ANIMAL TISSUE
INTO
HUMANS

A Report by

THE ADVISORY GROUP
ON THE ETHICS OF
XENOTRANSPLANTATION

1 9 9 6

ISBN 0 11 321866 4

CONTENTS

SECTION TWO
ETHICS

SECTION THREE
AN ETHICAL FRAMEWORK

CHAIRMAN'S FOREWORD

It has become a commonplace, such is the pace of innovation and development in medicine that "frontiers"are identified, only to be crossed and assimilated with ease into the medical map in what seems like the blink of an eye. Thus, to describe xenotransplantation as a frontier in medical science is to invite a raised eyebrow from the world-weary and to risk relegating it to the status of this season's fashion. Yet, for once, the description may be apt. Those who need tissue for transplant, whether it be a solid organ such as a heart, the transplant of which could save the life of someone suffering from end-stage cardiac failure, or cells such as pancreatic islets which could dramatically change the circumstances of those suffering from insulin-dependent diabetes, may look to xenotransplantation as, at last, the answer to their needs. Others, however, may see in xenotransplantation a further example of humankind's wilful exploitation of animals. Others still baulk at the risks involved, particularly that existing or new infectious diseases will be let loose on the population beyond the animal facility and the hospital. Perhaps, this is one area where the word frontier is not hyperbole.

It is significant that the Secretary of State's charge to the Advisory Group was to concern ourselves with ethics. This reflects, indeed reinforces, the view that, whatever the issue involved, public policy should ultimately be grounded on ethical principles. But ethical analysis and any subsequent recommendations concerning public policy can only be of value if the facts to which analysis is applied is properly understood. In our case the facts are the current state of xenotransplantation. For this reason, the Report sets out at some length the "state of the art". Only then can the ethical complexities be identified and explored.

It must not be thought, however, that once involved in ethics, this is synonymous with some other-worldly commentary divorced from the real world of suffering and ill-health. The Group has had to make hard choices in a world in which easy choices are rarely an option. The Report's recommendations are the sum of these hard choices. Indeed, after the last full meeting of the Group, Dr Suckling, on further reflection, expressed reservations about the extent and scope of the further work on primates which the Group has recommended be undertaken and he has asked that these reservations be registered here. He has assured me that he is content with the rest of the Report and with all other recommendations. For their part, all of the other members affirm their support for what is said concerning the use of primates in research.

It was my privilege to Chair the Advisory Group. It will be clear that my contributions were more those of a conductor rather than a player. I gratefully relied on the extraordinary range of experience and expertise which my colleagues brought to the deliberations. I cannot thank them enough, not least because of the uncomplaining manner in which they responded to the extremely tight deadlines I set for the Group's work.

The Group could not have achieved anything without the dedication and ability of the Secretariat, led outstandingly by Rachel Arrundale. Carl Evans was a model of unflappable efficiency. It would be hard to find a better example of public service than the commitment shown by all of the team. I record here my very great thanks to them. Edmund Waterhouse, of the Department of Health, was a source of quiet wisdom. I am greatly indebted to him.

Professor Ian Kennedy
August 1996

THE ADVISORY GROUP ON THE ETHICS OF XENOTRANSPLANTATION

MEMBERSHIP

Chairman

Professor Ian Kennedy — Professor of Medical Law and Ethics, Head and Dean of the Law School, King's College, London.

Members

Professor Kay Davies — Professor of Genetics, Keble College, Oxford.

Ms Nicola Davies QC — Barrister.

Professor Robin Downie — Professor of Moral Philosophy, Glasgow University.

Mrs Judy MacArthur Clark — Consultant in Laboratory Animal Science and Ethics.

Ms Polly Toynbee — Journalist.

Professor Herbert Sewell — Professor of Immunology, Queens Medical Centre, University Hospital, Nottingham.

Professor John Salaman — (retired) Professor of Transplant Surgery at the University of Wales College of Medicine.

Dr Anthony Suckling — Director of Scientific Affairs, RSPCA.

Observer

Dr David Harper — Chief Scientific Officer, Department of Health.

Secretariat (Department of Health)

Ms Rachel Arrundale — Secretary

Dr Antonia Leigh — Scientific Secretary

Mrs Debby Dare — Assistant Secretary

Mr Carl Evans — Assistant Secretary

We would like to emphasise that all the Group members were appointed by virtue of their individual expertise and that they do not necessarily represent the views of any organisation with which they are associated.

SUMMARY OF MAIN CONCLUSIONS AND RECOMMENDATIONS

1   The **Advisory Group on the Ethics of Xenotransplantation** was appointed by the Secretary of State for Health with the following terms of reference:

> **In the light of recent and potential developments in xenotransplantation, to review the acceptability of and ethical framework within which xenotransplantation may be undertaken and to make recommendations**.

2.   Xenotransplantation is the transplant of tissue (including solid organs) between species. We are primarily concerned with xenotransplantation in the context of the use of non–human animals to provide tissue for transplant to humans. Interest in xenotransplantation has been reawakened by scientific developments which seek to enable humans to tolerate animal tissue (specifically that of the pig) by modifying the genetic make-up of the pig through the addition of particular human genes.

3.   We use the word tissue to refer to solid organs and other tissue. We use the word animal to refer to non–human animals. We describe animals from which tissue is taken as **source** animals.

4.   Our assessment of the ethical acceptability of xenotransplantation involves a two stage process: first whether this use of animals is unacceptable under any circumstances; secondly whether it may be acceptable under certain circumstances and, if so, what circumstances make it so. Our response to this second question led us to identify the benefits which xenotransplantation could bring and to weigh them against the possible harms, whether to animals, patients or the wider population.

5.   Our main conclusion is that it is not currently acceptable to move to trials involving humans due to the lack of knowledge at the present time concerning aspects of physiology, immunology and the risk of infection (see paragraphs 16, 17 and 20). We also recommend that a National Standing Committee should be established to oversee the development of xenotransplantation. Any applications to undertake trials would have to be approved by this Committee (see paragraph 47). The Committee should be established by law.

6.   We reached these conclusions concerning the ethical acceptability of xenotransplantation as follows:

❖   we recognise that some may regard all use of animals as wrong regardless of any potential benefits;

❖   we do not adopt this position, but rather a weighing of benefit versus harm;

❖   we consider that benefits to patients and the wider population may flow from the development and introduction of xenotransplantation;

❖   we consider that any benefits must, however, be set against the possibility of harm arising.

7.   Animals vary a great deal in their abilities and mental capacities and presumably in their capacity for suffering. The non-human primates (hereafter, primates), including chimpanzees and baboons, are at the higher end of this scale, and have close affinities with humans. We consider that these animals can be distinguished from other animals not least by virtue of their greater self-awareness and mental capacity. We consider that these features increase their capacity for suffering, particularly given the conditions under which source animals would be kept in order to ensure proper controls (e.g. biosecure and isolated accommodation). **We therefore conclude that it would be ethically unacceptable to use primates as source animals for xenotransplantation, not least because they would be exposed to too much suffering** [Para 4.28].

8.   But primates are also involved in the **research** being carried out into xenotransplantation, primarily as recipients of tissue transplanted from pigs. We regard such research as being necessary to protect the interests of potential patients. Can this use in research be justified? A primate used for research purposes may (indirectly) provide benefit for a large number of humans, due to the information generated from the research. Thus, the ratio of benefit to humans against harm to the primate may provide an ethical basis for the use of primates in research. By contrast, a primate used as a source animal could only benefit one or at best a very small number of humans. Further, the conditions which would prevail for primates to be used in research would not be those which prevail for source animals. We recognise the case for such research to take place and note that such research is currently permitted under the provisions of the Animals (Scientific Procedures) Act and thus: **We conclude that it would be ethically acceptable to use primates in the research into xenotransplantation, but only where no alternative method of obtaining information exists and this use should be limited so far as is possible** [Para 4.29].

9.   The pig is attracting the most interest as a potential source animal. We ask whether the use of this animal as a source for xenotransplantation is similarly ethically unacceptable?

We conclude that the use of the pig for xenotransplantation may be ethically acceptable. We conclude further, however, that the acceptability lies in balancing the benefit to humans against the harm both to the pig and to humans [Para 4.30].

10.   This conclusion entails an analysis which weighs not only the benefits to humans against the harm done to the pig, but also the benefits to individual patients against the potential harm both to those patients and to the wider human population.   The various harms which are intrinsic to xenotransplantation include the effects on the animal of genetic modification and the effects on the human of transplantation of animal tissue, the possible suffering of patients, the possible suffering of animals, and the potential harm caused by diverting attention away from other areas of research and resources towards this treatment.

11.   The pigs intended for use in xenotransplantation are genetically modified. **We take the view that some degree of genetic modification is ethically acceptable providing that there is a concomitant benefit to humans and that the pig neither suffers unduly nor ceases recognisably to be a pig** [Para 4.36].

12.   Further genetic modification of animals may be proposed over the coming years. **We take the view that there are limits to the extent to which an animal should be genetically modified and that constant monitoring both of animals which have been modified, so as to assess effects, and of proposed genetic modifications must take place** [Para 4.39].

13.   There is a general misgiving about transplanting animal tissue into humans and, in particular, concern about transplantation of certain tissues. **We take the view that the procedures currently proposed do not go beyond acceptable limits and, further, that the criterion for evaluating the ethical acceptability of xenotransplants depends on the function performed by the tissue involved** [Para 4.43].

14.   However, further developments may raise concerns. **We take the view, therefore, that new developments should be monitored to ascertain whether they appear to go beyond what may be acceptable limits** [Para 4.44].

15.   There remain medical risks which may result from xenotransplantation, related to physiology (the functioning of the tissue), immunology (the possible rejection of the tissue), and infection (transmitted from the animal through the tissue to the patient and possibly the wider population).

16.   **We conclude that the evidence on transplant function, organ growth and the functioning of the recipient's immune system within the transplant is too limited, at the current time, to justify a move to clinical trials. We recommend that further research should be carried out and analysed before such trials can take place. We note**

that some of this research may involve the use of primates and must therefore be read in the light of the recommendations we have made about their use [Para 4.50].

17.   We consider that the evidence on immunological rejection is too limited, at the current time, to justify a move to clinical trials. We recommend that further research should be carried out to investigate more fully the rejection processes associated with xenotransplantation and to determine an effective and acceptable immunosuppression regimen [Para 4.52].

18.   As regards the risks of infection, these vary between infectious agents. We consider that it is ethically acceptable to take the risks of infection associated with fungi, parasites, bacteria and prions provided that source animals are maintained in conditions which aim to minimise the risk of infection and provided that any infections which arise are monitored. We accordingly recommend that such conditions are established for animals reared for use in xenotransplantation [Para 4.55].

19.   Prion-related diseases can remain latent for long periods of time and it is currently only possible to positively identify their presence after death. We further recommend, therefore, that with regard to prion-related diseases, there should be a programme of culling of sentinel pigs over a wide age range to test for neuropathological changes [Para 4.56].

20.   Viruses cause the most concern particularly as it is possible that there are a number of porcine viruses which have not yet been identified. We conclude that there is insufficient knowledge about the known viruses to make it safe to proceed to clinical trials at the current time. We recommend that further research should be carried out on known viruses, including the porcine retroviruses, cytomegalovirus (CMV) and circovirus, before clinical trials may be considered [Para 4.58].

21.   Given that there are likely to be other pathogens which have not yet been identified, we asked ourselves whether it would **ever** be ethically acceptable to proceed with xenotransplantation. We conclude that, at the stage when it is considered that a full investigation of potential infection risks has been carried out, and the risks have been shown to be within tolerable margins, it would be ethically acceptable to proceed. This is subject to there being a system in place to monitor the emergence of any unusual disease or any unknown pathogens and to require, as a consequence, that appropriate additional research be completed in a proper fashion [Para 4.63].

22.   We attach importance to infection control and monitoring arrangements. It would be important to maintain infection control standards in the animal facilities. We recommend that such standards be designed and agreed and further recommend that animal facilities be monitored to ensure that these standards are observed [Para 4.66].

23.   The transport of animals (or of tissue) between sites and the removal of tissue are points in any production process where biosecure conditions might more easily be breached. **We recommend that particular attention be paid to these, in terms of both establishing and monitoring standards** [Para 4.67].

24.   There is one further issue relating to the risk of infection. We are not aware of any assessment of the risks to animals through the mutation of animal pathogens in human hosts and **we recommend that this issue should be considered further** [Para 4.70].

25.   We have recommended that a range of investigations be undertaken with the aim of providing further information on the physiological, immunological and infection effects of xenotransplantation. **We recommend that this programme should be co-ordinated, so far as is possible, and the results monitored and assessed with a view to determining whether further research is needed and whether clinical trials are acceptable** [Para 4.71].

26.   There is a limit to the information which may be provided through trials on primates. **We recommend that those who have responsibility for co-ordinating the programme should do so with particular regard to this point** [Para 4.72].

27.   Infection control arrangements in animal facilities may cause some degree of harm to the animals. Our concerns relate to the procedures involved in the xenotransplantation production process; to the infection-free environment, including monitoring arrangements; to some specific restrictions on the movement of pigs; and to the potential wastage of animals.

28.   The procedures which would take place in a xenotransplantation production process and which would cause us concern are:

❖   the removal, and then replacement, of eggs from sows under anaesthesia (so that the human gene may be micro-injected into the egg).

❖   hysterectomy and removal of the piglets from the sow.

❖   the serial tissue sampling which takes place to test for genetic modification and for infectious agents.

However, these are intrinsic parts of the programme and are currently unavoidable. Although these procedures are *currently* unavoidable, every effort should be made to minimise suffering through development of alternative techniques.

29.   Tissue will be removed from the animal under appropriate anaesthesia and, usually, the animal will be killed immediately. However, the sequential removal of tissue is a possibility. **We conclude that the sequential removal of solid organs is ethically unacceptable and**

further, we take the view that the sequential removal of any tissue is ethically unacceptable [Paras 4.93-4.94]. We exclude here the taking of blood and tissue for monitoring purposes.

30.   Controlled environments, such as specific pathogen free conditions, may raise specific concerns about animal welfare. For example, there may be a lack of rooting or bedding material, low levels of natural light and possible social isolation. **We recommend that such issues be addressed in the design of SPF facilities for xenotransplantation to determine whether improvements can be made** [Para 4.95].

31.   We are also concerned, specifically, about the use of farrowing crates. This, of course, is not unique to xenotransplantation and we recognise that there is currently no practical alternative available. **We recommend that research to establish appropriate alternatives to farrowing crates should be encouraged** [Para 4.96].

32.   The issue of **wastage** of pigs arises at various points in the process of producing pigs for xenotransplantation. **We recommend that wastage rates be monitored closely during any future development of xenotransplantation** [Para 4.97].

33.   Research into aspects of xenotransplantation will continue for some considerable time, including the transplantation of pig tissue to primates. **We therefore take the view that further research involving primates should be kept to the minimum necessary, and that, wherever appropriate, other means of generating reliable information be used. We also recommend that the welfare of the animals used should be closely monitored and supervised** [Para 4.98].

34.   We conclude, generally, that: **from the point of view of animal welfare, the use of pigs for xenotransplantation is ethically acceptable so long as continued efforts are made to avoid or minimise the harm caused** [Para 4.99].

35.   We are concerned that resources for xenotransplantation are allocated fairly and justly and with regard to alternative services. **We recommend therefore that the National Specialist Commissioning Advisory Group (NSCAG) consider the purchase of the various xenotransplantation services, should their development reach the stage at which central support for the treatment costs might be appropriate during clinical evaluation. NSCAG could also consider the purchase of xenotransplant services, should they become established, but not widely provided, services. We further recommend that in its considerations, the NSCAG should take account of the various concerns which we have expressed in this Report** [Para 4.106].

36.   Xenotransplantation may have a detrimental effect on the allotransplantation programme in that public perception of its success, or otherwise, could affect the supply of human organs.

Our concern relates to the risk of reducing the supply. **We accordingly recommend that consideration be given to means of educating the public about xenotransplantation** [Para 4.110].

37. The advent of xenotransplantation may also affect the development of other therapies, should investment be directed at it rather than more generally. **We take the view that Government, through the relevant mechanisms, should ensure that research into therapeutic responses for those whose conditions currently call for transplantation, in addition to xenotransplantation, is adequately supported** [Para 4.112].

38. The assessment of the ethical acceptability of xenotransplantation also depends on the existence and availability of other therapies. If there are no such therapies, xenotransplantation would appear to have the advantage. However, if such therapies exist, or could be developed in the relevant timescale, it becomes more difficult ethically to make the case for xenotransplantation. No unique benefit would flow from it to outweigh the ethical concerns which are intrinsic to it.

39. Allotransplantation is currently the treatment of choice for those patients who could benefit from xenotransplantation, but the allotransplant programme is restricted due to the shortage of organs and other tissue. We asked ourselves whether this programme could be improved. **We conclude that more organs, and other tissue, *could* be obtained from cadaveric donors.** This could be achieved primarily through continued attention to improving management of the organ retrieval system and to training those involved. **We recommend that due attention continue to be given to improving donation rates** [Para 5.19].

40. Further options for increasing the availability of cadaveric organs and tissue would exist, should there be changes in UK law. **We do not, however, recommend such changes.** We are not convinced that they are justified on the basis of current evidence. **We recommend, however, they be kept under review** [Para 5.20].

41. There appears to be potential for therapies other than xenotransplantation to be developed in response to the conditions currently requiring transplantation, in particular, artificial organs and somatic cell gene therapy. **We recommend that appropriate means be found to support and encourage continued research into the development and application of gene therapy and artificial organs** [Para 5.40].

42. Health promotion measures and preventive medicine might assist in avoiding the need for transplantation. There seems to be some potential for such measures to make some impact. However we emphasise that some of the relevant medical conditions are not amenable to these measures. We nevertheless **recommend that such measures should continue to be pursued** [Para 5.49].

43.   We conclude that there are indeed other procedures, either in existence (such as health promotion methods) or in development (such as artificial organs) which may provide alternatives to xenotransplantation. We repeat that such methods must be pursued in tandem with xenotransplantation. We do not consider that it is possible to predict, at the present time, which therapies are most likely to meet the needs of the patients whose conditions currently call for transplantation. We consider that these means of meeting the needs of patients must be explored as they potentially offer the benefits of xenotransplantation without some of its inherent harms.

44.   We have outlined a number of conditions in paragraphs 11 - 37. **We conclude that only if the conditions which we have outlined are met could xenotransplantation be considered to be ethically acceptable**[Para 6.2]. These conditions include the prohibition of primates as a source species, conditions designed to minimise the risks to the patient and the wider population, and conditions designed to minimise the harms to the animal.

45.   What we are concluding, in effect, by those of our conditions which refer to the state of scientific knowledge, is that current knowledge is not yet such as to allow us to support the introduction of xenotransplantation at the present time. Given the constantly changing nature of science, the conditions we have established are necessarily conditions arising from what we currently know. They are, therefore, necessary but not sufficient conditions [Para 6.7].

46.   We therefore conclude that some mechanism should be put in place to ensure that these conditions are met and that no research into xenotransplantation involving humans should be carried out until there is evidence that these conditions have been met. We also note that any approval of clinical trials would not presuppose a move to a therapeutic programme. The outcomes of clinical trials, for each proposed xenotransplant therapy, should be carefully assessed before any such move to a therapeutic programme is contemplated. There is also a clear need for the progress of clinical trials to be closely monitored and to be stopped, should it be thought appropriate in the light of adverse effects. Similarly, any therapeutic programme must be monitored and discontinued if thought appropriate in the light of adverse effects [Para 6.8].

47.   We therefore **conclude that a Standing Committee on xenotransplantation is required to monitor and review these matters and accordingly recommend the establishment of such a committee. We further recommend that such a Committee should have a national role and that it should be established by primary legislation** [Para 6.9].

48.   The second element in our terms of reference concerns the nature of any ethical framework within which xenotransplantation, were it to proceed, could ethically be undertaken. The development of this framework involves consideration of the further ethical concerns which arise, should xenotransplantation proceed to involve humans, first, in clinical trials, and potentially, in therapeutic programmes. Consideration of the framework also involves

consideration of the current legal framework and discussion of the responsibilities of the proposed National Standing Committee.

49.   The further ethical considerations which arise relate to the patient, the professionals who would be involved, the clinical sites in which xenotransplantation procedures would take place and our recognition of the ethical difficulties which xenotransplantation poses.

50.   One issue is whether children and those incapable of giving valid consent should be considered for inclusion in clinical trials. **We recommend that children should not be included in trials, at least until all the initial concerns about safety and efficacy have been satisfactorily resolved. We take the same view as regards those incapable of giving valid consent** [Para 7.7].

51.   Consent is an exceptionally complex concept from both an ethical and legal standpoint. We are content to conclude here that the principles ordinarily applied both in the context of therapeutic research and treatment should equally apply to xenotransplantation. However, there are certain particular issues which are raised by xenotransplantation and which call for particular comment. **We recommend that they should be incorporated into any consent arrangements, so that the patient may be properly informed** [Para 7.11].

52.   We note the need of the patient to assimilate a considerable volume of information, as part of the consent process. **We recommend that a system of counselling, independent of the transplant team, should be in place and that prospective xenotransplant recipients should have access to it, both before any clinical trial and if judged appropriate, subsequently, should any xenotransplant programme be established** [Para 7.13].

53.   The potential psychological and social effects of xenotransplantation are an issue of potential significance and on which there is little evidence. **We recommend that the psychological effects of xenotransplantation should be kept under review and that consideration should be given to funding research into these effects** [Para 7.14].

54.   Some patients, for whatever reason, might choose not to opt for a xenotransplantation procedure. **We recommend that patients who choose not to opt for xenotransplantation should not be penalised in any way in their medical care** [Para 7.15].

55.   The relatives of patients who would be undergoing a new and untried form of treatment also deserve consideration. **We recommend that the clinical site where the xenotransplantation procedure takes place should address the needs of relatives as well as the needs of patients** [Para 7.20].

56.   A variety of professionals would be involved in xenotransplantation such that a wide variety of related issues would need to be addressed. These include their training needs and the consequent provision of training and the complementary nature of the roles of the professions involved. **We recommend that these issues be addressed as a matter of priority, taking advice from interested professional groups** [Para 7.25].

57.   We also consider registration of those who would be involved with the source animals to be important. The Institute of Animal Technology produces guidelines which apply to Registered Animal Technicians. The British Veterinary Nursing Association produces similar guidelines for Veterinary Nurses. **We consider that such guidelines (currently non-statutory) should apply to all animal technicians and veterinary nurses involved in xenotransplantation, together with an appropriate system of monitoring compliance with them** [Para 7.24].

58.   We recognise that, as in the rest of the population, the views of the professionals in veterinary and human health care will vary. **We consider that those whose work may involve them in xenotransplantation must be given information about xenotransplantation and its effects, so that they are able to make a personal decision** about their involvement. **Further, we take the view that any person in such a situation should have the right to "opt-out" of this work without prejudice to career or employment.** This right should be protected by legislation [Para 7.26].

59.   It is clear from the above that any clinical site where xenotransplantation took place would have a range of responsibilities to fulfil. **We recommend that those clinical sites in which it may be proposed that xenotransplantation should take place be assessed at the early clinical trial stage. We further recommend that any assessment should be based on the conditions which we have outlined** [Para 7.28].

60.   We have concluded that the conditions which we have outlined are such that they should be backed by primary legislation. If a legal framework (whether in one law or a combination of laws) were to exist which could serve the needs which we have identified, this would obviate the need to recommend primary legislation. However, we conclude that, although there are provisions in current legislation which address many of our concerns, they do not entirely meet the needs which we have identified. As a consequence, **we recommend that a comprehensive statutory framework of regulation be put in place, taking account of and drawing upon existing law wherever it is relevant and appropriate** [Para 8.4].

61.   **We further recommend that such legislation should, among other things, ensure that the animals involved in xenotransplantation are brought and remain within the provisions of the Animals (Scientific Procedures) Act 1986 (ASPA) by appropriate amendments** [Para 8.35].

62.   We have recognised that the Animals (Scientific Procedures) Act can meet a number of our concerns about animal welfare and that a well-established and highly regarded system of inspection exists. But xenotransplantation would raise new issues and **we therefore recommend that an appropriate code of practice be issued under ASPA and that this should take into account the concerns which we have expressed** [Para 8.36].

63.   We have already noted it is possible that biosecure conditions be breached during the transport of tissue or animals. **We therefore recommend that the movement of tissue be brought within regulatory control in the primary legislation which we propose** [Para 8.45].

64.   We consider that any proposed use for food of animals which are part of any xenotransplantation programme should be regulated. The EC Novel Foods Regulation meets our concerns on this point but we note that labelling may not be required for those animals which are the product of a xenotransplantation programme but are not genetically modified. **We recommend that consideration should be given to whether such animals should be used as food and, if so, whether labelling on food produced from them is required** [Para 8.49].

65.   We considered both domestic and European legislation which relates to medicines and medical devices. We have noted the highly regarded regulatory structures which exist under such legislation. However, it is our opinion that these could not be said, beyond significant doubt, to apply to xenotransplantation and that, therefore, the existing legal framework is inadequate to answer our concerns about risks to patients and to the wider population arising from tissue from animals which are part of a xenotransplantation programme. **We recommend that the legislation which we propose take account of these regulatory structures so as to ensure that a similar structure is put in place to regulate any procedure involving xenotransplantation** [Para 8.67].

66.   We consider that clinical trials of xenotransplantation procedures should be considered to be "medical research". **We recommend that the approval and monitoring of such trials should be conditional on the approval of and monitoring by the National Standing Committee** which we propose [Para 8.74].

67.   We have expressed the view that there are potential limits to the ethical acceptability of the genetic modification of animals for the purposes of xenotransplantation and to the animal tissue which may be transplanted into humans. **We recommend the National Standing Committee monitor developments and examine any which could cause public concern [Para 8.75].**

68.   It is possible that the private sector may wish to undertake xenotransplantation. We **recommend that guidance be issued to Health Authorities that the prior approval of xenotransplantation procedures by the National Standing Committee should be**

regarded as a condition for obtaining or remaining registration under Part II of the Registered Homes Act 1984. We further recommend that any new primary legislation on xenotransplantation should seek to ensure that similar conditions apply for independent facilities as for NHS hospitals [Para 8.77].

69. Developments in xenotransplantation are taking place around the world and several different groups, including the Food and Drug Administration in the United States and the World Health Organisation, are developing guidelines. **We recommend that appropriate account be taken of international developments and that there should be liaison with the EC and with other Member States and with appropriate international organisations, particularly in the framing of appropriate legislation and regulations** [Para 8.85].

70. We have concluded that new, specific, primary legislation to regulate xenotransplantation is required in the interests of patients, public health and animal welfare. We recognise, however, the pressure on Parliamentary timetables. **We therefore recommend, as an interim measure only, that our recommendations, particularly with regard to the National Standing Committee, are taken forward on a non-statutory basis until such time as legislation can be brought forward.** Such an interim body should not be regarded as a substitute for legislation [Para 9.2].

71. **We recommend that the National Standing Committee should have overall national responsibility for overseeing the development of xenotransplantation; that is, the transplant of viable, replicating, animal tissue into humans.** Its role will cover, broadly, the **setting of standards** for continued research into and, if appropriate, the introduction of xenotransplantation, and **ensuring their implementation**. Given the range of expertise which would necessarily be represented on such a Committee it could additionally be responsible for a range of related, additional, functions. The Committee would be charged with ensuring that the recommendations contained in this Report are implemented [Para 9.3].

72. As regards overseeing the development of xenotransplantation, **we further recommend that in carrying out its responsibilities, the National Standing Committee should work with other interested bodies in an appropriate way so as to co-ordinate the work being undertaken, thus minimising duplication, and to call upon the skill and expertise necessary to undertake its role successfully** [Para 9.6].

73. We note that the Animal Procedures Committee does not directly consider each of the many licence applications made. **We recommend that the Home Secretary treat xenotransplantation as a special case, and request the APC to consider which mechanisms may be needed to deal in a co-ordinated manner with all applications which involve xenotransplantation** [Para 9.8].

74. We see a need for close liaison between the National Standing Committee on Xenotransplantation and the Animal Procedures Committee. **We accordingly recommend that the National Standing Committee should act in co-ordination with the Animal Procedures Committee and measures to achieve this should be addressed as a matter of urgency.** [Para 9.9].

75. We have argued that the National Standing Committee should approve any applications for clinical research involving xenotransplantation but we also recognise the role of Local Research Ethics Committees. Thus, we **recommend that the National Standing Committee should co-ordinate its activities with those of LRECs.** We further **recommend that any proposal for research into xenotransplantation which involves humans must be approved by the National Standing Committee prior to approval by a properly constituted LREC.** We also **recommend that the arrangements for the co-ordinated working of the proposed National Standing Committee with LRECs should be addressed as a matter of urgency and further that these arrangements should seek to minimise the problems of delay and bureaucracy** [Para 9.10].

76. **We recommend that the proposed National Standing Committee should be funded by, and be under the aegis of the appropriate UK Government Departments** [Para 9.12].

77. We have recommended that, as a temporary measure, the National Committee should be set up on an interim basis. **We recommend that such a committee be supported by some means of control, through, for example, appropriate guidance to LRECs, and that the Committee should be empowered, where necessary, to bring matters of concern to the attention of Ministers** [Para 9.14].

SECTION ONE

INTRODUCTION
AND
BACKGROUND

CHAPTER ONE:

INTRODUCTION

XENOTRANSPLANTATION

1.1   Xenotransplantation is the transplant of tissue (including organs) between species. In this report, we are primarily concerned with xenotransplantation in the context of the use of non-human animals to provide tissue for transplant into humans.

1.2   Throughout the report, we use the word tissue to refer to solid organs and other tissue including, for example, bone, bone marrow and isolated cells. We use the word "animal" to refer to non-human animals. We describe animals from which tissue is taken as **source** animals.

1.3   Animal tissue and proteins have been used in humans for many years as the main or partial component of medical devices and medicines. Well known examples are porcine heart valves and insulin derived from both pigs and cows. These uses of non viable, non replicating, animal material are not considered here. Our concern is with living tissue.

1.4   Xenotransplantation is not new. The first reported transplants of animal tissues into humans took place early in the 1900s and met with very little success. However, the development of immunosuppressive drugs and the success of allotransplantation (that is, human to human transplantation) prompted a number of xenotransplant experiments in the 1960s. These included two series of experiments to transplant kidneys from baboons and chimpanzees to humans. Attempts to transplant hearts have been made sporadically since the 1960s, involving chimpanzees, baboons, pigs and sheep and have not been successful. More recently, there have been attempts to transplant livers either as a full transplant (again unsuccessful) or as temporary support (with limited success).

1.5   Notwithstanding the previous lack of success, certain recent developments have reawakened interest in xenotransplantation. In the transplantation of solid organs, new research has focused on enabling humans to tolerate an animal (pig) organ by modifying the genetic make-up of the pig, by the addition of particular human genes. There is also growing interest in the transplantation of other tissue, including the transplantation of fetal pig cells, as potential therapies for diabetes and Parkinson's disease.

ETHICS

1.6   We were charged by the Secretary of State for Health as follows:

In the light of recent and potential developments in xenotransplantation, to review the acceptability of and ethical framework within which xenotransplantation may be undertaken and to make recommendations.

1.7   We draw attention to the two central features of these **terms of reference**. The first is whether xenotransplantation is acceptable. The second, which only arises if xenotransplantation is found to be acceptable, involves a consideration of those elements which would comprise a framework within which xenotransplantation could be ethically undertaken.

1.8   The term "ethics" is used regularly in everyday life, and in the professions, in a variety of ways. "Ethics" can be another word for our ordinary sense of what is right and wrong. But ordinary intuitions can be inconsistent and unclear, especially when we are dealing with unfamiliar problems. "Ethics" in the sense of moral philosophy, can assist when the intuitions of everyday life are inadequate. In this sense, ethics is a matter of examining the moral judgments of ordinary life in the light of new developments; in our case new developments in science, biotechnology and their economic implications.

1.9   In the examination which follows, we seek to reach a view on what is ethically appropriate with a view to make public policy recommendations within a legal framework.

Our ethical enquiry is based on certain assumptions. These are:

1   Ethical judgments are inescapable. They are not simply for rarefied people in rarefied circumstances but are unavoidable in medicine, science and ordinary life.

2   Ethical judgments are all pervasive. Dramatic issues which happen to be topical tend to be highlighted, but ethical decisions are made many times in the course of a normal working day.

3   Ethical considerations are indivisible in the sense that there are not separate public and private areas of ethics. Ethical judgments made by the professions should be open to attitudinal changes in society. Moreover, they should take note of science, public health and economics.

4   Ethical decisions must be made in the everyday world of "give and take" and of constantly changing information. In other words, "absolutes" may need to be tempered by realities.

5   Ethical decisions can change as new knowledge becomes available which shifts the balance of arguments.

1.10   It follows that we do not see our brief as being confined to an examination of a few specific ethical arguments, such as those to do with animal rights. We recognise the need to apply ethical thinking to **all** issues raised by or inherent in xenotransplantation; it will be inadequate to say that our ethical view on xenotransplantation is "such and such" and go on to say that there then remain practical, public health or financial problems which need to be resolved. Ethics encompasses all these spheres. We must thus engage in a complex analysis rather than merely reach a simplistic judgment. In such an analysis we must, above all, weigh the relative claims of animals and patients and the relative claims of the individual patients and the wider human population.

1.11   In formulating public policy, therefore, our ethical analysis in essence involves the process of balancing benefit against harm. In adopting this approach, we do not ignore general theories of ethics. We understand, for example, that some will argue that the proper approach for us to take is to recognise that patients in appropriate circumstances have a right to a transplant. Others will argue that we owe such patients a duty to make transplantation available. Adopting one or the other of these approaches does not, however, obviate the need critically to enquire into the ratio of benefit over harm which xenotransplantation may entail. This is because it would be idle to argue that someone may demand of the state that its health care system provide a form of therapy which, on balance, would do more harm than good. Such a demand may be valid from the point of view of the individual who believes that he may benefit from xenotransplantation, or is prepared to take the risk of failure. But the desires or perceived needs of a particular individual (or group) cannot supplant the obligation of the state to introduce as treatment only that which, by reference to the community at large, may on balance be of benefit.

WHY CONSIDER XENOTRANSPLANTATION?

1.12   During the last year, it has been reported that progress has been made in resolving one of the major problems associated with transplanting solid organs from animals to humans: that the organ would be rejected by the human recipient in a matter of minutes. Clearly, if this is so, it could have significant implications in terms of providing an alternative and additional source of organs for transplant for those patients whose medical condition could benefit from such a transplant.

1.13   Allotransplantation, the transplant of tissue from human to human, has brought significant benefits to an increasing number of patients over the past three decades. It is widely thought, however, that the supply of organs and other tissue falls far short of meeting the need of those who could benefit.

1.14   Other procedures intended to meet these patients' needs have been the subject of considerable attention. They include the development of artificial organs, strategies involving the use of conventional medical and surgical approaches in novel ways and the possibility of developing gene therapies. While some have been successful, for example kidney dialysis, these other procedures have not currently removed the need for transplantation and there is a view that progress in this direction will be, at best, limited.

THIS REPORT

1.15   Arising from this renewed interest in xenotransplantation, there are three central questions which we must address. They are:

1   In the light of current scientific knowledge, does xenotransplantation offer an ethically acceptable solution to the problems associated with the shortage of tissue for transplantation and to the problems caused by other medical conditions?

2   Are there ways to improve the current programme for obtaining human tissue so as to meet all or a greater part of the demand for transplantation of tissue?

3   Are there currently other procedures for responding to the needs of those whose conditions call for transplantation and are such procedures likely to be developed in the relevant timescale?

In this report, we address each of these questions in turn. We recognise here that there are certain difficulties in this approach. By studying xenotransplantation and its inherent costs and benefits first, we may give the impression that the possibility that there may be alternatives to xenotransplantation has already been dismissed or is, at best, an afterthought. We would like to emphasise that this is not the case.

1.16   We adopt our approach for two reasons. Firstly, our remit is explicitly to do with the ethics of xenotransplantation and we wished to focus on this early in the report. Secondly, we discuss first what may be termed the intrinsic ethical issues: those which are particular to xenotransplantation. These are the ethical issues which xenotransplantation raises, and which may determine its acceptability, regardless of whether there are alternatives (Question 1: Chapters 3 and 4). Indeed, if it is considered that there are no ethical difficulties raised by xenotransplantation, the only consideration that need be given to alternative methods is whether *they* should be discontinued. However, if there are thought to be ethical problems raised by xenotransplantation, a judgement about its acceptability is also affected by the current or potential availability of alternatives. Indeed, it is the very concerns intrinsic to xenotransplantation which suggest that we should be careful to exhaust other possibilities first. This involves a consideration of what may be called extrinsic ethical issues: those which are not particular to xenotransplantation but have to do with the proper place of xenotransplantation, in a world where it may not be the only, or the best, way forward (Questions 2 and 3: Chapter 5). The ordering of our analysis does not, therefore, connote any preference; rather, after discussion, it seemed best to us to discuss first the intrinsic, and second the extrinsic, arguments.

METHOD OF WORKING

1.17   The Group was asked to report by the Summer of 1996. It met for the first time on 19 December 1995 and met ten further times during 1996. We conducted a consultation exercise and invited submissions both through writing directly to a number of individuals and organisations and through advertising in the national and specialist press in early February 1996. We received over 300 responses to this exercise and are grateful to all those who wrote to us. We were both stimulated and challenged by the submissions. We found the exercise indispensable and our work would have been diminished without it.

1.18   There are no quotations from the consultation exercise in the report as we undertook to keep the content of the submissions confidential to the Group. However, we have been careful to deal with the points raised by the exercise in the report. A summary of these points can be found at Annex B, with a copy of the consultation letter and a list of those who submitted evidence to us.

1.19   We also undertook several visits. The Group visited the facilities of Imutran plc and PPL Therapeutics. We are grateful to both firms for the access they gave us. We are particularly grateful to Imutran plc, who are at the forefront of developing xenotransplantation in the UK, for the information they have provided about their work. Without this knowledge our task would have been much more difficult and our findings less informed. The Chairman and Secretary of the Group also met officials of the United States' Food and Drug Administration in Washington DC to discuss its approach to xenotransplantation. We thank, in particular, Dr Amy Patterson and Dr Phil Noguchi for their time and hospitality.

1.20   One of the main ethical concerns which we identified early on is the possibility that infectious disease may be transmitted from the source animals to the human recipients and, possibly, to the wider population. We worked in collaboration with the Advisory Committee on Dangerous Pathogens (ACDP) on this issue and in April 1996 we jointly hosted a Workshop on Infectious Disease and Xenotransplantation. This collaboration has been invaluable and we wish to thank the Chairman of the ACDP, Dr Michael Crumpton, his colleagues and the Secretariat for their assistance and advice. We also thank those who attended and spoke at the Workshop. A report of the Workshop is attached at Annex C.

1.21   We have also taken advice on a number of specialised medical issues from those doctors appointed to advise the Chief Medical Officer on their area of expertise. We are grateful to them.

1.22   The United Kingdom Transplant Support Service Authority (UKTSSA) is responsible for supporting transplant services in this country. In the past few months, members of the Authority have also made themselves responsible for providing the Group with their statistics and, even more importantly, their analysis and insights. We are grateful to Dr John Evans, the Chairman, Mrs Balderson, the Chief Executive, and to their staff.

1.23   The Nuffield Council on Bioethics produced a report "Animal-to-Human Transplants: the ethics of xenotransplantation" in March 1996. We were much assisted by the analysis and observations it contained. We were also grateful for the assistance lent to us by the Secretariat of the Nuffield Council.

CHAPTER TWO:

CURRENT KNOWLEDGE ABOUT XENOTRANSPLANTATION

INTRODUCTION

2.1   The first question we have raised is:

> **1**   In the light of current scientific knowledge, does xenotransplantation offer an ethically acceptable solution to the problems associated with the shortage of tissue for transplantation and to the problems caused by other medical conditions?

Before we begin to answer this question, we must review experience with, and the current scientific knowledge of, xenotransplantation.

2.2   Procedures involving the transplant of animals' organs into humans have been attempted since the early 1900s, although, to date, these have met with minimal success. This failure can be attributed to three main factors – the physiological differences which exist between the various animals used as sources and humans, the ability of the human immune system to defend the body by attacking and destroying foreign tissue, and infection.

2.3   Xenotransplantation poses physiological difficulties, due to such issues as the size and function of the organs or tissue transplanted. These difficulties vary from tissue to tissue.

2.4   The human immune system's ability to attack – or **reject** – foreign tissue is a problem in both allotransplantation (except in the particular case of transplantation between identical twins) and xenotransplantation.   In allotransplantation, this reaction is minimised by matching the recipient to the donor and controlled by the use of drugs which suppress the reaction of the immune system (**immunosuppression**).   Improved immunosuppressive techniques in the 1960s and 1970s brought about increasing success in allotransplantation.   However, they were not found to be effective enough in countering the problems of rejection met when animal organs were transplanted to humans.   In the 1990s, improved understanding of the human immune system, improvements in immunosuppressive therapy and the development of molecular genetic techniques have provided new means of countering tissue rejection, mainly through the genetic modification of the animal.

2.5   But such control of the immune system also adversely affects the body's ability to defend itself against harmful infections, arising from infectious agents present in the transplanted tissue, the external environment or the patient's own body. These may include infectious agents which are rarely the cause of disease in healthy individuals, but which can give rise to **opportunistic** infections in immunosuppressed patients. Strong immunosuppression has also been associated with the formation of tumours.

NOTE ON OTHER USES OF ANIMALS IN MEDICAL PRODUCTS

2.6   Animal products have been used for many years in medical devices and medicinal products. Examples of medical devices which include animal tissue are cattle bones which have been used as a bone substitute for humans; cattle tendons or ligaments for orthopaedic use; cattle collagen, a surgical material; bovine or porcine heart valves to replace defective human heart valves; catgut sutures made from sheep intestines for surgical use where a temporary suture is required. These tissues are usually obtained by the manufacturer from other industries, for example from herds and flocks used for farming. In all of these products the tissues undergo a series of processes which are designed to destroy or inactivate transmissible infectious agents.

2.7   Porcine insulin has also been used for years to treat patients with insulin-dependent diabetes, prior to the availability of human recombinant insulin. Similarly porcine Factor VIII is used for haemophiliacs who have inhibitors to human Factor VIII. Cattle are also used to produce surfactants, the drug aprotonin is produced from cattle lung, and gelatin is made from their hides and bones.

2.8   These uses of non-viable animal products are not considered further in this report.

CASES OF XENOTRANSPLANTATION TO DATE

2.9   The history of clinical procedures involving xenotransplantation demonstrates the problems associated with xenotransplantation: physiological differences, immunological rejection and infection.

SOLID ORGANS

HEART

2.10   The first heart xenotransplant took place in 1964 in the USA and involved the transplant of a heart from a chimpanzee to a human.[1] However, the small chimpanzee heart failed to cope with the circulatory load of the adult human being and the heart functioned for only two hours.

2.11   In 1968, a sheep's heart in the USA and a pig's heart in the UK were transplanted into human patients but failed immediately. The transplant of the pig's heart was a heterotopic transplant (that is where a heart is implanted, but the original heart is not removed). The failure of these transplants has been attributed to the severe form of rejection associated with xenotransplantation, **hyper–acute rejection**.[2]

2.12   Two further heterotopic heart xenotransplants were attempted in South Africa in 1977. One involved a baboon and the other, a chimpanzee. However, the hearts functioned for only 6 hours, and 4 days respectively, as, again, they could not sustain the full circulatory load.[3]

2.13   In 1984, in the USA, a baboon's heart was transplanted into a 15 day old girl, "Baby Fae", who was born prematurely with hypoplastic left heart syndrome. The baboon heart failed twenty days after the transplant. This was thought to be due in part to blood group incompatibility.

2.14   In 1992 a pig's heart was transplanted into a human patient in Poland, but the patient died 24 hours after transplantation. This relatively extended survival was thought to be due mainly to lessening of the rejection process through the absorption of pre-formed antibodies by the cross-circulation of two pig hearts before the transplant.[4]

---

[1]   Hardy, J.D., Chavez, C.M., Kurrus, F.D., Neely, W.A., Eraslan, S., Turner, MD., Fabian, L.W. & Labecki, T.D. (1964). Heart transplantation in man. Developmental studies and report of a case. Journal of the American Medical Association. **188**, 1132-1140.

[2]   Cooper, D.K.C. & Ye, Y. (1991). Experience with clinical heart xenotransplantation. In: Xenotransplantation. The transplantation of organs and tissues between species. Cooper, D.K.C., Kemp, E., Reemtsma, K. & White, D.J.G. (Eds). Springer Verlag. pp 541-557.

[3]   Barnard, C.N., Wolpowitz, A. & Losman, J.G. (1977). Heterotopic cardiac transplantation with a xenograft for assistance of the left heart in cardiogenic shock after cardiopulmonary bypass. South African Medical Journal. **52**, 1035-1038.

[4]   Czaplicki, J., Blonska, B. & Religa, Z. (1992). The lack of hyperacute xenogeneic heart transplant rejection in a human. Letters to the editor and invited comments from Salomon, D.R. The Journal of Heart and Lung Transplantation. **11**, 393-397.

KIDNEY

2.15   Attempts at renal xenotransplantation, using a range of animal species as sources, have taken place since 1905. Specifically, in the USA in 1963-1964, six kidney heterotopic xenotransplants from chimpanzees to humans were carried out. The patients were all suffering from terminal kidney failure (uremia). After the xenotransplants, the patients survived for periods varying from days to months; one patient surviving for nine months. The functioning of the kidneys varied, and kidney malfunction due to uncorrected electrolyte imbalance was reported. However, bacterial infection, due to the immunosuppressive regimen and consequent complications, was the principal cause of death.[5]

2.16   Six baboon to human kidney transplants also took place in the USA around the same time. Again, the patients were all suffering from terminal uremia. The patients survived for periods varying from several weeks to around three months after the procedure. It was reported that initial function was normal in the kidney but repeated episodes of rejection, followed by bacterial infections (possibly related to the high levels of immunosuppressants used), contributed to the patients' deaths. Rejection of the baboon kidneys was more vigorous than that seen in the transplant of chimpanzee kidneys and the organs did not function as well.[6]

2.17   In 1991 in the UK, pig kidneys were successfully used for extra-corporeal perfusion (that is, temporary support through linking the patient's blood supply to the pig's kidney outside the body) for several hours. Before the perfusion procedure, the patient had pre-formed anti-pig antibodies absorbed out by the first kidney. Another kidney was used extra-corporeally on the same patient a few weeks later and worked well for one and a half hours after which the procedure was terminated by removal of the kidney.[7]

LIVER

2.18   Extracorporeal perfusion of human blood using animal livers to support patients in hepatic coma has also been attempted. In 1966 in the USA, pig livers were used for short-term extra-corporeal support and in some cases neurological improvement and metabolic and clinical benefit were reported.[8]

---

[5]   Reemtsma, K., McCracken, B.H., Schlegel, J.U., Pearl, M.A., Pearce, C.W., DeWitt, C.W., Smith, P.E., Hewitt, R.L., Flinner, R.L. & Creech, O. (1964). Renal heterotransplantation in man. Annals of Surgery, **160**, 384-410.

[6]   Starzl, T.E., Marchioro, T.L., Peters, G.N., Kirkpatrick, C.H., Wilson, W.E.C., Porter, K.A., Rifkind, D.,Ogden, D.A., Hitchcock, C.R. & Waddell, W.R. (1964). Renal heterotransplantation from baboon to man: experience with 6 cases. Transplantation. **2**, 752-776.

[7]   Cairns, T.D.H., Taube, D.H., Stevens, N., Binns, R. & Welsh, K.I. (1991). Xenografts - future prospects for clinical transplantation. Immunology Letters. **29**, 167-170.

[8]   Eiseman, B. (1966). Treatment of hepatic coma by extracorporeal liver perfusion. Annals of the Royal College of Surgeons, England. **38**, 329-348.

2.19   In 1992/1993 two baboon to human liver transplants were performed in the USA. The patients died at 26 days and 70 days following the transplants. The livers never achieved normal function and the patients died from complications associated with the transplant procedure; these included peritonitis and fungal infection acquired as a consequence of the heavy immunosuppression that was employed.[9]

2.20   In 1995, in the USA, a pig liver was heterotopically transplanted to provide temporary metabolic support for a patient with fulminant hepatic failure (severe liver injury) until a human organ could be transplanted. The removal of anti-pig antibodies from the patient before the procedure and immunosuppressive therapy was instituted with the intention of reducing the reaction of the immune system. However, the patient suffered brain damage and died 34 hours after the xenotransplant.[10]

LUNGS

2.21   Research is being conducted into the transplantation of lungs between different animal species. In Japan, this work has involved the transplantation of lungs from one species of nonhuman primates to another (baboon to Japanese monkey).[11]

OTHER TISSUE

PANCREATIC ISLETS OF LANGERHANS

2.22   Islet cell clusters in the pancreas (known as islets of Langerhans) produce insulin. In diabetics, these clusters either fail and no longer produce insulin (Type 1 diabetes) or produce ineffective insulin (Type 2 diabetes). Substitute islets of Langerhans may be transplanted to produce insulin with a view to treating insulin-dependent diabetes.

2.23   In 1994 in Sweden, pancreatic islet cell clusters from genetically unmodified pig fetuses were transplanted into ten people with Type 1 diabetes. The porcine islet cell clusters survived in the human diabetic recipients for several months. However, insulin production was markedly suboptimal. [12]

---

[9]   Starzl, T.E., Tzakis, A., Fung, J.J., Todo, S., Demetris, A.J., Manez, R., Marino, I.R., Valdivia, L. &. Murase, N. (1994). Prospects of clinical xenotransplantation. Transplantation Proceedings. **26**, 1082-1088.

[10]   Makowka, L., Cramer, D.V., Hoffman, A., Breda, M., Sher, L., Eiras-Hreha, G., Tuso, P.J., Yasunaga, C., Cosenza, C.A., Wu, G.D., Chapman, F.A. & Podesta, L. (1995). The use of a pig liver xenograft for temporary support of a patient with fulminant hepatic failure. Transplantation. **59**, 1654-1659.

[11]   Nakajima, J., Kawauchi, M., Kawaguchi, G., Takeda, M., Matsumoto, J. & Furuse, A. (1995). Characteristic findings of pulmonary arteriography in xenografted lung of the primates. Transplantation Proceedings. **27**, 310-312.

[12]   Groth, C.G., Korsgren, O.,Tibell, A., Tollemar, J., Moller, E., Bolinder, J., Ostman, J., Reinholt, F.P., Hellerstrom, C. & Andersson, A. (1994). Transplantation of porcine fetal pancreas to diabetic patients. The Lancet. **344**, 1402-1404.

NEURAL TISSUE

2.24   In late 1995, brain tissue from non-genetically modified pig fetuses was transplanted into the brains of patients with Parkinson's disease in the USA, in an attempt to re-establish the production of the brain neurotransmitter, dopamine.[13]   Outcomes are awaiting detailed medical reports.   The same treatment procedure could be applicable to other neurodegenerative disorders such as Huntington's and Alzheimer's disease.[14]

BONE MARROW

2.25   In late 1995, baboon bone marrow was transplanted into an AIDS patient in California in an attempt to reconstitute his immune system.   Baboon bone marrow cells are resistant to HIV infection and the theory was that these cells would be accepted by the host and help to restore his failing immune system.[15]   However, in early 1996, it was announced that the baboon cells had not survived in the patient.[16]

2.26   The transplantation of xenogeneic bone marrow is also now being considered as a means of inducing tolerance (a state of specific immunological unresponsiveness to avoid rejection) in the human's immune system in advance of a solid organ xenotransplant, thus improving the chance of acceptance of the organ.

SKIN AND CORNEAS

2.27   Skin and corneas are used in allotransplantation and could also be suitable for xenotransplantation. Pig skin has been used in the past as a skin dressing for severe burns (but this did not work well and is no longer common). Viable skin from genetically modified pigs could be suitable for xenotransplantation, most probably as temporary dressings. For corneas, animal research is being conducted into the comparison of rejection mechanisms in corneal transplants between species (guinea pig to rat) and between animals of the same species (rat to rat).[17]

---

[13]   Transplants from animals - researchers turn to pig cells to treat Parkinson's Disease. The Washington Post, 16 January 1996.

[14]   Krazanowski, J.J. (1994). Recent advances in neural transplantation - relevance to neurodegenerative disorders. The Journal of the Florida Medical Association. **91**, 689-694.

[15]   AIDS patient given baboon bone marrow (1995). Nature. **378**, 756.

[16]   Baboon xenotransplant fails but patient improves (1996). The Lancet, **347**,457.

[17]   Takano, T. & Williams, K.A. (1995). Mechanism of corneal endothelial destruction in rejecting rat corneal allografts and xenografts: a role for CD4+ cells. Transplantation Proceedings. **27**, 260-261.

BLOOD

2.28   Research has been carried out into the potential use of transgenic pigs to produce artificial blood substitute based on human haemoglobin. The view is taken that more research is needed before it could be used as a blood substitute.[18]

GENE THERAPY

2.29   There have been recent developments in the transplantation of encapsulated genetically modified animal cells to humans for therapeutic purposes.[19] Trials using animal cells from several sources (for example, mice or hamsters) have either taken place in the US and Switzerland and proposals are awaiting approval in several European countries.

THE UK SITUATION

2.30   In the UK, Imutran plc are developing genetically modified pigs for use as source animals for xenotransplantation.   Their interest is primarily with the transplant of solid organs.   In September 1995, they announced the results of research involving the heterotopic transplant of pig's hearts into cynomologous monkeys (see paragraph 2.68) and their intention to move to xenotransplants involving humans over the next 12 months.

THE ANIMALS INVOLVED

2.31   This brief history of the use of animals in xenotransplantation demonstrates that a range of animals have been used for this purpose, with, on the whole, little success. The animals can loosely be divided into non-human primates (hereafter **primates;** for example, chimpanzees and baboons) and non-primates (eg pigs and sheep). Currently, attention centres on the (genetically modified) pig.

---

[18]   O'Donnell, J.K., Martin, M.J., Logan, J.S. & Kumar, R. (1993). Production of human hemoglobin in transgenic swine: an approach to a blood substitute. Cancer Detection and Prevention. **17**, 307-312.

[19]   Aebischer, P., Schluep, M., Deglon, N., Joseph, J-M., Hirt, L., Heyd, B., Goddard, M., Hammang, J.P., Zurn, A.D., Kato, A.C., Regli, F. & Baetge, E.E. (1996). Intrathecal delivery of CNTF using encapsulated genetically modified xenogeneic cells in amyotrophic lateral sclerosis patients. Nature Medicine. **2**, 696-699.

2.32   Not all animals are an appropriate source of tissue for transplantation into humans. The appropriateness of the choice of animal depends on several factors:

❖   the anatomical and physiological properties of the animal;

❖   the genetic make-up of the animal;

❖   the feasibility of breeding the animal in large numbers;

❖   the potential risk of transmitting infection from animal to human; and

❖   the ethical acceptability of using the particular animal for the purpose of producing organs for transplant to humans.

2.33   **Anatomical and physiological** similarity is important. Examples of anatomically appropriate species for transplant to humans are pigs, kangaroos and primates (chimpanzees, baboons, gibbons, orangutans). Pigs are considered to be the most suitable as they can be allowed to develop until their hearts are an appropriate size and they have broadly similar renal, cardio-vascular and pulmonary anatomy to humans. The baboon, by contrast, is generally too small to be an appropriate source for most organs.[20] Indeed, there are problems with the size of both chimpanzees' and baboons' hearts which contributed to the recipients' deaths in two cases detailed above (paragraphs 2.10 to 2.12). For the transplantation of pancreatic islet and neural cells, the only consideration is whether the animal can supply a sufficient amount of cells.

2.34   **Genetic similarity** of species is also important. Those which are genetically closely related are termed **concordant** species; those which are not closely related are **discordant**. Transplants between concordant species are more likely to be successful as the transplanted tissue is less likely to be rejected. This is because humans have natural antibodies (called **xenoreactive natural antibodies**) to discordant species in their blood, but do not have these natural antibodies to concordant species. Species which are concordant with humans are non-human primates (eg baboons and chimpanzees), whilst pigs are discordant with humans. Again, the success of xenotransplants relative to the species used is demonstrated in clinical experience to date. Those involving the use of primates tended to have longer survival. It is also important to note that further distinctions can be drawn between members of concordant species. For example, chimpanzees are genetically more like humans than are baboons.

---

[20]   Sachs, D.H. (1994). The pig as a xenograft donor. Pathologie Biologie. **42**, 217-219.

2.35   The animal's **breeding** ability is also important when considering the introduction of a breeding programme, to supply the required amount of tissue for transplantation. The main criteria to be taken into account are that the animals should mature quickly, have a rapid breeding cycle and can be amenable to captivity in farm-like surroundings. Pigs reach sexual maturity at around 6 months and produce large litters (10 - 12 piglets born, and 9-10 weaned, per litter).   The longer it takes to breed herds of a particular animal sufficient to supply sufficient numbers of organs, the less viable a large scale xenotransplantation programme becomes.

2.36   There are **ethical considerations** to be taken into account with the use of any animal. We explore these at length in Chapter 4.   Here we point out that different (and differing) ethical considerations may apply to animals of different species.   It may, for example, be considered ethically unacceptable to use an endangered species (eg chimpanzees) as a source of organs.   By contrast, it may be considered acceptable to use animals such as pigs which have been bred in captivity for many centuries.

2.37   Finally, the qualities which are more likely to make a xenotransplant successful (that is, the similarity of a species to a human eg primate to human) could increase the **risk of transference of disease-causing pathogens**.   Thus, pigs, in most instances, would be considered to pose less of a risk than baboons. Different considerations also apply to wild-born animals as opposed to captive-bred animals, as it is less possible to control infections in wild-born animals. Thus, there would be a further reason (apart from scarcity) which would counsel against the use of wild-born animals which are concordant to humans.   They are also more difficult to breed in captivity on the necessary scale and in conditions which would minimise the existence of pathogens. Indeed, in any event, it may be considered unacceptable to keep them in this way. Paragraphs 4.78 - 4.86 discuss this in more detail.

2.38   An evaluation and balancing of these various criteria has led to current attention being focused on the pig as the source animal for xenotransplantation.

THE STATE OF CURRENT SCIENTIFIC KNOWLEDGE

2.39   The success of xenotransplantation depends on the resolution of problems which relate to three distinct issues: physiology, immunology, and the inherent risks of infection. As noted above, much recent attention has concentrated on immunology and attempts to make a species which is discordant to humans (the pig) an acceptable animal source.   However, overcoming immunological reactions is only of interest if it is thought that the tissue will function as desired when transplanted.   Thus, we consider physiology first.

PHYSIOLOGY

2.40   The solid organs most likely to be transplanted are hearts, kidneys, and possibly lungs; that is, the organs in shortest supply in the allotransplantation programme. Livers may also be used for extracorporeal perfusion. Problems relate to the relative growth rates of xenotransplants in humans, the relative lifespan of the organs and the function of xenotransplants in humans. Due to the lack of success of xenotransplants to date there is little information on whether organs from a pig or primate would continue to function effectively in a human and, if they do, whether their function would be adequate to support human life and health in the medium to longer term. As regards other tissue, there are also potential difficulties with the transplantation of pig islet cells to humans, in that it is uncertain whether the insulin-producing capacity of these cells could maintain an appropriate blood glucose control in the human in the longer term.

HEART AND LUNG

2.41   The heart and lungs primarily have a mechanical function. Thus, animal hearts and lungs should be able to perform the same function as the human organ. However, as demonstrated by experience to date (paragraphs 2.10 and 2.12), it is crucial that they are, or could grow to, an appropriate size after transplantation.

KIDNEY AND LIVER

2.42   By contrast, the kidneys and even more so, the liver undertake much more complex biochemical and metabolic functions many of which may be species specific.

2.43   Pig kidneys may well be of clinical value even though they differ in structure and function from the human kidney. For example, a pig's kidney is almost unique in lacking a region known as the proximal tubule brush-border, which is important for biochemical filtering and exchange of important molecules, for example, uric acid. This could cause problems in humans as, while the human kidney reabsorbs about 90% of uric acid, the pig's kidney secretes it.[21]

2.44   Successful liver xenotransplants from species discordant with humans (such as pigs) may be difficult to achieve due to the complexity of the biochemical interactions of the liver with the rest of the body. The liver is the main source of blood clotting and fibrinolysis factors, as well as of many other complex functional proteins. If the porcine factors were to interact poorly with the relevant human proteins, recipients of pig livers could suffer from bleeding disorders.[22]

---

[21]   Simmonds, A. & Roch-Ramel, F. (1994). Pigs aren't people. Letter to New Scientist. 23 July 1994, pp 45-46.
[22]   Fabre. (1995). Nudging xenotransplantation towards humans. Nature Medicine. **1**, 403-404

Proteins produced by the pig's liver may also be functionally incompatible with those of a human recipient. In addition, the "foreignness" of these pig liver *products* could result in an immune response from the recipient. The antibodies thereby generated could cause immune complex disorders, for example, serum sickness type illnesses in the recipient.

2.45 There are also incompatibilities between a pig's liver functions and what a human needs. This is illustrated by reference to certain critical enzymes which control essential cellular functions. For instance, in contrast to humans, the pig's liver lacks the important enzyme guanase.[23]

2.46 Xenotransplants of kidneys and livers could possibly be used as short-term extra-corporeal support, rather than as substitute organs for patients with acute liver or kidney failure whilst their own organs are recovering. Extra-corporeal support could also be used for patients waiting for human organs to become available.

PANCREATIC ISLET CELLS

2.47 There may be physiological difficulties associated with the transplant of pig islet cells to humans. This is because there is a difference in homeostatic control of blood glucose levels. Humans have a higher normal blood glucose level than pigs. These higher glucose levels could act as a continuous stimulus to pig islet cells, inducing them to overproduce insulin and consequently die of exhaustion or alternatively, cellular adaptation could occur. It could also be possible to manipulate genetically the pig cells' response so that the stimulus for insulin production is re-set at a higher level. However, this is a complex problem.

2.48 Intense efforts have been made to achieve long term survival and functioning of isolated cell xenotransplants. However, to date overall results in restoring function have been relatively disappointing.

IMMUNOLOGY

2.49 The main problem in all forms of transplantation whether allotransplantation or xenotransplantation is that of tissue rejection. Current thinking and research contemplate the xenotransplantation of both solid organs and other tissue (including isolated cells). The rejection processes associated with xenotransplantation are commonly described in relation to solid organs and much of the current research work, particularly that on genetic modification, aims to address the rejection of solid organs from animals. We, therefore, consider first the problem of the rejection of solid organs. Then we will consider the rejection processes associated with other tissue, including isolated cells.

---

[23]   Simmonds, A. & Roch-Ramel, F. (1994). Pigs aren't people. Letter to New Scientist. 23 July 1994, pp 45-46.

2.50 Immunosuppressive drug therapy plays a central role in reducing rejection in allotransplantation. Currently the most important drug is Cylosporin-A. It was introduced into widespread clinical practice in the 1980s. It was initially used in human kidney transplantation and quickly resulted in an improvement in the rate of survival of these transplants. Recipients of cardiac and liver transplants also benefited from the drug. At first, Cyclosporin-A was used on its own but now it is common to use it in combination with other immunosuppressive agents. The challenge has been to avoid over-immunosuppression whereby patients develop life-threatening infections and, on occasions, tumours. Over time, relatively safe and effective immunosuppressive protocols have been established for allotransplantation.

2.51 These immunosuppressive protocols have not altogether eliminated the problem of rejection. Transplant recipients are still obliged to undergo drug therapy indefinitely. Thus, the search has continued for better immunosuppression and in recent times, new immunosuppressive agents have become available for clinical use.

THE PROCESSES OF REJECTION: ORGANS

2.52 Based largely on the experience with allotransplantation and xenotransplants between different animal species, four main types of rejection mechanism are documented. They apply largely to solid organs although cells may also be susceptible (see paragraph 2.73). They are termed: **hyperacute, acute vascular, acute cellular and chronic rejection**. As regards, transplants between discordant species, **hyperacute rejection** can take place within seconds or minutes of the surgical completion of the organ transplant. If hyperacute rejection is overcome, there is the possibility of another form of early rejection called **acute vascular rejection** which also causes a devastating attack on the blood vessels of the transplanted organ. If both of these types of rejection are overcome, there is the possibility of the development over weeks and months of a form of rejection based on cellular mechanisms; **acute cellular rejection**. Finally, after many months to years survival, transplants may become susceptible to **chronic rejection**, as has occurred in allotransplantation. Hyperacute rejection has been observed in xenotransplants. The possible effects of acute vascular rejection, of acute cellular rejection and of chronic rejection in the context of xenotransplantation are either not known at present or are sparsely documented, but parallels have been drawn from the long term experience of allotransplantation where these changes have been closely studied.

Hyperacute rejection

2.53   Hyperacute rejection is associated with xenotransplantation and occurs particularly in transplants between discordant species. Hyper-acute rejection is caused by naturally occurring antibodies and by complement activation (see Figure 1). Humans have pre-existing natural antibodies that bind to molecules (called xenoantigens; specifically the Gal-epitope) on the surface of the cells of transplants from discordant species.[24] These are known as xenoreactive natural antibodies (XNAs). The recipient's XNAs react with the endothelial cells (which line the blood vessels) as soon as blood flow is established to the transplant. The antibodies then react with the recipient's complement which is present in the blood. Complement (which is a group of proteins in the blood) becomes activated and acts to destroy the foreign cells of the transplanted organ by triggering a violent series of inflammatory processes. Normally, the complement proteins are prevented from attacking the body's own cells by the action of complement regulating proteins (Regulators of Complement Activity or RCAs), which are carried on the surface of cells. The most important of these regulators of complement activity are decay-accelerating factor (DAF, cluster differentiation CD55), membrane cofactor protein (MCP, CD46), complement receptor protein (CR1) and CD59 a membrane inhibitor of reactive lysis. When the correct regulatory proteins are present, they "down-regulate" (or reduce) complement activation and hyper-acute rejection. If they are not present, hyper-acute rejection will take place, sometimes within seconds, and the organ which has been transplanted will fill with clotted blood as its internal structure is destroyed. Regulators of complement activity are species specific, although they may be partially effective in preventing or moderating complement activation in a concordant species. This means that human regulators will only regulate human or, to some extent, a closely related species', complement; the regulators on the animal organ from a discordant species (eg pig) will only regulate the complement of their own species and will have no effect on the human complement of the organ recipient. Thus there have been efforts to find a way of expressing human regulators in pig cells, to make pig xenotransplants resistant to hyperacute rejection (see 2.64 and Figures 1 and 2).

---

[24]   Vaughan H.A., Loveland B.E., Sandrin M.S.(1994). Gal a(1,3)Gal is the major xeno epitope expressed on pig endothelial cells recognised by naturally occurring cytotoxic human antibodies. Transplantation. **58**, 879-882.

HYPERACUTE REJECTION

Figure 1: Xenoreactive Natural Antibodies (XNA) in the blood of the human recipient (1), targets the blood vessel lining cells (2) called endothelial cells (EC) of the transplanted pig kidney. This results in XNA binding to the EC and the activation of complement (3) with a resultant severe inflammatory process leading to hyperacute rejection (4) and death of the xenograft kidney.

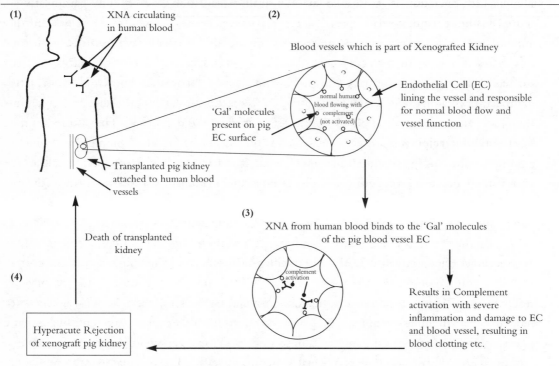

(1) XNA circulating in human blood

(2) Blood vessels which is part of Xenografted Kidney

normal human blood flowing with complement (not activated)

Endothelial Cell (EC) lining the vessel and responsible for normal blood flow and vessel function

'Gal' molecules present on pig EC surface

Transplanted pig kidney attached to human blood vessels

(3) XNA from human blood binds to the 'Gal' molecules of the pig blood vessel EC

complement activation

Death of transplanted kidney

Results in Complement activation with severe inflammation and damage to EC and blood vessel, resulting in blood clotting etc.

(4) Hyperacute Rejection of xenograft pig kidney

Figure 2: **COMPLEMENT ACTIVATION (by XNA binding to EC) and the role of regulators of Complement Activation (RCA) in preventing Hyperacute Rejection**

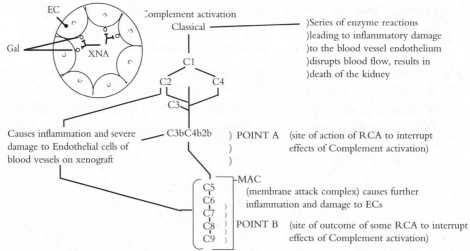

EC

Gal

XNA

Complement activation
Classical

C1

C2   C4

C3

C3bC4b2b

Causes inflammation and severe damage to Endothelial cells of blood vessels on xenograft

)Series of enzyme reactions
)leading to inflammatory damage
)to the blood vessel endothelium
)disrupts blood flow, results in
)death of the kidney

) POINT A   (site of action of RCA to interrupt
)   effects of Complement activation)
)

MAC (membrane attack complex) causes further inflammation and damage to ECs

C5
C6
C7
C8
C9

POINT B   (site of outcome of some RCA to interrupt
                effects of Complement activation)

Regulators of Complement Activation (RCA):-
the human genes for RCA have been introduced into Pig cells and RCA protein appear on the surface of the pig endothelial cells of the blood vessels where they neutralise the effects of complement activation ie prevent hyperacute rejection of the xenograft.

Examples of RCA	Site/ Function of RCA in neutralising Complement Activation
DAF (CD55)	membrane protein on EC)
	) interrupt events at Point A
MCP (CD46)	membrane protein on EC)
CD59	membrane protein - interrupts events at point B

Acute vascular rejection

2.54   If hyper-acute reaction is avoided, a xenotransplant may still be vulnerable to the process of **acute vascular rejection**.[25]   This reaction is likely to affect transplants whether from concordant or discordant species and tends to take place within days of the transplant procedure. The endothelial cells of the transplant are attacked and activated by newly formed antibodies and particular host blood cells which invade the transplant. These add to the blood clotting and inflammation, thereby promoting the rejection.

Acute cellular rejection

2.55   Even if acute vascular rejection can be overcome, acute cellular rejection and further rejection processes may take place. This reaction affects not only transplants between discordant and concordant species, but also allotransplants between unrelated members of the same species.

2.56   Acute cellular rejection involves specialised infection-fighting cells known as T cells, which act to destroy foreign cells in a process that is independent of antibody reaction. The response is similar to the reaction which occurs in allotransplantation and which may be controlled by the administration of immunosuppressive drugs. However, xenotransplant survival may require stronger immunosuppression than that used for allotransplant survival[26], as many more foreign antigens would potentially be present on xenotransplanted tissue compared with allotransplanted tissue. Indeed, recently published research indicates that some human T cell responses against pig xenoantigens are stronger than comparable allo-responses.[27]

Chronic rejection

2.57   Xenotransplants may also undergo **chronic rejection**. Clinical experience with allotransplants has shown that some transplants are rejected after months or years. The mechanisms involved are not fully understood but are thought to involve humoral and cellular mechanisms which lead to a slow but progressive reduction in transplant function. There is frequently a narrowing of arteries which restricts the amount of blood perfusing the transplanted organ.

---

[25]   Bach, F.H., Robson, S.C., Winkler, H., Ferran, C., Stuhlmeier, K.M., Wrighton, C.J., Hancock, W.W. (1995). Barriers to xenotransplantation. Nature Medicine. **1**, 869-873.

[26]   Steele, D.J.R. & Auchincloss, H. (1995). Xenotransplantation. Annual Review of Medicine. **46**, 345-360.

[27]   Dorling, A., Lombardi, G., Binns, R., Lechler, R.I. (1996). Detection of primary direct and indirect human anti-porcine T cell responses using a porcine dendritic cell population. European Journal of Immunology. **26**: 1378-1387.

RESPONSES TO THE PROBLEM OF SOLID ORGAN REJECTION

2.58　Improved understanding of the immunology of transplantation and of molecular genetics has created the possibility of countering many of the problems associated with the rejection of solid organs which have obstructed xenotransplant work to date.

Hyper-acute rejection

2.59　**Hyper-acute rejection** can be avoided by using the organ of a concordant species (that is, one to which humans do not have xenoreactive natural antibodies), by pre-treating the intended human recipient in advance of an organ transplant or by modifying the animal from which the organ is taken. Because of the need to look towards discordant species as sources, current research has concentrated on the latter two options.

2.60　Treatment of the intended recipient in advance of the xenotransplant　There is some potential for treating human recipients in advance of a xenotransplant. One method involves treating the patient's blood before the transplant to remove the xenoreactive antibodies. This should prevent the reaction which leads to complement activation. This technique was used in the extra-corporeal kidney procedure in 1991 (paragraph 2.17). However, in many instances, the recipient's immune system would regenerate the potentially damaging xenoreactive antibodies and measures would need to be taken to prevent this.

2.61　Another approach is to inject a protein complement inhibitor into the recipient of the xenotransplant. There are some early reports of successes with this approach. Pig hearts were transplanted into monkeys, who were then infused continuously with a complement inhibitor. These hearts survived for up to 32 days. Other experiments have shown that this complement inhibitor significantly delays hyperacute rejection in guinea pig to rat, and pig to primate, organ transplants. Work is now underway to develop a new second generation complement inhibitor.[28]

2.62　The ultimate goal would be to enable an organ recipient to tolerate the transplanted tissue. Such a technique is exemplified by the process known as **mixed chimerism** which, if completely successful, could obviate the need for potentially harmful immunosuppressive drugs.

2.63　Mixed chimerism depends on the immunological properties of bone marrow. The proposal is that, before the animal to human transplant, bone marrow would be taken from the animal which would supply the organ and transplanted into the intended organ recipient. The immune system of the organ recipient would be partly disabled by irradiation prior to the bone marrow infusion. This would allow the bone marrow from the animal to be accepted (not rejected) and grow within the recipient. Hence, the recipient would exhibit what is called a

---

[28]　TP10's potential in xenotransplants. Scrip No. 2068, 13 October 1995

chimeric state, with living human cells co-existing with the transplanted animal cells. After the transplant, the recipient's immune system would be allowed to regenerate, but as it would then include the animal's cells, the theory is that, after the solid organ transplant, the immune system would not recognise the new organ as "foreign" – and a state of immune tolerance is said to exist. Tolerance has been notoriously difficult to achieve, but some success has been reported recently with pigs and monkeys, using the mixed chimerism approach.

2.64   **Modifying the organ source** Research into modifying the source animal has concentrated largely on the genetic modification of pigs. There have been different approaches to countering hyper-acute rejection. The two main ones being considered are: (a) modifying the pig's genes by deleting the gene coding for the Gal epitope from pig embryos, so as to remove the cell surface antigen recognised as foreign by human xenoreactive antibodies, or (b) modifying the pig's genes to produce human regulators of complement activity (RCA) on their endothelial cell membranes, by injection of the relevant human gene into pig embryos. These genetically modified pig embryos are then implanted into sows.

2.65   **Deletion of a gene** Genetic elimination of the Gal epitope on a xenogeneic cell substantially reduces human antibody binding and the complement activation process. This approach is not yet possible in pigs but could provide an efficient and permanent way of eliminating the major effect of xenoreactive antigens and complement activation in hyperacute rejection. Such techniques have been shown to work in intact mice. But the work has not been without its complications. The mice produced without the Gal epitope all developed cataracts, and were blind.[29]

2.66   **Addition of a gene** This involves the modification of pigs to produce human regulators of complement activity (RCAs) on their endothelial cell membranes. Regulators of complement activity are species specific. Pigs have been bred to express human RCAs as well as pig RCAs on the lining of the organs. The theory is that this will mean that the pig's organs would still able to down-regulate the effects of their own complement activation, but, more importantly in the context of xenotransplantation, the organs would also be able to resist human complement activation when transplanted.

2.67   Only a small proportion of the piglets born following this genetic modification technique carry the human gene which has been introduced and the ones that do (known as transgenic pigs), carry it in varying amounts. However, the number of transgenic pigs can be quickly increased. The pigs which carry the relevant human gene are bred with normal pigs to produce piglets who have one "copy" of the human gene. These are known as heterozygous pigs and they produce the gene stably from one generation to the next. Cross-breeding heterozygous pigs

29   Tearle, R.G., Tange, M.J., Zannettino, Z.L., Katerelos, M., Shinkel, T.A., Van Denderen, B.J.W., Lonie, A.J., Lyons, I., Nottle, M.B., Cox, T., Becker, C., Peura, A.M., Wigley, P.L., Crawford, R.J., Robins, A.J., Pearse, M.J. & D'Apice, A.J.F. (1996). The a-1,3-galactosyltransferase knockout mouse -implications for xenotransplantation. Transplantation. **61**, 13-19.

produces offspring which have two sets of copies of the gene. These are known as homozygous pigs and are theoretically preferred as they will produce more of the desired human protein than will the heterozygotes.

2.68 There is experimental evidence to support this approach involving the addition of a gene. Transgenic pigs have been modified to express one of the human regulators of complement activity (decay accelerating factor (DAF, CD55)) on their organs. First, *ex vivo* perfusion studies involved passing human blood through transgenic pigs' hearts and through the hearts of control pigs (which had not been genetically modified in this way). The transgenic pigs' hearts continued beating for up to four hours, whereas the unmodified pigs' hearts showed a decline in function within minutes.[30] Secondly, in an *in vivo* experiment, transgenic pigs' hearts from heterozygous pigs which expressed high levels of DAF were transplanted into ten unmodified cynomologus monkeys whose own hearts were still present. The monkeys were also given immunosuppressive therapy. Two monkeys survived for over 60 days. The other eight monkeys did not survive due, for example, to the side effects of the immunosuppressive drugs. The animals were killed if they showed signs of distress in accordance with Home Office regulations. The survival rates were particularly significant. None of the hearts suffered hyper-acute rejection where the transgenic pigs were modified to express human-specific regulators of complement activity.[31]

2.69 Research is now being carried out to develop pigs modified for more than one human regulator of complement activity. The reason for this is that the three main regulators of complement activity (DAF, MCP and CD59) each block different stages in a complex series of complement activation reactions. Experimental evidence has shown that DAF has the greatest effect as it inhibits an earlier, central point in the activation reaction. However, evidence also exists that transgenic pig cells which express DAF plus one or both of the other factors can give additional protection against the complement activation process.[32] Experiments have demonstrated, to some extent, the success of the technique. Hearts from transgenic pigs expressing DAF and CD59 were transplanted, heterotopically, into the necks of three baboons. The hearts resisted the rejection processes and continued to beat for between 4 and 30 hours.[33] In more recent experiments pigs' hearts which express low levels of human CD59 have been transplanted into baboons. Again there was evidence of reduced tissue damage.[34]

---

[30] Cozzi, E., White, D.J.G. (1995). The generation of transgenic pigs as potential organ donors for humans. Nature Medicine. **1**, 964–966.Recombinant xenotransplants: what will the first one look like? Biotechnology News, 20 October 1995, 2-3.

[31] Recombinant xenotransplants: what will the first one look like? Biotechnology News, 20 October 1995, 2-3.

[32] Byrne, G.W., McCurry, K.R., Kagan, D., Quinn, C., Martin, M.J., Platt, J.L. & Logan, J.S. (1995). Protection of xenogeneic cardiac endothelium from human complement by expression of CD59 or DAF in transgenic mice. Transplantation. **60**, 1149-1156

[33] McCurry, K.R., Kooyman, D.L., Alvarado, C.G., Cotterell, A.H., Martin, M.J., Logan, J.S. & Platt, J.L. (1995). Human complement regulatory proteins protect swine-to-primate cardiac xenografts from humoral injury. Nature Medicine. **1**, 423-427.

[34] Diamond, L.E., McCurry, K.R., Martin, M.J., McClellan, S.B., Oldham, E.R., Platt, J.L. & Logan, J.S. (1996). Characterization of transgenic pigs expressing functionally active human CD59 on cardiac endothelium. Transplantation. **61**, 1241 - 1249.

Avoiding acute vascular rejection

2.70   Research is currently being carried out to understand the biological basis of acute vascular rejection. Recent findings suggest that in xenotransplantation it may result from reactions against blood endothelial cells similar to those involved in hyperacute rejection, with additional activity associated with various groups of recipient white blood cells.[35] Accordingly, strategies to avoid or overcome acute vascular rejection are still being developed. Approaches may involve drug treatments and the genetic manipulation of the cells (endothelial cells) which line blood vessels to prevent them from becoming activated and thus damaged.

Avoiding acute cellular rejection

2.71   It is speculated that the intense cellular response associated with acute cellular rejection in xenotransplants may be similar to that found in allotransplantation. Accordingly, it is believed that this rejection process should be amenable to the standard immunosuppressive drug regimen which are currently in use. The relative intensities of the cellular rejection in xenotransplant against allotransplant have not been compared critically and there are significant areas of uncertainty. It is yet to be determined whether there will be unique aspects to the cellular rejection associated with xenotransplants. As noted, some recent laboratory based studies suggest that xenotransplants may stimulate more vigorous cellular based rejection compared to allotransplants.[27]

Avoiding chronic rejection

2.72   As has been said, if a xenotransplant were to survive hyperacute rejection, acute vascular rejection, and acute cellular rejection, it might, as in the case of allotransplants, still be susceptible to the ill-defined chronic rejection process, and fail over a period of months to years.

REJECTION PROCESSES: ISOLATED CELLS

2.73   We have already seen that the xenotransplantation of isolated cells includes the transplantation of porcine fetal pancreatic islet cells, with the aim of producing insulin in people with Type 1 diabetes, and porcine fetal brain cells, with the aim of producing dopamine in patients with Parkinson's Disease. Such transplanted cells are relatively protected from immunological rejection including that mediated by blood antibodies (for example, xenoreactive natural antibodies and hyperacute rejection). This is due to the fact that, at least initially, they do not have a direct blood supply. However, over time, these cells would develop a blood supply and be exposed to antibodies, thus becoming susceptible to humoral rejection mechanisms, unless measures were taken to protect them. Furthermore, some weeks to months after implantation,

---

[35]   Platt, J.L. & Parker, W. (1995). Another step towards xenotransplantation. Nature Medicine. **1**, 1248-1250.

even without a blood supply, if left unprotected, they can become invaded by white blood cells (especially T cells) which can move through tissues to identify sites of implanted isolated (eg islet) cells. Cells would, therefore, ultimately become susceptible to all types of immunological rejection.

2.74   However, in the case of Parkinson's disease, the dopamine producing cells are implanted directly into the brain. The brain is seen as an immune privilege site in that brain tissue presents anatomical and physiological barriers to elements of the immune response and the transplanted cells are thus relatively protected from immune rejection processes.

TRANSPLANTED CELLS: STRATEGIES FOR PROTECTION FROM REJECTION

2.75   Transplanted cell clusters, for example, islet cells, may be protected by encapsulating them in biocompatible materials to exclude both antibodies and the recipient's T cells. The development of transgenic animals and their use as a source of cells would offer protection from hyperacute rejection. Islets in suspension are also readily amenable to modification by gene transfer. Genes could be inserted which could potentially help to counter other forms of the rejection process at the site of cell implantation. Genes for molecules like Fas Ligand (FasL) can, in the vicinity of the transplanted cells, suppress or kill the incoming recipient's T cells and thus prevent acute cellular rejection.[36]

FUTURE RESEARCH WORK

2.76   Several groups may undertake clinical trials this year. For example, in the USA, one group has received approval from the Food and Drug Administration (FDA) to use livers from genetically modified pigs as *ex vivo* support for ten patients with liver-failure waiting for human organs to become available. Paragraph 2.30 details the position in the UK.

---

[36]   Lau, H.T., Yu, M., Fontana, A., Stoeckert, C.J. (1996). Prevention of islet allograft rejection with engineered myoblasts expressing FasL in mice. Science, **273**, 109-112.

INFECTION

2.77 If the transplant were to function correctly and not be rejected, there would remain the possibility that an infection could be transmitted from the source animal to:

(a) the tissue recipient, with the further possible consequence of morbidity or even death, either as a result of the infection itself or because the infection has caused transplant failure; and

(b) the recipient's immediate contacts and possibly to the wider population.

2.78 Infections can be transmitted from animals to humans as a result of normal contact. Such infections are known as **zoonoses**. Xenotransplantation brings animal tissue into unusually intimate contact with human tissue, bypassing the natural barriers to infection (for example, skin and mucosal surfaces). The infections caused in this way have been termed as **xenozoonoses**.[37]

2.79 A range of infectious agents could cause disease following xenotransplantation. These include parasites, bacteria, fungi and viruses and, possibly, prions.

2.80 The unique circumstances brought about by xenotransplantation would give rise to several possibilities for the transmission of infectious diseases:

❖ Microorganisms, which under normal circumstances are considered as species specific, could infect a new host ie the human recipient.

❖ Microorganisms which cause no illness in the source animal, or are latent (that is, dormant) without producing symptoms at the time of tissue removal could give rise to an infection in the human recipient.

❖ The immunosuppressed environment could make the human transplant recipients more susceptible to microorganisms.

❖ An animal microorganism from the transplanted organ/tissue could combine with a human microorganism to generate a new and dangerous disease-causing organism. This is particularly relevant to viruses.

There is also another possibility which is not specifically one of transmission but which relates to the action of animal microorganisms. These may maintain species specificity but undergo local reactivation in the animal tissue, leading to transplant disease and failure.

---

[37] Michaels, M.G. & Simmons, R.L. (1994). Xenotransplant-associated zoonoses - strategies for prevention. Transplantation. **57**, 1-7.

2.81   The micro-organisms in question could be **known**; that is, they have already been identified, whether or not they cause disease. However, it is also possible that there are **unknown** agents, which have not yet been identified. It is possible that these do not cause disease in the host animal or have not yet been identified as doing so.

2.82   In the following section we give an overview of the infectious agents which cause concern in the context of xenotransplantation (it is not comprehensive, nor is it designed to be so). Information is drawn in some measure from the Report of the Workshop on Infectious Disease and Xenotransplantation which is attached at Annex C. As attention currently focused on the pig as the source animal, we similarly focus on known pig infectious agents and the potential for unknown infectious agents. However, examples are also drawn from experience with other animals. We concentrate on which pathogens are known, whether they are known to be transmissible between species (and in particular, between a source animal species and humans), and whether they can be excluded from the particular tissue to be transplanted, the source animal, or the source herd.[38] [39]

2.83   This last point raises issue of control. Not all pathogens that may infect the pig, or other animals, need be a concern in xenotransplantation. There are ways to reduce the risks posed by infectious agents and we outline these first.

STRATEGIES FOR CONTROL

2.84   Various measures can be taken to control or reduce the risk of transmission of infectious agents from source animals to humans.

2.85   The **choice of animals** to be used would be important. For example, wild-born animals may be thought to carry more risk than animals bred in captivity. Wild-born animals have an unknown history of infection and would have been susceptible to environmental infection. As noted earlier, evidence suggests that most pig pathogens are less likely to infect humans than are primate pathogens.

2.86   **Captive breeding conditions** could be designed to exclude known pathogens and to keep the potential source animals in circumstances which would greatly reduce the risk associated with infectious agents. One such method is known as **specific-pathogen-free** breeding. The aim is to reduce the access of pathogens to the herd; for example through control of feeding, air and exclusion of contact with animals outside the herd. Such methods are logistically more difficult to implement for primates than for pigs. Breeding techniques such as artificial insemination and delivery techniques such as hysterectomy could also contribute to reducing the risk from pathogens. At the stage of tissue removal, aseptic removal conditions would be required.

---

[38]   Allan, J.S. (1995). Xenograft transplantation and the infectious disease conundrum. ILAR Journal. **37**, 37-48.
[39]   Chapman, L.E., Folks, T.M., Salomon, D.R., Patterson, A.P., Eggerman, T.E. & Neguchi, P.D. (1995). Xenotransplantation and xenogeneic infections. The New England Journal of Medicine. **333,**1498-1501.

2.87   **Screening programmes** would be an integral part of the process. Such screening could include checks on the animal's general health and tests for specific bacterial, fungal, viral and parasite infection.   It would also be possible to keep **sentinel** animals, which would not be used as sources of tissue, but which would be killed periodically to enable thorough testing through post-mortem examination. Such testing is of use only for **known** pathogens.

2.88   If pathogens were identified appropriate action could be taken. This could be to treat the animal so that such pathogens would not be passed on, to rule out particular tissue for transplant (since, for example, certain bacteria are only present in particular parts of the animal), or to exclude the animal as a tissue source. For certain infections, follow-up action may need to be taken as regards the rest of the herd.

2.89   Where the risk is **unknown**, controls rely on screening the source animal for signs of infectious disease before the transplant and post transplant surveillance of the tissue recipient. This would include lifelong follow up of the person to check for the occurrence of unexpected illnesses and the study of data on all transplant recipients with a view to identifying any common patterns. Previously unrecognised infections should still be detectable but it may take longer to reach a diagnosis. The aim would be to detect xenogeneic infections in recipients before they could spread to the general population (if, indeed, they could do so). Should the disease be highly infectious but have a long latent period before symptoms show, the task of prevention would be that much harder.

2.90   Such control methods affect the welfare of the animal. We explore the various methods in use and their implications in Chapter 4.

THE PATHOGENS

2.91   In this section, we explore what is known in particular about pig pathogens, and more generally about pathogens which have been shown to be zoonotic. A more comprehensive review can be found in Annex C.

Fungi

2.92   Fungi are members of a diverse group of single or multicellular microorganisms. Some fungi cause disease in humans and other animals. However, in the context of xenotransplantation fungi are only thought to be of concern if they were present in the transplanted tissue. The use of animals bred in a specific pathogen free environment, with pre-transplant testing carried out for known fungi, would reduce the potential risk of infection. Fungal infection presents a risk to the recipient but would not be passed on to the recipient's contacts and is not, therefore, a risk to the wider population.

2.93   **Examples** of fungi in pigs are aspergillus, which is present in the respiratory tract, and candida, which can be present in the alimentary tract.

Parasites

2.94   Parasites are organisms which are able to live in or on, and cause damage to, another organism. The use of animals bred in specific pathogen free environments, accompanied by pre-transplant testing for known parasites, would reduce the potential risk of infection. It is possible to block most routes of infection for pig parasites. However, latent (dormant) parasite infections would not necessarily be detected unless organisms were transferred to the human recipient in the transplanted tissue. There is, therefore, a potential concern for the morbidity and mortality of the recipient (although effective anti-microbial agents exist for certain parasites). There would not, however, be a risk to the health of the wider population.

2.95   **Examples** Parasites such as *Toxoplasma gondii* can infect pigs, humans and other mammals. Both wild and captive bred baboons, and pig populations, show evidence of toxoplasma infection. This could pose a serious risk of transmission from the source animal to the human recipient after xenotransplantation. However, for pigs, a source of toxoplasma infection is contact with cat faeces and it is possible to block this route of infection.

Bacteria

2.96   Bacteria are members of a group of single-celled microorganisms. In the context of xenotransplantation they could be controlled by breeding animals in specific pathogen free environments. They would not be eliminated, however, since not all potential pathogens are detectable in animal tissues using available diagnostic tests. It is also possible that bacterial infections could be identified using a generic PCR amplification approach. If the animals became infected, and the infection is identified, they could be treated with antibiotics and tested for the eradication of the bacteria before any organs/tissues were removed for transplants. We are aware that opinion is divided about the use of antibiotics on source animals. Antibiotics can act to suppress infection but can also encourage the emergence of drug resistant microorganisms. In the context of xenotransplantation, it might be better to let any infection be expressed fully so that it could be identified. If bacteria are identified, a decision would then be taken about the use, or otherwise, of the animal as a source of tissue. However, it is also the case that immunosuppression might lead to the failure of standard antibiotic therapy, such that patients could require greater doses and longer use of antibiotics.

2.97   Despite the availability of various treatments, there remains the possibility of transmission of bacterial infection to the wider population.

2.98   **Examples** *Mycobacterium tuberculosis* can be transmitted to humans from non-human primates, which show few clinically apparent symptoms until the late stage of the disease when the infection has disseminated to multiple organs. It should be noted that there are increasing numbers of antibiotic resistant strains in humans. *Yersinia* spp, *Salmonella* spp, and *Campylobacter* spp are also known to cause zoonotic diseases, are capable of being transmitted between primates and humans and are commonly recognised in pig populations. These organisms would be unlikely to pose a risk unless the animal had the organism in its blood stream at the time an organ was transplanted. Thus, checks would have to be made for microorganisms in the source animal's blood stream.

Viruses

2.99   Viruses are micro-organisms, some of which can reside and replicate in human or other animal cells. Viruses are the source of considerable concern. Certain viruses are known to be zoonotic and animal viruses have caused fatal disease in humans. The infected humans have also, in certain cases, then transmitted these viruses to contacts. Viruses are difficult to treat with drugs and can mutate rapidly to resist the immune system; thereby infecting humans more readily. Viruses can be transmitted from person to person, through three main routes: through blood contact, ingestion and via the aerosol route. Therefore, they would pose an infectious hazard to the human recipient of animal tissue and, potentially, to the wider human population, if the appropriate infection route were not controlled.

2.100   The breeding of source animals in specific pathogen free environments would help to reduce the risk of viral infection. Also, it would be possible to vaccinate the animals against particular viruses. However, vaccination can only be of use for known viruses.

2.101   A further major problem lies in the inability to identify even known viruses. Infection with viruses can be difficult to detect. Even where the virus is known and a test has been developed, the test may be insensitive or give false positive results. PCR (the Polymerase Chain Reaction) is useful when sequences are known for specific viruses, but there appears to be a lack of generic primers for more general virus identification.

2.102   There are many examples of **known** viruses which cause zoonotic disease.

Known zoonotic viral infections

2.103   Many viral infections in animals can be transmitted to humans, either directly or by insect vectors. The majority of these infections do not occur in the UK, although animals imported from countries where they are endemic may be infected. In many cases, the animal hosts are rodents. However, larger mammals, including primates, are sources for some infections. Of most concern are infections that may be asymptomatic in animals, since infections that cause clinical disease can ordinarily be excluded by a period of quarantine. Examples of viral infection which have caused disease in humans include the following.

2.104   *Filoviruses* such as Ebola and Marburg virus have infected the human population with mortality rates of up to 90%. The source of infection and route of introduction to the human population in outbreaks in Africa are largely unknown. However, the laboratory outbreak of Marburg virus infection in Germany in 1967 was caused by close contact with the blood and tissue from African Green monkeys originally caught in Uganda. Primates are not however thought to be the natural hosts of these viruses.

2.105   There is only a limited potential for transmission of filoviruses within the human population because human to human transmission requires close contact with the blood of an infected person. The rapid onset of symptoms and death caused by these infections probably also plays a part in limiting spread. It is consequently easy to identify infected animal and infected humans. This is in marked contrast to infections with viruses which have been far more successful in establishing themselves in the human population because of the time that elapses between infection and symptomatic disease or death. An example is, the human immunodeficiency viruses, HIV1 and HIV2. These are *retroviruses* which we discuss below.

2.106   There also exists an example of zoonotic infection attributable to a medical product. In the 1950s, millions of people were exposed to monkey parvovirus, simian virus 40, a virus known to be oncogenic in laboratory animals, when they received contaminated polio vaccines made in monkey kidney cells. Subclinical (that is, symptomless) infection was documented in exposed persons by serum antibody and virus isolation studies.

Viruses of concern in pigs

2.107   A range of viruses found in pigs could be of concern. These include polyomavirus, parvovirus, circovirus, cytomegalovirus, reproductive and respiratory syndrome virus, and influenza virus. Herpesviruses and retroviruses, in particular, are a cause of concern.

2.108   Once *herpesviruses* have established infection, the infection is permanent. Moreover, the virus can remain latent for a long period of time. A common herpes virus in humans is the herpes simplex virus (HSV) type 1 and 2. In Old World Monkeys, Herpes B Virus is both able to establish latency and to recombine with HSV. The probability of such recombination in humans is low, though the result would probably be severe (see Annex C). Herpes B Virus has been transmitted from monkeys to humans with fatal results and, in one case, a victim infected his wife.

2.109   In the pig, herpesviruses include pseudorabies virus (aka Aujeszky's disease) and cytomegalovirus (CMV). We are told that pseudorabies virus can infect a related species eg cattle but there are no known cases of human infection. Moreover, we note that pseudorabies virus is not known to be present in pig herds in the UK. CMV has posed significant problems in allotransplantation. Since CMV can be transferred to the fetus *in utero*, it could not be eliminated from source animals by SPF breeding conditions. This is a matter of concern as CMV is common in British pig herds. It is not known whether porcine CMV can infect humans nor whether human cells can be infected in experimental conditions.

2.110   Generally, we are told that herpesviruses are of concern because:

❖   Herpesviruses are more likely to cause severe disease if transmitted to another closely related species. Pigs which are less closely related to humans than primates are therefore considered a better source animal for xenotransplants into humans in this respect.

❖   There are likely to be a number of *unknown animal herpesviruses*. Three new *human* herpesviruses have been discovered in the last ten years and it is fully expected that more will be revealed in the next ten years. Less is known about animal herpesviruses than human herpesviruses. It is more likely, therefore, that more unknowns remain.

❖   The hazard of recombination whereby new recombinant herpesviruses would be generated, would clearly be considerable. However, there is only a small probability of this occurring. There are no reports of herpesviruses recombining with each other, except when they are very closely related, for example, HSV1 and HSV2. It should also be noted that when genes have been exchanged between herpesviruses by genetic manipulation, the normal outcome is to create a virus the pathogenicity of which is only equally or less than the original material.

❖   *Latent viruses could be reactivated*. This effect could be exacerbated by interactions with other infectious agents, either released from the recipient to reactivate viruses in the donated organ, or vice versa. These agents could be herpesviruses or other viruses. In turn, viruses other than herpesviruses could be reactivated by these mechanisms. Equally importantly, the immunosuppression of recipients can promote viral reactivation.

Retroviruses

2.111   Retroviruses have been found in many vertebrate species, including non-human primates. There are three main sub families of retroviruses: *Oncovirus, Foamyvirus and Lentivirus*. In primates, endogenous baboon retroviruses and foamyviruses have been identified. The potential infection risks of these are not known.

2.112   Oncoviruses are related to leukaemia viruses and occur in baboons and pigs. They are known to infect human cells in culture. Foamyviruses are common in apes and old world monkeys, including baboons. Some monkey handlers have become infected and viral DNA has been found in their blood but, as far as is known, they have to date not become ill. Lentiviruses include the human immunodeficiency virus (HIV). HIV2 is genetically similar to simian immunodeficiency virus (SIV) which leads to an AIDS-like illness in primates.

2.113 *Endogenous Retroviruses* are retroviruses which are transmitted genetically from one generation to the next. We are told that retroviruses which are probably endogenous have also been identified in pigs but neither their relation to other retroviruses nor the mechanism of their association with potentially malignant disease is known. It is however, likely, that these viruses are uniformly present in porcine tissue as the viral DNA is incorporated within the porcine genome. It has recently been reported that one of these retroviruses has infected human cells in culture. Endogenous retroviruses also illustrate the limits of control. We are told that, as such viruses are transmitted genetically, they will be present in each cell of every member of a strain infected by the virus. Such viruses could only be eradicated by breeding animals to exclude the virus. If we can identify the presence of such viruses, but cannot then eliminate them, the object would be to determine their ability to infect and harm human recipients and to control such infectivity.

2.114 The main concerns associated with endogenous retroviruses are that:

❖ they are more likely to be transmitted between distantly related species i.e. they are xenotropic. Thus, in this regard, it is not possible to say that pigs are safer than primates.

❖ retroviruses which are not normally pathogenic in their natural host (ie such as the porcine endogenous retroviruses) could, if transferred to new species, replicate and become pathogenic in their new host. This may be because the natural host species has adapted to keep the endogenous virus under control, or because the endogenous virus is inherently non-replicating and non-pathogenic in its natural host species.

PRIONS

2.115 Prions are a modified form of protein. They are thought to be the transmissible agents that cause fatal neurodegenerative diseases in humans (e.g. Creutzfeldt Jakob Disease, CJD) and in a range of animals including sheep (scrapie), and cattle (bovine spongiform encephalopathy (BSE)). Collectively these diseases are known as spongiform encephalopathies. In humans, inadvertent transmission has been documented through certain transplanted tissue such as human dura mater (part of the lining of the brain) and through the administration of human derived pituitary growth hormone. Prion-related diseases do not seem to pass horizontally or vertically in many species (but an exception is sheep and cows may pass infection to their calves). Naturally occurring prion diseases have not been described in pigs. In experiments, pigs have not been shown to be vulnerable to infection through eating contaminated food, although they did become infected when infected material was introduced directly into the brain. It would be possible to exclude animal feed from the source animals' diet to eliminate any risk from feeding. However, *if* present in the animal source and in the transplanted tissue and transmitted to the human recipient, any resultant disease would be unlikely to be transferred to any other contact. Transmissible spongiform encephalopathy, *if* transmitted, therefore poses a potential risk to the recipient of the organ, but not to the wider population.

2.116 Primates are known to be susceptible to experimental challenge with these types of agent. We are also told that it is theoretically possible for spontaneous disease to arise in primates, although it might be expected that any such diseases would have a very low incidence.

SUMMARY

2.117 As regards the three main concerns associated with xenotransplantation; we conclude as follows:

❖ **Physiology:** although it would appear that hearts and lungs may be capable of functioning as intended in the recipient, questions remain about kidneys, livers and islet cells, in view of the more complex biochemical functions which they perform.

❖ **Immunology:** research is proceeding into the neutralisation of hyper-acute rejection and there are indications that such research is having some significant success. However, the operation and control of other rejection processes are not well known, particularly as neither human nor primate recipients of foreign tissue have survived for long enough for these processes to be studied.

❖ **Infection:** SPF or similar conditions could reduce many of the risks associated with fungi, parasites and bacteria but are thought to be of more limited use in reducing the risks from viruses, which would have the greatest potential for onward transmission. Prion-related disease has not been identified in pigs. This is not to conclude that it may not constitute a risk, but we note however that, measures could be taken to eliminate certain routes of transmission.

SECTION TWO

ETHICS

CHAPTER THREE:

POTENTIAL BENEFITS

INTRODUCTION

3.1   Having surveyed the current state of scientific knowledge of xenotransplantation, we can now begin to examine the ethical acceptability of xenotransplantation and begin to answer what we have called, Question 1:

In the light of current scientific knowledge, does xenotransplantation offer an ethically acceptable solution to the problems associated with the shortage of tissue for transplantation and to the problems caused by other medical conditions?

3.2   The case **for** the ethical acceptability of xenotransplantation rests on a simple claim: that clear benefits to patients will follow, or are at least likely to follow, from the practice. If that claim can be established, or shown to be highly probable, then there is a case for saying that xenotransplantation is ethically acceptable since it will produce benefits to patients.

3.3   From what we have seen of the science of xenotransplantation in Chapter 2, it seems that practical difficulties remain.   However, if these are overcome, there could be significant benefits for patients. Of solid organs, it is most likely that xenotransplantation of hearts, lungs and kidneys would be beneficial. The liver may not be suitable for xenotransplantation, although it may have a role in extra-corporeal perfusion.   Of tissue transplants, although these are in an earlier stage of development, it is possible that effective interventions could be developed for Parkinson's disease and diabetes.   Bone and skin xenotransplantation are also possible.

3.4   Therefore, patients requiring such transplants, and whose need is not being met through other means, could benefit if xenotransplantation were to become successful. We note here the possibility that there may be other ways of meeting the needs of these patients but consider this issue in more detail in Chapter 5.

3.5   It is widely thought that the need of patients requiring transplantation is not being met because there is a shortage of human tissue.   We will first consider the nature of this shortage of both solid organs and other tissue.   Then we look in more detail at the potential benefits which xenotransplantation could bring for these and other patients.

THE TRANSPLANTATION OF HUMAN TISSUE

3.6   The successful development of human to human **solid organ** transplantation began in 1954, when a single kidney was transplanted between two identical twins. Allotransplantation now includes renal, liver, heart and lung transplantation. Pancreatic and small bowel transplantation are still in the development stage. However, as the number of people for whom a transplant might be successful has increased, other developments such as road safety campaigns, have reduced the numbers of organs available.

3.7   A wide range of **human tissue, other than solid organs**, is used for therapeutic purposes. Whole blood is used to replace blood lost through, for example, haemorrhages or during surgery. Blood components are also used in the treatment of haemophilia and of burns patients. Bone marrow is transplanted in the treatment of leukaemias and certain inherited diseases. Corneas are transplanted in cases of corneal ulceration and heart valves are used during surgery. Bone itself is transplanted to reconstruct limbs following accidents, joint deterioration or bone cancer. There are also therapies which involve tissue replacement rather than tissue transplantation. Tissue inducing substances, such as human growth factors, stimulate the growth of replacement cells or tissue. Research is proceeding into the transplantation of cells to produce substances absent or lost in patients suffering from certain diseases (for example, dopamine in patients with Parkinson's disease and insulin in those with certain types of diabetes). Finally, cells can be grown around artificial supporting matrices to form tissue masses which can then be transplanted. For skin grafts, the matrix alone can be used to stimulate the growth of the patient's own blood vessels and cells.

THE NATURE OF THE TISSUE SHORTAGE

SOURCES OF HUMAN ORGANS

3.8   Human organs for transplantation are obtained from individuals who have died (cadaveric donors) and, to a much lesser extent, from volunteer living donors, who are almost always genetically related, or married, to the intended recipient.

3.9   For **cadaver** organs to be used, the donor has to die in hospital and almost always in an intensive care unit. Death is often the result of a road traffic accident or a cerebrovascular accident (stroke). It is legally permissible, under the Human Tissue Act 1961, to remove organs from a dead body for the purposes of transplantation, provided that permission is given either in advance by the deceased or subsequent to death by the relatives of the deceased. Public policy in the UK is that organ donation is a gift and permission is always sought from family members.

3.10   To give a picture of the scale of transplantation, 1003 (including 36 from overseas) cadaveric donors became available in 1995.

TABLE 1:

CADAVERIC SOLID ORGAN DONORS REPORTED TO UKTSSA, 1 JANUARY – 31 DECEMBER 1995 [40]

Donor Type	Country of Donation						
	England	Wales	Scotland	N Ireland	IRL	Overseas	Total
Kidney only	134	8	17	7	22	9	197
Kidney & Thoracic	21	2	4	-	7	-	34
Kidney & Liver	226	19	31	9	27	-	312
Kidney Thoracic & Liver	231	6	29	8	25	-	299
Thoracic only	5	-	-	-	-	16	21
Liver only	10	-	-	-	3	10	23
Thoracic & Liver	5	-	-	-	1	1	7
Pancreas only	1	-	-	-	-	-	1
Kidney & Pancreas	9	-	-	-	1	-	10
Kidney, Thoracic & Pancreas	5	-	-	-	-	-	5
Kidney, Liver & Pancreas	30	3	-	-	3	-	36
Kidney Thoracic Liver Pancreas	50	2	-	1	2	-	55
Total	**730**	**40**	**81**	**25**	**91**	**36**	**1003**

---

[40]   United Kingdom Transplant Support Service Authority UKTSSA) Annual Report 1995/96. Statistics for the United Kingdom & Republic of Ireland as notified to the UKTSSA.

3.11   The supply of cadaver organs is restricted both by the ability to retrieve them in an undamaged state and by the length of time for which they may be kept before being transplanted into the selected recipient.   Some organs, notably lungs, can be difficult to retrieve in a good condition. Lungs deteriorate rapidly after death.   They are also often damaged in trauma cases and as a by-product of other diseases in donors.

3.12   Unlike tissue, organs cannot be banked and the amount of time from their removal from the donor to implantation into the recipient is crucial.   In the case of hearts and lungs, this can only be a few hours; after retrieval they are perfused, double packed in plastic and packed in crushed ice.   Kidneys are more robust and can be kept for up to 36 hours in crushed ice.   The United Kingdom Transplant Support Service Authority (UKTSSA), the Special Health Authority which supports the transplant service in the UK and Republic of Ireland, maintains a national waiting list database with clinical and other details of the prospective recipients.   When organs are donated these details are used to identify suitable recipients for the available organs as quickly as possible.

3.13   The number of potential cadaveric donors has fallen over the last 20 years.   This is due, among other things, to the success of road safety campaigns such as making crash helmets compulsory for motor cyclists and to improvements in the treatment and prevention of stroke.   The number of intra-cranial haemorrhage (stroke) deaths in the UK has fallen by about three-quarters since 1970, from 18,225 in 1970 to 4,527 in 1994, although there was a small increase in 1995 to 5,235[41].   Over the same period deaths from road traffic accidents have more than halved from 7,883 in 1970 to 3,679 in 1995[42].   These figures are projected to fall further in the medium to long term as strategies such as that of the *Health of the Nation*[43], which includes targets to reduce the numbers of deaths from accidents and strokes, bear fruit.

3.14   Further, those patients who die of strokes may not be suitable donors due to changing medical practice.   It used to be the case that many stroke victims were placed in intensive care on ventilation in an attempt to save their lives, while an accurate assessment of their likely prognosis was made.   Now, it is possible to assess very rapidly the severity of the stroke and the likelihood of the patient's recovery.   Those patients with no chance of recovery will not be placed in intensive care as this will not be in their best interests.   The consequence is that organs are now available only from those patients who are thought to have a chance of recovery and are consequently ventilated in intensive care units, but who fail to recover and die.

---

[41]   Office for National Statistics (England and Wales) and the General Register Offices for Scotland and Northern Ireland. Note: Figures from Scotland and Northern Ireland are provisional.

[42]   Office for National Statistics (England and Wales) and the General Register Offices for Scotland and Northern Ireland. Note: Figures from Scotland and Northern Ireland are provisional.

[43]   Department of Health. The Health of the Nation: A Strategy for Health in England, HMSO 1992.

3.15 Donation from **living donors** is predominantly restricted to kidneys, liver-lobes and lung-lobes (where two donors are required, each of whom donate one lobe). Hearts (and very infrequently lungs and livers) can also become available through domino donation; that is where a patient receives, for example, a heart/lung transplant from a cadaver and donates his or her own heart to another patient. In all, only 184 living donors donated organs during 1995.

TABLE 2:

ORGANS DONATED FOR TRANSPLANT FROM LIVING DONORS REPORTED TO THE UKTSSA, 1 JANUARY – 31 DECEMBER 1995[44]

Organ	Country of Donation					
	England	**Wales**	**Scotland**	**N Ireland**	**IRL**	**Total**
Kidney	134★	4	11	2	1	152
Heart	28★★	-	-	-	-	28
Lung(s)	2	-	-	-	-	2
Liver	1	-	-	-	-	1
Cornea	1	-	-	-	-	1
Total	**166**	**4**	**11**	**2**	**1**	**184**

★ includes 5 cases where the donor was unrelated

★★ 1 donated (domino) heart was not subsequently used

3.16 The supply of living donors may, like cadaveric donors, vary over time. In 1995, there was a notable reduction in the number of live liver donations; one case in 1995 compared with 7 in 1994. The number of live donor kidney transplants increased to 152 in 1995 (compared with 126 in 1994, and 140 in 1993). The number of domino heart transplants also rose in 1995 by 17%. The number of such cases has doubled since 1993[45]. Further, ordinary live donors must be genetically related to the recipient. The donation of organs from unrelated live donors is regulated by the Unrelated Live Transplant Regulatory Authority (ULTRA), established under the Human Organs Transplant Act 1989. ULTRA reviews any proposed transplant of an organ from a live donor genetically unrelated to the recipient.

---

[44] United Kingdom Transplant Support Service Authority (UKTSSA) Annual Report 1995/96. Statistics for the United Kingdom & Republic of Ireland as notified to the UKTSSA.

[45] United Kingdom Transplant Support Service Authority (UKTSSA) Annual Report 1995/96. Statistics for the United Kingdom & Republic of Ireland as notified to the UKTSSA.

SOURCES OF OTHER HUMAN TISSUE

3.17   As with solid organs, tissue can be obtained from cadavers or from live donors, often as a by-product of other surgery. For example, bone is retrieved from cadavers or as a consequence of procedures such as hip-replacement operations. Fetal material, which may be the result of spontaneous or induced abortion, may also be used, although certain safeguards (such as the use of an intermediary to eliminate contact between the source and the users of fetal tissue) are laid down in guidelines[46].

3.18   Tissue can be preserved and banked for future use. Most stored tissue is either freeze-dried and sterilised (eg bone) or cryopreserved (eg skin, heart valves). **Bone** cannot usually be used in a "living state" as the presence of bone marrow means that it would be rejected by the recipient's immune system. It is reported (British Association of Tissue Banks) that bone is in short supply and that most bone banks have waiting lists of patients.

3.19   **Skin** may be retrieved from cadavers, but retrieval must take place within 18 hours of the donor's death. It is cryopreserved and can be stored as "living skin" for a number of years. Again, the British Association of Tissue Banks reports that there are shortages. Skin can also be retrieved from living donors (usually a close relative), particularly in cases of burns where the need is urgent.

3.20   Pancreatic islet cells are retrieved in clusters (islets of Langerhans) from pancreases obtained through cadaveric donation employing a process of mechanical disruption and enzymatic digestion.

DEMAND FOR TRANSPLANTATION

DEMAND FOR SOLID ORGANS

3.21   The demand for human tissue has been best recorded and demonstrated in the case of human organs. Many people are waiting both in the UK and internationally, for transplants. The size of the waiting lists gives some indication of the level of demand for transplants. At the end of 1995 6,133 patients in the UK still remained registered on the waiting list[47] (see table 4). However, the underlying levels of demand may be higher than these waiting lists indicate. For example, medical advances may make transplantation a plausible option for many people who, until recently, would not have been considered suitable for transplantation. Further, many of the diseases which can be treated by transplantation are more common in the elderly. But the elderly are less able to tolerate the toxic effects of the combination of immunosuppressive drugs

---

[46]   Polkinghorne J (Chairman) (1989) *Review of the Guidance on the Research Use of Fetuses and Fetal Material.* London, HMSO.

[47]   United Kingdom Transplant Support Service Authority (UKTSSA) Annual Report 1995/96. Statistics for the United Kingdom & Republic of Ireland as notified to the UKTSSA. Note: Waiting list statistics do not include data for Republic of Ireland

commonly used in transplant procedures. As immunosuppressive drugs and techniques are refined it is possible that more of these patients could be transplanted. However, elderly patients are also more likely to have other medical conditions. It is also possible that, if there were an unlimited supply of organs, transplantation might be considered an appropriate therapy for a wider range of conditions.

3.22   Figures on the number of organs donated for transplant are given in table 3; figures on numbers of potential recipients on waiting lists are given in table 4; figures on transplants undertaken are given in table 5; and figures on the number of transplants per million population in Europe and the USA for 1995 are given in table 6.

Table 3:

UK and REPUBLIC OF IRELAND TRANSPLANT WAITING LISTS AND ACTIVITIES IN 1995

Figures taken from United Kingdom Transplant Support Service Authority (UKTSSA) Annual Report 1995/96.

ORGANS DONATED FOR TRANSPLANT - Reported to UKTSSA
1 January - 31 December 1995

	Cadaveric	Living	Total
Kidney	1868	152	2020
Heart	331	28	359
Heart/Lung	66	-	66
Lung(s)	129	2	131
Liver	793	1	794
Pancreas	110	-	110
TOTAL (Solid Organs)	**3297**	**183**	**3480**
Cornea	2264	1	2265
TOTAL	**5561**	**184**	**5745**

Table 4:

NUMBERS WAITING FOR TRANSPLANTS IN UK. (31.12.95)

Organs	Number waiting
Kidney (includes pancreas & Kidney)	5241
Heart	344
Heart/Lung	165
Lung(s)	224
Liver	153
Pancreas	6
TOTAL (Solid Organs)	**6133**
Cornea	401
(this does not reflect true clinical need. Patients not usually registered in advance)	

Table 5:

NUMBERS OF ORGANS TRANSPLANTED IN UK (1995)

Organs	Number Transplanted
Kidney	1949
Heart	338
Heart/Lung	58
Lung(s)	113
Liver	687
Pancreas	16
TOTAL (Solid Organs)	**3161**
Cornea	2528

Table 6:
ORGAN TRANSPLANTS PER MILLION INHABITANTS (*PMP) IN EUROPE AND USA – 1995

Transplant Organisation	E.T **	E.F.G France	H.T. Greece	I.T. Italy	L.T Portugal	O.N.T. Spain	SK.T ***	SW.T Switzerland	U.K. & Ireland	U.S.A.
Cadaveric Kidney Transplants PMP*	27	24	4.2	18.3	36.8	46	26.3	22.6	27.2	32.4
Living Kidney Transplants PMP*	1.8	-	8.5	1.9	0.2	0.9	8.1	5.8	2.3	12.1
Heart Transplants (Heart-lung included) PMP*	6.8	7.4	1	6.9	0.5	7.2	4.9	6.1	6.5	9.5
Single Lung-Double Lung Transplants (Heart-lung PMP included) PMP*	1.5	1.4	0.1	0.75	-	1.1	2.7	2.6	2.7	3.7
Liver Transplants PMP*	8.2	11.1	0.7	7.1	7.0	18.1	7.5	6.7	11.3	15.3
Kidney - Pancreas Transplants PMP*	1	0.8	-	0.3	-	0.6	0.9	1.1	0.5	3.6

Source: Council of Europe Transplant Newsletter March 1996.   Note: The 1995 data has not been completely validated and should be considered as preliminary.

*   PMP – Per million population

**   E.T. – EUROTRANSPLANT – Austria, Belgium, Germany, Luxembourg, The Netherlands

*** SK.T.– SCANDIATRANSPLANT – Denmark, Finland, Norway, Sweden

Hearts

3.23   The two common indications for heart transplantation are complex congenital heart disease (which may require heart/lung transplantation) and end-stage heart failure due either to cardiomyopathy (weakening of the heart muscle leading to enlargement of the heart) or to ischaemic heart disease. Heart/lung transplants are indicated for pulmonary hypertension and may be used in patients with cystic fibrosis.

3.24   The UKTSSA Annual Report[48] for 1995 shows that 359 hearts were donated during 1995 but that, at the end of the year, 344 people remained on the waiting list; and that 66 heart/lung transplants became available but that 165 people were still awaiting transplants at the end of the year. Transplantation survival analysis gives, for patients receiving their (first) transplant in 1991/92, an estimated 1 year survival (ie. still alive with a functioning heart 1 year after the transplant) rate of 72%. The corresponding figure for heart/lung patients is 63%.[49]

3.25   Estimates from the USA[50] indicate that incidence is 23 per million population aged 45-74 and 166 per million population aged 75-94. Applied to the population in England and Wales, this would suggest an annual incidence of around 55,000 new patients each year for the 45-74 age group. If restricted to the 45-64 age group, the suggested incidence would be around 25,000.

3.26   There were 13,000 deaths from heart failure and cardiomyopathy in the UK in 1995, 3,000 of which occurred in people below the age of 75.[51] Transplantation is currently indicated in those patients who either do not respond to pharmacological treatment or who cease to respond to such treatment. Life expectancy in this group is very low (below one year). Heart transplantation is actively considered as a treatment option in patients under 60 years of age, occasionally in patients between 60-65 years of age and very rarely in patients over 65 years of age.

3.27   If xenotransplantation were to provide an unlimited supply of organs, it is possible that more patients with cardiomyopathy could be transplanted although the problems of concomitant disease and immunosuppression remain for elderly patients and could restrict the numbers who could benefit. Other groups who could potentially benefit are patients with cardiogenic shock, following acute myocardial infarction (heart attack). These are patients who survive their heart attacks if they are in hospital but who develop cardiogenic shock and die within a few days.

---

48   United Kingdom Transplant Support Service Authority (UKTSSA) Annual Report 1995/96. Statistics for the United Kingdom & Republic of Ireland as notified to the UKTSSA Note: Waiting list statistics do not include data for Republic of Ireland

49   Information supplied by UKTSSA – The survival rate figures are described as 'estimated' because the technique for analysis makes optimum use of all available data, where outcome at 1 year is not yet known.

50   Kannel, William B and Belandger, Albert J. Epidemiology of heart failure, American Heart Journal Vol 121 No 3 Part 1, March 1991

51   Office for National Statistics (England and Wales) and the General Register Offices for Scotland and Northern Ireland. Note: Figures from Scotland and Northern Ireland are provisional.

Additionally, approximately 1% of adult patients undergoing heart surgery develop cardiogenic shock in the early post-operative period and this similarly has a high mortality rate. Although transplantation for this condition is currently feasible it rarely occurs, as the patients' short life expectancy precludes waiting for an organ. It is thought that around 2,000 people per year suffer cardiogenic shock. There are also a small number of complex heart operations that may benefit from transplantation, though it is unlikely that they would amount to much more than 200 cases per year.

Lungs

3.28   Lungs can be transplanted as part of a heart/lung block, or as a double lung pair, or as a single lung. Lung transplantation is currently predominantly used as a treatment for cystic fibrosis and chronic pulmonary obstructive disease, but not all those who suffer from these conditions receive a transplant. There were 135 deaths from cystic fibrosis in the UK in 1995[52]. Around 95% of sufferers die before the age of 30 and around half do so before the age of 20 although overall life expectancy has now increased to 40. Chronic obstructive pulmonary disease (COPD) covers a broad range of diseases, including emphysema and chronic bronchitis, and is generally degenerative and fatal. As with heart failure, the prevalence of most COPD diseases rises rapidly with age and there is a limited range of alternative treatments other than transplants. There were 31,000 deaths from these conditions in the UK in 1995.[53] Other diseases which are suitable for lung transplantation include fibrosing alveolitis, pulmonary hypertension and bronchiolitis obliterans. Data providing approximate estimates of the need for lung and heart/lung transplants in the US would suggest a need for around 3500-4000 such transplants per annum in the UK for patients below the age of 65.[54] If transplantation were feasible for more elderly patients, this figure would be much larger.

3.29   It is also possible that transplantation could be a treatment option for patients with lung cancer, although such therapy is not likely to be successful if the cancer has spread to other parts of the body. There were around 76,000 cases of lung cancer in the UK in 1994/95[55], although again the majority are in more elderly patients.

3.30   113 patients received lungs in 1995 and 224 patients were on the waiting list at the end of the year.[56] The estimated 1 year transplant survival rate for patients receiving their (first) transplant in 1992/93 is 63%[57].

---

52   Office for National Statistics (England and Wales) and the General Register Offices for Scotland and Northern Ireland. Note: Figures from Scotland and Northern Ireland are provisional.

53   Office for National Statistics (England and Wales) and the General Register Offices for Scotland and Northern Ireland. Note: Figures from Scotland and Northern Ireland are provisional.

54   Laing, P. (1996). Sandoz - The Unrecognised potential of xenotransplantation. (Published by Salomon Brothers).

55   Source: Hospital Episode Statistics (England); Scottish Morbidity Records (ASD/SMR1); Patient Episode database for Wales (note Database 70% complete); and Hospital Inpatient System (Northern Ireland)

Kidneys

3.31   Transplantation is the treatment of choice for end-stage renal failure. It is generally accepted that 80 patients per million of the population below the age of 80 are likely to benefit from renal replacement therapy (this may rise to 90-100 per million population if patients over the age of 80 are included). End-stage renal failure may follow acute renal failure or be the final stage of a chronic renal condition eg analgesic nephropathy, reflux nephropathy, nephritides, uncontrolled hypertension, adult polycystic kidney disease and diabetes. Combined pancreas/kidney transplants are sometimes indicated for diabetes. This is discussed in paragraph 3.40.

3.32   Dialysis, discussed in more detail in paragraph 5.37, is an alternative treatment which can support people in end stage renal failure. Around 19,200 people are on dialysis in England. If there were an unlimited supply of organs, many patients currently being maintained on dialysis could be transplanted. This would result in an initial surge in demand while the waiting list was being cleared.   In the longer term, some 50 patients per million population may be suitable for transplantation, meaning the annual number of new transplants would be around 2500 in England. Again, this assumes that some 30 per million population who are in end-stage renal failure may remain unsuitable for transplantation despite the fact there would be organs available.

3.33   Although 2020 kidneys were donated during 1995, at the end of the year 5241 people were still waiting for a transplant.[58]   The estimated 1 year transplant survival rate for patients receiving their (first) cadaveric kidney transplant in 1991/92 is 69%.[59]

3.34   There could also be some circumstances in which xenotransplants would be the only transplant option. There is an increasing pool of kidney patients who have become highly sensitised to other individuals as a result of previous transplants and transfusions. Xenotransplantation could become a possible option for them if there were no cross-reactivity with the source animal (pig) antigens. Children, for whom there appears to be a shortage of donors of a suitable size, could also benefit from xenotransplantation.

[56]   United Kingdom Transplant Support Service Authority (UKTSSA) Annual Report 1995/96. Statistics for the United Kingdom & Republic of Ireland as notified to the UKTSSA. Note: Waiting list statistics do not include data for Republic of Ireland.

[57]   Information supplied by UKTSSA – The survival rate figures are described as 'estimated' because the technique for analysis makes optimum use of all available data, where outcome at 1 year is not yet known.

[58]   United Kingdom Transplant Support Service Authority (UKTSSA) Annual Report 1995/96. Statistics for the United Kingdom & Republic of Ireland as notified to the UKTSSA. Note: Waiting list statistics do not include data for Republic of Ireland.

[59]   Information supplied by UKTSSA – The survival rate figures are described as 'estimated' because the technique for analysis makes optimum use of all available data, where outcome at 1 year is not yet known.

Livers

3.35   The main indications for liver transplantation are chronic liver failure caused by cirrhosis (non-alcoholic and, less commonly, alcoholic), hepatitis, and biliary atresia in childhood and acute liver failure caused by viral hepatitis or toxic drugs (eg paracetamol). Liver transplantation has also been used as a treatment for liver cancer. It is also possible to replace part of the liver with the equivalent section of a donor organ[60], again to give it support until it can regenerate. In 1995, in the UK, 86 patients died of acute and subacute liver failure, 4,739 died of chronic liver failure and 608 of primary cancer of the liver.[61]

3.36   In 1995, 794 livers were donated and 153 people remained on the waiting list at the end of the year.[62] The estimated 1 year transplant survival rate for patients receiving their (first) liver transplant in 1991/92 is 69%.[63]

3.37   In some instances, livers are also employed for extra-corporeal support (where the patient is linked to the liver which remains outside the body). It is for this purpose that xenotransplantation could most likely be beneficial. The aim of such support is to assist the patient's liver and give it time to regenerate. This could be of use for those patients whose livers are damaged through the toxic effect of drugs.

DEMAND FOR OTHER HUMAN TISSUE

Pancreatic islet cells

3.38   The transplantation of the pancreas or the transplantation of pancreatic islet cells is designed to treat diabetes. Some diabetics are deficient in the pancreatic endocrine function and it is this deficiency that transplantation aims to correct.

3.39   In the UK, of those patients on the waiting list for kidneys in 1995, 46 also required a pancreas while 6 patients needed a pancreas transplant only. 110 pancreases were donated during 1995.[64] The surplus was used largely for research. The one-year patient survival rate is assessed as 91% and the one year insulin independence rate was 70%.[65]

---

[60]   McNair A N B et al. (1995) Recent Advances, Hepatology. British Medical Journal, Vol 311.

[61]   Office for National Statistics (England and Wales) and the General Register Offices for Scotland and Northern Ireland. Note: Figures from Scotland and Northern Ireland are provisional.

[62]   United Kingdom Transplant Support Service Authority (UKTSSA) Annual Report 1995/96. Statistics for the United Kingdom & Republic of Ireland as notified to the UKTSSA. Note: Waiting list statistics do not include data for Republic of Ireland.

[63]   Information supplied by UKTSSA - The survival rate figures are described as 'estimated' because the technique for analysis makes optimum use of all available data, where outcome at 1 year is not yet known.

[64]   United Kingdom Transplant Support Service Authority (UKTSSA) Annual Report 1995/96. Statistics for the United Kingdom & Republic of Ireland as notified to the UKTSSA

[65]   Hakim, N. (1996). Pancreatic Transplantation. UKTSSA Users Bulletin Issue 19

3.40   Diabetes constitutes a group of chronic disorders with common features. It is estimated that around 2.4% of the UK population have clinically diagnosed diabetes. The number of currently undiagnosed individuals may increase this number to around 3%. There are three main forms of diabetes: insulin-dependent diabetes mellitus (Type 1) in which the pancreatic islet cells, present at birth, cease to function (around 15% of people with diabetes); non-insulin-dependent diabetes mellitus (Type 2) in which the islet cells produce insufficient insulin, or do not target the insulin correctly (around 85% of people with diabetes); and gestational diabetes (or diabetes of pregnancy). Type 1 diabetics are treated by dietary restrictions and parenteral insulin and type 2 by dietary restrictions and oral therapy, plus parenteral insulin if the diabetes cannot be otherwise managed. However, within 10 years of a diagnosis of diabetes, complications associated with diabetes usually develop. These include diabetic retinopathy, renal failure (which can itself lead to a need for a kidney transplant), peripheral vascular disease, and coronary heart disease. Transplantation of islet cells would be considered primarily for Type 1 diabetics, although it could also be considered for some Type 2 diabetics, particularly those dependent on insulin.

3.41   Pancreas, and islet cell, transplants aim to remove the need for daily insulin injections and are designed to prevent the long-term complications associated with diabetes. They offer the promise of improving the patient's quality, and length, of life.

3.42   Pancreas transplantation carries the usual problems associated with immunosuppression. For this reason, pancreas transplants tend to be considered only for diabetes patients who are already suffering from complications. For instance, such patients may have diabetes-induced renal failure and may therefore already have received a kidney transplant (and receiving immunosuppressive drugs already) or may be on dialysis and require a pancreas/kidney transplant. Alternatively, patients may be considered for pancreas transplantation if they have diabetic complications such as neuropathy or there is extreme difficulty in controlling the diabetes. But transplantation of the pancreas remains problematic. The procedure is technically complicated and problems arise with the leakage of powerful digestive enzymes from pancreatic tissues. Combining kidney and pancreas transplants has been a more successful means of overcoming these difficulties. However, we are told that the number of pancreas transplants worldwide is in decline, reflecting the generally poor success rates in most centres.

3.43   The difficulties with pancreas transplants mean that islet transplantation surgery is a preferred option. This obviates major surgery and the difficulties associated with whole organ transplants. But this procedure is also technically difficult and there has been only limited clinical success to date. Partial success is reported with 20% of the patients achieving transitory insulin independence (7% of the patients did not need exogenous insulin one year after transplantation[66]).

---

[66]   Inveradi L and Camillo R. (1996). Immunology Today, Vol.17, Number 1

3.44 Islet cell transplantation has been attempted using islet cells from both humans and from (non genetically modified) pigs. There are problems associated with using islet cells from human donors, in particular with the yield and purity of the islet preparations. There is an estimated minimum number of islets required to be transplanted in order to establish normal blood sugar level control. This number is rarely obtained from a single donor. Multiple donors are therefore needed and islet preparations must be pooled and cryopreserved (frozen) until sufficient cells of a particular donor type are accumulated. This is particularly difficult given the problems of cadaveric donor shortage. Further, the preparation of islets is a time consuming, albeit straightforward, procedure and, as with whole pancreas transplants, the islet preparation may become contaminated with pancreatic digestive enzymes which is thought to be detrimental to the outcome of transplantation. One possible alternative is the use of human fetal islets, which retain the capacity for growth, but this option brings with it the ethical difficulties associated with the use of fetal tissue.

3.45 The use of islet cells from an animal is perceived as a better option for two reasons. First, the supply, preparation and manipulation of islets from an animal source would greatly alleviate many of the difficulties associated with islets from human sources. In principle, a sufficient number of genetically uniform islets, prepared under conditions of strict quality control for viability and purity, could be made available at a time most suited for transplantation. Secondly, islets from animal sources also have an important theoretical advantage over allotransplants. It has been shown that well-matched human islet transplants into Type 1 diabetic patients are rapidly destroyed. This is due to the occurrence of an accelerated form of the original auto-immune disease which made the recipient diabetic. The recipient's T cells, responsible for the original auto-immune islet destruction recognise a human self-antigen and induce an inflammatory destruction of the islets. It is most unlikely that the pig islet cells will express the human self-antigen and so they would theoretically be resistant to the recurrence of autoimmune disease. Further, the pig cells could deliberately be selected or manipulated to ensure that rejection was unlikely to happen (see paragraph 2.75).

Neural tissue

3.46 The loss of dopamine, a chemical messenger within the centre for movement in the mid-brain, is thought to result in Parkinson's disease. There are more than 120,000 people with Parkinson's disease in the UK. Parkinson's disease is a progressive neurological disorder affecting learned voluntary movements such as walking, talking and writing. The main treatment is drug therapy and, with optimal drug treatment, life expectancy is normal. However, the quality of the patient's life can be severely impaired in the majority of cases over time by the side-effects of the drug therapies. Clinical trials have been conducted of the transplantation of human fetal cells into the brain to produce substitute dopamine. Again, the cells need to be obtained from multiple (around five or six) sources. We are told that results from a few centres show clearly that human fetal cells will survive, connect, produce dopamine and restore some aspects of motor function. However, the availability of the cells and, again, the ethical questions surrounding the use of fetal tissue have limited these procedures. Researchers are actively pursuing the use of pig fetal cells (both unmodified and genetically manipulated).

Bone

3.47 Bone is often used in joint replacements, in revision surgery which is required if such joint replacements fail, in reconstructive surgery following accidents and in some cases of bone cancer. Bone is often processed and may be used as bone paste for other reconstructive procedures. Animal bone (processed bovine bone) is already used but it does not always work well as it does not incorporate into the human body and can result in sterile cysts. It is thought that bone from genetically modified animals could have better results. The current information available suggests that in 1994/95 there were around 26,000 operations performed in the UK using bone grafts and around 50, 000 procedures using bone paste or cement.[67]

Skin

3.48 Skin transplantation can be used to treat burns and ulcers. Often, the skin to be transplanted can be taken from another part of the patient's body. With seriously injured patients, who require grafting over more than 50% of the body surface area, the patients' own grafting sites are limited. We are told that in these cases the provision of early skin cover is related to long-term survival.

3.49 Donated skin from the recently deceased or living relatives may be used. However it is also possible to use cultured skin, whereby layers of fragile keratinocytes can be grown in tissue culture from a small sample of the patient's own skin. This takes time (3–4 weeks) and the delay can often cause problems. Further, the skin produced is frequently small in area and fragile. There are, however, several ways of improving survival and durability in cultured skingrafts. One method is to use a dermal collagen layer upon which they are spread. Another is to crop the patient's own donor sites (however limited) at intervals. In some cases (eg the scalp) thin grafts can be retrieved every week. These grafts can be expanded by being meshed or used in strips, interspersed with homografts or cultured skin. There are also various artificial skin preparations. These have been moderately useful for dressing, and helping to deslough burn wounds.

3.50 Pig skin is already used in a processed and sterilised form. Genetically modified pig skin, which could be used as "living" tissue, could offer better outcomes. It could be particularly useful in the case of burns. The current information available suggests that in 1994/95 there were around 400 skin grafts performed, not using the patient's own skin, in the UK.[68] The figures available do not distinguish between the sources of these grafts.

---

[67]   Source: Hospital Episode Statistics (England); Scottish Morbidity Records (ASD/SMR1); Patient Episode database for Wales (note Database 70% complete); and Hospital Inpatient System (Northern Ireland)

SUMMARY

3.51   There appears to be a range of conditions which could, potentially, benefit from xenotransplantation, in that;

1.   xenotransplantation could provide sufficient tissue to meet the need eg for heart transplantation

2.   tissue for xenotransplantation could be supplied as it was needed so that those patients whose conditions would preclude waiting for an organ could be treated eg patients in cardiogenic shock or burns patients.

3.   xenotransplanted tissue may be better than human tissue for some procedures, for example, in the case of islet cell transplantation.

---

68   Source: Hospital Episode Statistics (England); Scottish Morbidity Records (ASD/SMR1); Patient Episode database for Wales (note Database 70% complete); and Hospital Inpatient System (Northern Ireland)

CHAPTER FOUR:
CONCERNS

INTRODUCTION

4.1   In Chapter 3, we considered the case **for** xenotransplantation. Now, we examine the other side of the coin. There are important ethical arguments **against** xenotransplantation. It is these which we must consider now. They can be placed in two categories. There are those arguments which lead to the conclusion that xenotransplantation is not acceptable in any circumstances, no matter what benefits it may seem to bring, and there are arguments which suggest that only in some circumstances, or with certain safeguards, may it be acceptable.

4.2   We must begin with the first and principal question: is the use of animals as a source of tissue ethically acceptable? If the answer is no, all other questions fall away. Xenotransplantation should not proceed. If the answer is otherwise, there then arise a number of further questions, each of which must be satisfactorily resolved before a final view can be taken as to the ethical acceptability of xenotransplantation.   They can be seen as gateways through which the argument must pass.

4.3   We note at this point that we consider the harm intrinsic in xenotransplantation, both to the animal and to the patient, in terms of the pig. We do so as scientific evidence suggests that it is the pig which is the most appropriate source of tissue for transplant to humans and because most research and development effort focuses on this animal. However, other animals may in future be considered as sources for xenotransplantation. We consider that the issues of principle that we examine here would remain the same even if points of detail would differ.

THE PRINCIPAL QUESTION: THE USE OF ANIMALS

4.4   Religious and secular traditions of ethical thinking in the west have tended to give animals a low status. The Bible sets the tone in the very first chapter of Genesis when God places human beings above animals. Religious thinkers have followed this lead. For example, Aquinas holds that we have no duty of charity towards animals as such, although we should not be cruel to them in case this develops habits of cruelty which might carry over into our dealings with human beings. Some secular thinkers such as Descartes take the line that animals are like machines which might move and emit sounds but have no feelings. Kant finds supreme ethical worth in the exercise of the autonomous or purely rational will. Human beings have the capacity for autonomous action and are on that account 'ends in themselves'. Animals do not have that capacity so their value is simply to be a means to human ends. Like Aquinas, Kant holds that the only reason we should be kind to animals is to train ourselves in kindness, which can then be shown to human beings. In essence, the Judaeo-Christian religious tradition excluded animals from ethical consideration because they were thought to lack soul, and the secular tradition rejected them because they lacked reason, or some reason-dependent ability such as the ability to use language.

4.5   During the last few decades, the situation has changed dramatically. There has been an explosion of popular interest in the natural world including animals, as evidenced, for example, by the appearance of the 'green movement,' the spread of vegetarianism and the commercial success of products 'not tested on animals'. Basically there are two distinct but overlapping movements. The 'animal rights' movement, which opposes any exploitation of animals for human ends; and the environmental movement, which opposes the exploitation of the natural environment, including animal species, for human ends. The environmental movement is divided in two: 'shallow' environmentalists and 'deep' environmentalists. The 'shallow' environmentalists oppose the exploitation of the planet because this will eventually harm human beings: the 'deep' environmentalists think that the present, what they view as reckless, exploitation of the environment is wrong in itself. These popular and political movements have significant theoretical underpinning. Any review of xenotransplantation must take account of these various arguments and recognise the fact that, whatever view we take here, there will be a responsible body of opinion which will oppose it.

4.6   There are a range of arguments against the use of animals for xenotransplantation: the religious, those based on considerations of what is "natural" and "unnatural", and those based on the assertion of animal rights.

THE RELIGIOUS ARGUMENT

4.7   One kind of religious argument is to the effect that every living thing is sacred, and therefore it would be wrong to kill an animal for human benefit. A second sort of religious argument is that animals, or some animals including pigs, are unclean and therefore their organs ought not to be transplanted into human beings. These arguments depend on beliefs which not everyone shares and which cannot be established beyond doubt.

NATURALNESS AND UNNATURALNESS

4.8   Some people might argue that animal transplants are unethical because they are 'unnatural'; that it is 'contrary to nature' that a human being should be given, for example, an animal heart or kidney.

4.9   As we have seen, the animal most likely to be used for xenotransplantation is the pig. There would appear to be a simple argument in favour of using the pig. It begins by reminding us that there is a consensus moral position that the pig's right to life is outweighed by the benefits its carcass will bring to human beings as food. (This position is, of course, compatible with continuing to maintain that in the process of rearing and slaughtering the pig has a right to have its suffering minimised). Now, the argument goes, if there is a consensus that it is ethically justifiable to eat pigs, what can be wrong with using their organs or tissue for the purpose of transplant? Indeed, some who regard it as wrong to use pigs and other animals as food (because other foods are available) may admit that animal parts can legitimately be used for human therapeutic purposes, if there is no non–animal substitute.

4.10   There is, however, a difficulty with this simple argument which is best appreciated by using the (admittedly ambiguous) terms 'natural' and 'unnatural'. It can be argued that whereas the eating of animal flesh may or may not be ethically right, it is, at least, 'natural' in the sense that many other animal species in fact do it and (as has been claimed by some) human beings are biologically carnivorous or at least omnivorous. On the other hand, the transplant of animal tissue into human beings is 'unnatural' in the sense that it is a human artifact. This of course does not mean that it is wrong - perhaps every medical intervention is in that sense 'unnatural'. It does, however, mean that the analogy between eating animals and using them for transplantation is misleading. Further it suggests that the "natural" - "unnatural" distinction may offer guidance as to what is ethically acceptable.

4.11   It is difficult to assess this argument. Those who are impressed by it will support the use of the term 'unnatural' by saying that the scientists are 'playing God'. This of course has been said of the introduction of many life saving therapies, and perhaps our tendency to use the word 'unnatural' here simply reflects an understandable fear of the unknown. But it is also possible to be too sophisticated and too much impressed by science. What is being proposed is (a) inserting the genes of one species into that of another, and (b) transplanting organs and tissues so treated into the human species. Such a process seems profoundly different from previous medical interventions. Hence, the use of the term 'unnatural' is difficult to repress. Furthermore, it is clear that unnatural may sometimes also mean wrong. The two are not, however, inevitably related. It may be that before it can be found to be ethically unacceptable, something has to be both unnatural and to have predominantly harmful consequences when set on a scale of benefits and harms. Thus, any conclusion as to whether xenotransplantation is or is not "natural" will not prevent the need to examine the various arguments which suggest that xenotransplantation may bring more harm than good.

ANIMAL RIGHTS

4.12   The third set of arguments which may suggest that xenotransplantation is ethically unacceptable from the outset are the arguments falling under the general heading of "animal rights". The claim that animals have rights has often been dismissed on superficial grounds, such as that it would be absurd to expect animals to vote. There are clearly important differences between humans and other animals and, if animals had rights, the differences would affect what rights animals have. In general, rights safeguard interests. Human animals certainly have more, and more complex, interests than non-human animals; but all animals, human and non-human, share certain interests, such as in avoiding suffering and leading a life. These fundamental rights have been called natural or inalienable rights. It can be maintained that, if there is a human natural right to life, or to be safeguarded against unmerited suffering, there must in logic be similar rights for animals, for they too have these vital interests.

4.13   The origins of the modern western conception of rights are in a tradition of ethical thinking which goes back to the Greeks. This ancient tradition recognised that actual human laws might, in specific jurisdictions, be unjust. The tradition appealed to a 'natural law' or *ius naturale* to which we all have access through our reason and in terms of which we might judge actual laws. The idea was taken up in Roman law as *ius gentium* – a basic system of law which could be applied despite the varied systems in the conquered territories of the Roman Empire. During the medieval period it was given support by being identified as the law God intended to apply to all rational creatures.

4.14   During the 17th century the tradition of natural law was transformed into that of natural rights, and the doctrine was extensively used in the 17th and 18th centuries as a justification for opposing oppression by rulers, in America and France, for example. The tradition of natural rights (or the 'rights of man') culminated in 1948 with the United Nations' Declaration of Human Rights. In this Declaration and ever since the vocabulary of rights has spread from the narrow moral concerns of the earlier theorists with minimum protection against oppression to cover every aspect of health, welfare and education.

4.15   In order to understand the potentially confusing contemporary proliferation of rights it is necessary to draw some distinctions.

(a)   The rights which emerged from the ancient tradition of natural law can be called universal rights. They are 'moral' in the sense that they are thought to exist whether or not a given legal jurisdiction recognises them, and they are 'universal' in that they belong to all human beings.

(b)   The rights which are recognised or created by a given jurisdiction are legal rights. There is always pressure to convert natural or human rights into legal rights, although there are of course many legal rights which have nothing to do with human rights.

(c)   There are also many specific moral rights which are not human rights. For example, if A borrows a book from B on the understanding that it will be returned on Tuesday, then B has a moral right to its return. But this is not a human right – it is not universal or of paramount importance to human life.

4.16 Rights, legal and moral, have also been classified by the jurist Wesley Hohfeld as claims, powers, liberties and immunities. A claim is a right (say) to have a sum of money paid back, or to have a job application considered; a power is a right (say) to enter and search a property; a liberty is a right (say) of adults over the age of 18 to vote; an immunity is a right (say) of a student in full-time education not to pay National Insurance. In all cases there is the implication that another person, a state, or people in general have a reciprocal duty to observe the right.

4.17 What follows from the general overview is that if animals are to be said to have rights it can only be in the sense of claims (as distinct from powers, liberties or immunities). The essential claim will be to have their interests considered. If this position is accepted we are granting or recognising in animals moral rights (although of course these moral rights may become legal rights if they are recognised by a system of law). Presumably, the animal interests which rights would principally protect would be that of protecting and preserving animal life and having animal suffering minimised.

4.18 Opposition to this position is based either on misunderstanding it, or on building a certain set of assumptions into the concept of rights.

4.19 *Misunderstandings* include the belief that we are attributing to animals a more complex set of rights than we are actually doing. For example, we are not suggesting that animals have voting rights. It is also a misunderstanding to say that animals cannot have rights because they cannot perform duties. There is no impediment to saying that someone - a baby or an incompetent adult - may hold rights without being able himself to perform duties. Hence an animal can have rights without being able to perform duties. The duties entailed by rights are reciprocal duties laid on *others* to observe the rights.

4.20 Further, it is a misunderstanding to assert that only human beings can hold rights. This simply begs the question, which is whether animals other than human animals can hold rights. This kind of objection is based on an arbitrariness which is easy to understand psychologically but is nevertheless illogical. The illogical nature of the position emerges if we look at a comparable case. Until this century, it was widely held that women could not have rights because they were women. But the factors in virtue of which men had rights - such as an interest in avoiding arbitrary imprisonment or in voting for a government - were factors applying also to women. Those denying women rights held by men are now labelled 'sexist'; those denying non-human animals vital rights enjoyed by human animals have been labelled 'species-ist'.

4.21 As for opposition to animal rights based on certain *assumptions,* the most important assumption about rights which makes it hard to accept that animals have (minimal) rights is that rights are absolute or that rights are "trumps". But not even *human rights* are absolute. In times of war people's rights to liberty, property or even life may be overridden by other considerations, such as public utility. And lesser moral rights (such as to have a book returned) are more easily overridden.

4.22   Putting this opposition aside, to say that animals have rights need be to say no more than that in any circumstances in which they may suffer, their claim to be free from suffering must weigh in any assessment of the benefits and harms of any proposed course of action. They have a right to consideration. The extent of this right will vary according to the capacity which the animal has for suffering, and clearly higher primates have greater capacity than lower animals, and human beings have greatest of all. This is the position we hold. We consider that animals have rights in this minimal sense.

4.23   We note that the same position can be reached by another route. Our society recognises that a moral duty, and also a limited legal duty, is owed to animals to prevent them from suffering and to care for their welfare. Indeed, we may go further and also recognise a duty to refrain from using animals where practical and appropriate alternatives are available. If we fail in these duties it follows that the animals have been wronged. And if they have been wronged, they can be said to have (minimal) rights.

4.24   Objections to our view may take two opposing forms. Some would argue that our minimal view of the rights of animals is claiming *too little*. While we argue for the position that animals have a right to be considered in the total calculus of harm and benefit, some would maintain that because animals are the *subjects of a life* they have rights in a much stronger sense. For those who hold this position *any* use of animals which involves their death or suffering for human benefit will be ruled out. This position must be respected, but it is not our position.

4.25   Other philosophers, and many members of the public, might maintain that our minimal position on animal rights is claiming *too much*. For it follows from our position that not every use of animals for human benefit is justifiable. For example, it would follow (say) that the considerable cruelty involved in bull fighting cannot be justified in terms of the minor gratification of the spectators. Presumably the manufacturers who advertise their products as 'not tested on animals' are reflecting what we see as a growing consensus that not every human use of animals can be justified.

OUR POSITION

4.26   Notwithstanding these objections, we hold to our position: that animals do have rights in this minimal sense. This means that while there is no fundamental right not to be used for xenotransplantation, animals may not be so used in circumstances which violate unjustifiably the minimum rights they may have.

4.27   Their interests must, therefore, be considered in any assessment of the benefits and harms arising from the introduction of xenotransplantation. Such a consideration, in our view, is required in reaching a view on the ethical acceptability of xenotransplantation.

4.28   As a first step, we have already indicated that animals vary a great deal in their complexity and presumably in their capacity for suffering. Primates, including chimpanzees and baboons, are at the higher end of this scale, and have close affinities with humans. We consider that these animals can be distinguished from other animals not least by virtue of their greater self-awareness and mental capacity. We consider that these features increase their capacity for suffering, particularly given the conditions under which source animals would be kept in order to ensure proper controls (e.g. biosecure and isolated accommodation). To use them for xenotransplantation would therefore, in our view, constitute too great an infringement of their right to be free from suffering.

We therefore conclude that it would be ethically unacceptable to use primates as source animals for xenotransplantation, not least because they would be exposed to too much suffering.

4.29   We reach this view quite apart from the fact that there may also be other reasons for ruling them out, such as the difficulty of rearing them in captivity, slowness of breeding and greater liability for causing cross-species infection. Primates are also involved in the research being carried out into xenotransplantation, primarily as recipients of tissue transplanted from pigs. Can this use in research be justified? A primate used for research purposes may (indirectly) provide benefit for a large number of humans, due to the information generated from the research. Thus, the ratio of benefit to humans against harm to the primate may provide an ethical basis for the use of primates in research. By contrast, a primate used as a source animal could only benefit one or at best a very small number of humans. Further, the conditions which would prevail for primates to be used in research would not be those which prevail for source animals. We recognise the case for such research to take place and note that such research is currently permitted under the provisions of the Animals (Scientific Procedures) Act and thus:

We conclude that it would be ethically acceptable to use primates in research into xenotransplantation, but only where no alternative method of obtaining information exists and this use should be limited so far as is possible.

4.30   Our next step is to ask whether the arguments which rule out primates also rule out the use of the pig. We conclude that they do not. While the pig may be exposed to harm, we do not regard it as so unjustifiable as to make the use of the pig unacceptable in principle. Instead, as regards the pig, the issue is one of balancing the rights of the pig to be free from harm, as we understand them, against the rights of the human who, as we have seen, could benefit from xenotransplantation. The ethical acceptability of the use of the pig then becomes a matter of balancing the potential benefits, which we have already outlined, against the harm involved, particularly, in using the pig, and reaching a view.

We conclude that the use of the pig for xenotransplantation may be ethically acceptable. We conclude further, however, that the acceptability lies in balancing the benefit to humans against both harm both to the pig and to humans.

4.31　This conclusion forces us now to analyse the range of ethical concerns having to do with the possible harm arising from the development of xenotransplantation. This harm includes, but is not limited to, harm done to the pig. It extends to harm done to possible patients and to the wider population. We must now negotiate what we termed earlier as "gateways". This will involve weighing not only the benefits to humans against the harm done to the pig, but also the benefits to individual patients against the potential harm both to those patients and to the wider human population. In our analysis we must take account of:

i　　the effects on the animal of genetic modification and the effects on the human of transplantation.

ii　　the possible suffering of patients who are led to expect improvement in their condition which does not take place because the transplanted tissue is rejected or does not function for a reasonable period of time; the possible harm to future human beings by the introduction of new strains of virus.

iii　　the possible suffering of the animals involved;

iv　　the possible harm caused by diverting attention from other areas of research which might improve the shortfall in human tissue availability;

v　　the possible harm caused by the 'opportunity cost' of the treatment i.e. that disproportionate resources will be diverted from other areas of health care to fund this programme.

THE GATEWAYS

GENETIC MODIFICATION

4.32　We have noted above that the use of animals (specifically, pigs) for xenotransplantation might be regarded as "unnatural". This is especially so when we bear in mind that the pigs will be bred with human genes. This argument is different from the claim that pigs have a right to have their suffering minimised. It is focused on whether the pig has a right to live and die as a pig. This is the first element of the harm to the pig which we have identified.

4.33   Not all xenotransplantation procedures involve the genetic modification of animals. For example, unmodified pig fetal cells have been transplanted into the brains of patients with Parkinson's disease. Many of the procedures now in development, however, involve the use of animals (usually pigs) genetically modified in such a way as to seek to stop the rejection process.

4.34   It is important to note at the outset that the ethical significance of any genetic modification should not be considered in terms of the number of genes involved, i.e. changing one gene out of fifty thousand, but in terms of the effect of that modification. The central concern must be with the notion of an identity in animals and whether procedures involving genetic modification alter the pig to such an extent that its integrity is threatened. Given that, for example, a pig has certain qualities that may be necessary for it to retain its essential identity as a pig, will genetically modified pigs bred for xenotransplantation lose this claim to identity? The question is made that much more difficult by the fact that it is not currently possible to identify the limits to genetic modification. The issue could be assessed from two points of view. From the human viewpoint the question may be whether the genetic modification changes the entity from what it was. From the animal's point of view, the question is: does it harm the animal?

4.35   The effect of the modification currently being considered is small. The developments to date propose the addition of up to three human genes (regulators of complement activity) to the pig's genome. The function of these genes is to neutralise the process of rejection of the transplanted tissue. Other potential developments include the deletion of a gene from the pig (as has already happened with, for example, mice).

4.36   The current procedure for genetically modifying pigs by the addition of genes has not seemed to cause the pigs any physical harm. The pigs do not appear to recognise themselves as anything but pigs. Furthermore, the pigs do not look like anything but a pig. The current transgenic pigs, modified and bred for xenotransplantation would, therefore, seem to have all the actions, reactions and habits of a 'normal' pig.

We take the view that some degree of genetic modification is ethically acceptable providing that there is a concomitant benefit to humans and that the pig neither suffers unduly nor ceases recognisably to be a pig.

4.37   Thus, the current genetic modifications are ethically acceptable. That said, we recognise that further modifications may be proposed in the future. It is more difficult to lay down benchmarks for the future. For example, it is perhaps more likely that harm will be caused to pigs through the deletion, rather than addition, of a gene. Mice bred to exclude one relevant gene have been born blind (see paragraph 2.65).

4.38   We have taken the view, however, that there is a limit to the harm that may be inflicted on an animal. Xenotransplantation should, in this respect, be treated as no different from other uses of animals, in that animals should not suffer pain which is deemed unacceptable in other circumstances, and they should suffer no deleterious changes to their form or in their function.

4.39   Over the coming years, however, there may be proposals for further genetic change. This may involve more extensive modification of genes affecting functions more closely related to identity or causing variations in their structure which have the effect of causing pain.

We take the view that there are limits to the extent to which an animal should be genetically modified and that constant monitoring both of animals which have been modified, so as to assess effects, and of proposed genetic modifications must take place.

TRANSPLANTATION

4.40   In parallel with the considerations of the genetic modification of the pig, questions of the possible effects on identity also arise when considering the transplantation of animal organs or other tissue into humans. This is the first example of the possible harm to the human patient which we discuss. The procedures proposed so far involve solid organs, either as transplants or as extra-corporeal support, and other tissue, including bone marrow, pancreatic islet cells and fetal cells. It is also possible that skin tissue and bone will be transplanted.

4.41   We need to consider whether there is a basic identity in humans with which it is wrong to interfere and whether these procedures alter humans such that their identity, as humans, is altered.

4.42   If xenotransplantation proceeds and develops, with the genetic modification of animals with human genes and the transplant of animal tissue into humans, the distinction between humans and animals could be perceived, at some point, to break down. An anxiety about the human/animal divide has been a constant theme in the history of human culture, partly due to the belief, noted earlier, that animals may be considered unclean. Perceived threats to the distinction could therefore be thought to be ethically unacceptable.

4.43   Quite apart from this general misgiving, concern exists about transplanting particular tissue, namely any tissue (eg. central nervous tissue) which might be thought to affect personality or behaviour. It is not possible to identify physiologically specific tissue which affects personality. Clearly however, the practice, currently undergoing trials, of transplanting pig fetal cells into the brains of patients with Parkinson's disease would undoubtedly, indeed is intended to, affect behaviour and thus affect personality. Thus the issue is both more profound and more elusive. The view may be taken that while incremental or transient changes in identity may be effected through a variety of medical (and non-medical) interventions, there is an irreducible essence called personal identity which in some sense depends on neural tissue. This issue cannot be resolved here. Suffice it to say that

We take the view that procedures currently proposed do not go beyond acceptable limits and, further, that the criterion for evaluating the ethical acceptability of xenotransplants depends on the function performed by the tissue involved.

4.44   We agree, however, that possible further developments may raise concerns.

We take the view, therefore, that new developments should be monitored to ascertain whether they appear to go beyond what may be acceptable limits.

RISKS

4.45   We now turn to the second instance of the possible harm to the human patient. We are concerned with the possible risks posed by xenotransplantation. These risks are not limited only to the possible patients, but extend also, potentially, to the human population. They constitute a very real ethical concern. We consider the information we have regarding such risks (as described in Chapter 2) and, in particular, form a view, whether, on the basis of the scientific knowledge, xenotransplantation may properly proceed to clinical trials.

4.46   We have identified three types of risk. They are:

(i)   the risk that the tissue will not function physiologically once transplanted and the consequent possible harm caused to the tissue recipient should the tissue not function normally. This is of particular, but not exclusive, relevance to the transplant of solid organs.

(ii)   the risk of the organ or tissue being rejected and the risk to the tissue recipient of an excessive immunosuppressive regimen which may be needed to prevent rejection but which also increases the risk of infection and possibly cancers.

(iii)   the risk of infection transmitted from the source animal to (a) human tissue recipients and (b) their contacts and the wider population.

PHYSIOLOGY

4.47   There is currently a lack of information about the way in which animal organs will function within the human body. Although the function of the heart is primarily mechanical and can be supposed to be similar in both pigs (whose organ size is similar to humans) and humans, there is as yet little evidence of the ability of a transplanted pig heart to support life in the medium to long term. The function of lungs is similarly mechanical and this function may therefore be achievable. However, research into the xenotransplantation of lungs is at only an early stage. Kidneys and livers, however, carry out complex biochemical and metabolic functions and there is little evidence on which to base a judgment about the likelihood of pig organs functioning correctly in human recipients. We consider it probable that a pig's liver could not carry out certain vital functions performed by a human liver, particularly in the long term. Further research work, which looks at the function of the organ, is needed before clinical trials could be considered. There also remain questions about the function of transplanted cells, for example the ability of pancreatic islet cells to produce sufficient insulin to support diabetics beyond the very short term. We note, however, that the failure of this function is not life-threatening.

4.48   We note, moreover, that research involving the transplant of a pig's liver into a baboon may not provide the necessary information concerning its functioning in humans, as some of the biochemical and metabolic functions involved are likely to be species specific.

4.49   There is also little evidence about whether animal organs transplanted into humans would undergo 'normal' growth. For example, we are not aware of evidence about the ability of pig hearts or lungs to grow in children once transplanted. Again, further research is required to cast light on these issues.

4.50   We are also concerned about the lack of evidence on the ability of the human recipient's immune system to work within a transplanted animal organ. If it is not able to do so, any infections, whether of human or animal origin, within the organ, may not be resisted and may lead to the transplant failure.

We therefore conclude that the evidence on transplant function, organ growth and the functioning of the recipient's immune system within the transplant is too limited, at the current time, to justify a move to clinical trials.

We recommend that further research should be carried out and analysed before such trials can take place. We note that some of this research may involve the use of primates and must therefore be read in the light of the recommendations we have made about their use.

IMMUNOLOGY

4.51   Overcoming the problems associated with hyperacute rejection has received much attention in research. This is understandable and progress has been made. However, overcoming hyperacute rejection is only the first step in overcoming the spectrum of the processes involved in rejection. Other rejection problems, as in allotransplantation, include acute cellular rejection. There is evidence that this will be stronger in pig to human transplants than in allotransplantation and the implication of this is that more immunosuppression will be required. No primate recipients of pig organs have yet survived for a length of time sufficient to be able to be sure that these rejection mechanisms have been overcome.

4.52 The level of immunosuppression therapy which may be needed in humans has yet to be determined. This is particularly important, because severe immunosuppression carries its own risks. Investigating appropriate levels of immunosuppression may involve further research on primates, although we note that appropriate levels in, for example, baboons may not directly correspond to appropriate levels in humans. Further research involving primates should be limited to that which can provide necessary information (see paragraph 4.48).

We consider that the evidence on immunological rejection is too limited, at the current time, to justify a move to clinical trials.

We recommend that further research should be carried out to investigate more fully the rejection processes associated with xenotransplantation and to determine an effective and acceptable immunosuppression regimen. Such work would be likely to involve primates and would aim to keep them alive for longer periods of time in a controlled medical equilibrium after the xenotransplant.

RISKS OF INFECTION

4.53 We concluded at the end of Chapter 2 that while breeding and rearing conditions for pigs designed to be as free as possible of infectious agents could reduce many of the risks attached to fungi, parasites and bacteria, such conditions were of more limited use in reducing the risk from viruses, which have the greatest potential for onward transmission. Risks of infection therefore remain, both to the recipient and to the wider population.

Risks to the recipient

4.54 We accept from the evidence presented to us that the risks of infection from fungi and parasites is probably small compared with other microorganisms and most likely limited to the tissue recipient only. As regards bacteria, we consider that there remains a risk that the source animal may pass bacterial infection to the tissue recipient. However, this risk can be reduced by maintaining the animal in specific-pathogen-free conditions and because antibiotics are available to treat such infections.

4.55 We accept advice that **prions** are unlikely to pose a risk to the tissue recipient and that it is unlikely that any pig bred for transplantation would be infected with a prion-related disease. We also accept that if any risk remained, this would be to the recipient alone. Further, long incubation periods are common in the development of prion-related disease such that, even if there were any infection, the tissue recipient may nonetheless benefit from years of "good quality" life from the transplant.

We consider that it is ethically acceptable to take the risks of infection associated with fungi, parasites, bacteria and prions, provided that source animals are maintained in

conditions which aim to minimise the risk of infection and provided that any infections which arise are monitored. We accordingly recommend that such conditions be established for animals reared for use in xenotransplantation.

4.56   We note, with particular regard to prion-related diseases, their long latency and the current ability only to positively identify and diagnose their presence after death.

We further recommend, therefore, that with regard to prion-related diseases, there should be a programme of culling of sentinel pigs over a wide age range to test for neuropathological changes.

Risks to the recipient, and potentially, to the wider population.

4.57   Viruses pose the greatest risk of infection. Particular concern centres around herpesviruses and retroviruses, although we recognise that other viruses could also pose a risk to patients which should not be discounted. Our particular concerns can be separated into those which relate to **known** viruses and those which relate to **unknown** viruses.

Known viruses

4.58   With regard to known viruses, our concerns relate to:

❖   the experience of a range of viruses which have been transmitted from animals to humans and have caused (often fatal) disease and, particularly, that this experience suggests that viruses can become more harmful when transferred to other species.

❖   the lack of information about the infectious potential of a range of porcine viruses, including cytomegalovirus, circovirus and the porcine endogenous retroviruses. This lack is exacerbated by the limited effectiveness of screening mechanisms for even known viruses.

❖   in particular, porcine retroviruses, due to recent information that one retrovirus had been found to infect human cells in culture. This concern is amplified by the fact that as endogenous retroviruses are inherited genetically, they cannot be excluded from animals which have them. The only means of potentially eliminating endogenous viruses is by breeding animals specifically to exclude them.

❖   the recombination of viruses: although we note advice that, for example, if herpesviruses recombine, the resultant virus is likely to be less pathogenic.

We conclude that there is insufficient knowledge about the known viruses to make it safe to proceed to clinical trials at the current time. This is particularly relevant to the porcine endogenous retroviruses.

We recommend that further research should be carried out on known viruses, including the porcine retroviruses, cytomegalovirus (CMV), and circovirus before clinical trials may be considered.

4.59   Appropriately designed experiments with known viruses in human cell cultures would give more information on the risk of their transmission and some indication of the risk from unknown viruses that may be present.

4.60   An indicative, but not exhaustive, list of research, including some particular experiments, which we consider it necessary to be undertaken before any question of clinical trials could be considered, is as follows. In so far as this work involves primates we repeat that this must be read in the light of the recommendations we have made about their use.

1.   Whether reactivated endogenous porcine retroviruses will infect a variety of human cells, the significance of this if so, and whether pigs which lack endogenous porcine retrovirus sequences can be selectively bred.

2.   Testing of other viruses eg circovirus and cytomegalovirus, detected in pigs to determine how they perform in experimental conditions, for example, through co-culture experiments.

3.   The potential for the elimination of cytomegalovirus – and other viruses – from source animals.

4.   Immunosuppression of source animals may amplify pathogens which are present but are usually controlled by the animal's immune system. Therefore, research could be carried out involving the immunosuppression of source animals and the search for evidence of unknown viruses through the use of various techniques such as:

    -    histological examination of suspect tissues on the basis of disease symptoms;

    -    culture of peripheral blood cells

    -    co-culture of peripheral blood cells (PBCs) with human cells (CD8+ and T cell depleted; these cells act to destroy viral infection. As this experiment is designed to allow the emergence of viral infection, they must be removed)

    -    In each instance these must be followed by electron microscopy and immunohistochemistry with tagging IgG (a diagnostic indicator) from source animals.

5.   Culture of peripheral blood cells from primate xenotransplant recipients, followed by electron microscopy, and immunohistochemistry with serum from source animals. This is to detect the presence of infectious agents in tissues morphologically (ie by looking at their form) and by antibody reactivity.

6.   Trials involving immunosuppressed primate recipients, with monitoring for the emergence of infectious agents.

Further areas for possible research are identified in Annex C; the report of the Workshop on Infectious Disease and Xenotransplantation.

Currently unknown viruses

4.61   With regard to unknown risks, our concerns relate to:

❖   the lack of available means of screening which would reliably identify viruses which are currently unknown.

❖   the probability that unknown viruses do exist: new viruses are still being discovered in humans and more work has been done to identify human viruses than has currently been done on porcine viruses.

❖   the ability for viral infection to be latent, sometimes for many years, before clinical disease develops. This increases the possibility that such viruses will spread before they have been identified and measures taken to control them.

4.62   With regard to pathogens which have not been identified, we acknowledge the limits of research. Unknowns will always remain. It will not be possible ever to rule out the risk that a previously unidentified virus will infect a recipient of animal tissue and that this recipient will then infect contacts and the wider population.

4.63   Given this, and the likelihood that there are other pathogens which have not yet been identified, we considered whether it would **ever** be ethically acceptable to proceed with xenotransplantation. We reached the view that there will be a stage at which researchers will have done as much as is possible to learn about infection risks associated with xenotransplantation but that, even at this point, unknowns will still remain.

We conclude that, at the stage when it is considered that a full investigation of potential infection risks has been carried out, and the risks have been shown to be within tolerable margins, it would be ethically acceptable to proceed. This is subject to there being a system in place to monitor the emergence of any unusual disease or any unknown pathogens and to require, as a consequence, that appropriate additional research be completed in a proper fashion.

4.64 We return here to the question of the use of primates as a source of tissue. We have recommended already that we consider this use of primates to be ethically unacceptable on the grounds of the suffering which they would be caused. We emphasise here that, even were this not our view, we could not support the use of primates as source animals. We take this view in the light of the evidence we have received that primates, because of their genetic similarity to humans, pose a much greater risk of transmitting either known or unknown infections to humans. We draw attention in this regard to Chapter 2 where the fatal effects of viral infections passed from primates to humans are documented.

MONITORING

4.65 We have recommended that source animals should be kept in conditions which aim to exclude known pathogens and that systems should be in place to monitor the emergence of new diseases or new pathogens. The importance of these measures cannot be over-estimated. We do however recognise that the imposition of such conditions have an impact on the welfare of the animals and we explore this below (paragraph 4.73 to 4.99).

4.66 We consider that there should be some agreed standards for the conditions in which the animals should be kept and that the list of pathogens to be excluded and the methods in use should be kept under review so that newly identified pathogens can be taken into account.

We recommend that such standards be designed and agreed and further recommend that animal facilities be monitored to ensure that these standards are observed.

4.67 We identify the transport of animals (or of tissue) between sites and the removal of tissue as points in any production process where biosecure conditions might more easily be breached and:

We recommend that particular attention be paid to these, in terms of both establishing, and monitoring standards.

4.68 Monitoring arrangements should be based on an agreed range of tests and sample collection, which should be carried out on both the source animal and the human recipient. These arrangements must be flexible and be able to take into account any emerging infections or viruses. The potential of viruses, in particular, to remain latent for long periods of time means that for human recipients life-long monitoring would be required. The use of sentinel animals which are killed to be tested for infectious agents is proposed. More work may need to be undertaken to determine the length of time for which sentinel animals should be kept.

4.69 We note also that controls should not be relaxed even if no adverse reactions were recorded following the first, or even a great number of, xenotransplants. Latency and the low probability of serious infections occurring could mean that no serious threat might emerge for some years.

4.70   There is one further issue relating to the risk of infection. This risk relates to the risk to the species of the source animal. We are not aware of any assessment of the risks to animals through the mutation of animal pathogens in human hosts: **We recommend that this issue should be considered further.**

SUMMARY

4.71   We have recommended that a range of investigations be undertaken in order to provide further information on the physiological, immunological and infection aspects of xenotransplantation. To repeat, these are to study transplant function and growth in the recipient, and the functioning of the recipient's immune system within the transplant; to investigate more fully the rejection processes associated with xenotransplantation and to determine an effective and clinically acceptable immunosuppressive regimen; and to investigate more fully known porcine viruses, including the retroviruses, CMV and circovirus. In this regard, we draw attention in particular to the list in paragraph 4.60.

We recommend that this programme should be co-ordinated, so far as is possible, and the results monitored and assessed with a view to determining whether further research is needed and whether clinical trials are acceptable.

4.72   We draw particular attention in this context to the fact that there is a limit to the information which may be provided through trials on primates. We would wish to avoid a situation where primates were being used without there being a clear view of the benefit which would follow.

We recommend that those who have responsibility for co-ordinating the programme should do so with particular regard to this point.

ANIMAL WELFARE

4.73   The risks to patients and to the wider population through the risk of infection which we have discussed constitute a serious ethical concern. These risks can be reduced through the imposition of certain conditions on the keeping of the source animals. And so, in reducing the harm to humans, increased harm may be caused to the source animals. Accordingly, the next ethical gateway which we must negotiate concerns the conditions under which animals used in any xenotransplant programme would be kept. Again, we concentrate on the pig and what is likely to happen to pigs involved in any future tissue production programme.

4.74   Since the solid organs or other tissue from transgenic pigs are destined for transplantation into humans, we have said that it will be necessary to ensure that all such material is produced under sterile conditions from animals that have a defined microbiological flora which includes the absence of known pathogens. The consequences for the pig are that husbandry methods must allow the production of pathogen-free tissue. Such methods are likely to be more restrictive and closely controlled than is usual in, for example, good agricultural practice.

4.75   We have taken the view that animals can be said to have rights, in the sense of a claim to have their interests considered. The animal interest which this sense of animal rights would seek to protect is presumed to be mainly that of having any suffering minimised and their welfare taken into account.

4.76   The "five freedoms" developed by the Farm Animal Welfare Council (FAWC) provide a starting point for the creation of a framework within which to consider the welfare of animals. Admittedly, these represent an ideal developed in the context of agriculture. These are:

i   Freedom from thirst, hunger and malnutrition (by ready access to fresh water and a diet to maintain full health and vigour)

ii   Freedom from discomfort (by providing an appropriate environment including shelter and a comfortable resting place)

iii   Freedom from pain, injury and disease (by prevention, or rapid diagnosis and treatment)

iv   Freedom to express normal behaviour (by allowing sufficient space, proper facilities and company of the animal's own kind)

v   Freedom from fear and distress (by ensuring conditions and treatment which avoid mental suffering).

4.77   The FAWC further note that in acknowledging these freedoms those who have care of animals should practise:

❖   caring and responsible planning and management

❖   skilled, knowledgeable and conscientious stockmanship

❖   appropriate environmental design

❖   considerate handling and transport

❖   humane slaughter.

4.78   We now look in more detail at the conditions (the Defined Health Status) being proposed for the keeping of pigs for xenotransplantation and the implications for the pigs. The conditions we describe are based on our knowledge of developments of xenotransplantation and on more general knowledge about Specific Pathology Free(SPF) conditions. It is an illustrative example.

4.79   One husbandry system being developed for such animal facilities is the Nurtinger system. This system attempts to reflect the natural environment of the pig by providing different physical environments and different functional areas. The system includes separate areas for sleeping, play, feeding, drinking and dunging. It aims to enable the pig to control its own temperature by being able to move in and out of the enclosed sleeping area as required. However, no bedding is normally provided.

4.80   Three types of unit might be developed to breed and develop the pigs. These reflect the stages involved in producing a large supply of xenotransplants. They can be described as: the breeding of transgenic animals, the expansion of the transgenic herd and the establishment of the source animal supply. The processes involved in each stage, should xenotransplantation proceed, are described below.

4.81   **Initial breeding of transgenic pigs:** The herd would be of high health status, and kept in conditions with low stocking density and good ventilation. The pigs would be impregnated by artificial insemination and the fertilised eggs surgically removed from sows to be micro-injected with the required human gene. Transgenic pigs produced by this unit would form the basis of herds through which the herd would be expanded. These pigs would stock the expansion herd through early weaning procedures.

4.82   Pigs used to **expand the transgenic herd** would be established using early weaning techniques. This would involve prophylactic medication and vaccination of the sows before they enter an isolated farrowing unit to the time of weaning (at five days of age), medication of piglets from birth to a few days after weaning, and the isolation of piglets after weaning. The herd would be sited in an isolated location (away from, in particular, other pig farms and the human population, which might be sources of infection). Strict biosecurity would be maintained. The pigs would undergo monitoring for pathogens of concern.

4.83   **The source animal herd** would be established as a specific pathogen free (SPF) herd. The piglets would be born via hysterectomy or hysterotomy, taken from the sow, and reared in groups in an isolated environment. They would be fed sterilised food for 2 weeks and, at this stage, would be gnotobiotic (ie, in this context, have a defined gut flora that has been deliberately introduced to the piglets in the isolator). After 2 weeks, the pigs would be moved to biosecure rooms were they would gradually be weaned onto a sterilised pig diet. They would gradually pick up normal flora but remain specific pathogen free. When mature, they could be used as the foundation stock of a new SPF high health status herd or in xenotransplantation trials with primates. The unit would have comprehensive barrier facilities, maintain strict biosecurity and the pigs would be routinely monitored for pathogens of concern.

4.84   **The source pigs** would be derived from the source animal herds by techniques known as Modified Medicated Early Weaning (MMEW) or Segregated Early Weaning (SEW). These are similar methods in which the sows are allowed to farrow in their herd of origin, piglets are weaned early (from 10-21 days) and then removed from the farm to an isolated location. The source pigs would then be reared in groups in biosecure rooms, possibly in a separate biosecure building. Some of each group of source pigs would be designated sentinels and killed for microbiological screening in advance of tissue being retrieved from their cohort.

4.85   Various procedures may be used to test for the presence, and control, of certain pathogens. They include serological monitoring, blood testing and nasal and tonsil swabs and vaccinations and prophylactic medication.

4.86   It is also possible that the pigs would need to be transported between the units or from the unit to the place where their tissue would be retrieved. If this were necessary, it is likely that they would be transported in sterilised vehicles supplied with HEPA filtered air.

4.87   The **retrieval of tissue** would be carried out by veterinary and surgical personnel and appropriate anaesthesia would be used.

4.88   We take the view that the general conditions described above represent a departure from the "five freedoms". We accept, however, that these "five freedoms" are seen as an ideal starting point for consideration of animal welfare rather than absolute principles. That said, we further take the view that harm suffered by the animals should be avoided where possible and kept to a minimum where unavoidable. We **regret** that animal suffering is caused but we conclude that these are inevitable compromises if xenotransplantation is to take place. Furthermore, a rigorous system of monitoring, inspection and enforcement is the necessary counterpart to such compromises.

4.89   We draw particular attention to the following as being harm which warrants continued consideration with a view to whether it could be avoided, now or in the future, or its effect mitigated. There are four broad areas of concern. These relate to the procedures involved in producing the animal tissue for transplant; to the maintenance of the infection-free environment, including the monitoring of the animals; to specific restrictions on movement; and to the potential wastage of animals.

4.90   We look first at the procedures involved.
Egg Removal and Replacement This procedure carries the potential for harm to the sow. It is, however, an intrinsic part of the development of transgenic animals and currently unavoidable. We note here that although this, and those procedures mentioned in 4.91 and 4.92 are *currently* unavoidable, every effort should be made to minimise suffering through development of alternative techniques.

4.91   **Hysterectomy and separation of piglet from sow** This causes harm both to the sow and to the piglets who, in moving to SPF conditions, will be kept in isolators for 14 days having no contact with the sow or sow's milk. Again this is an intrinsic part of the development of transgenic animals and currently unavoidable.

4.92   **Substantial programme of sampling** An animal kept for use in xenotransplantation would inevitably be subject to a programme of sampling of, for example, blood and tissue, to identify any potential infection in the animal and reduce any subsequent risk of transmission to a tissue recipient. This is an intrinsic part of the development of the programme and is currently unavoidable. Indeed, we consider it essential to protect the recipient and the public health.

4.93   **Sequential use of tissue** Tissue could be removed from a source animal sequentially on a series of occasions. As regards the removal of solid organs, this would involve the administration of an anaesthetic and all the attendant distress to the animal.

We conclude, therefore, that the sequential removal of *solid organs* is ethically unacceptable.

4.94   The sequential removal of other tissue poses a more difficult ethical question. On the one hand there is the harm associated with each intervention. On the other hand, since the animal will ordinarily otherwise be killed immediately after the first intervention, it could be said that this is a greater harm. On balance, however, **we take the view that the sequential removal of any tissue is ethically unacceptable.** The repeated distress to the animal, (as against the painless (to the pig) slaughter) cannot be justified. We here exclude the taking of blood and tissue for monitoring purposes.

4.95   The second group of concerns relate to the maintenance of the SPF environment. Controlled environments raise specific concerns centred on the design of flooring, minimal environmental enrichment for the animals (there may be no rooting material provided, for example), low levels of natural light and possible social isolation for the pigs.

We recommend that such issues be addressed in the design of SPF facilities for xenotransplantation to determine whether improvements can be made.

4.96   There would also be restrictions imposed on the pigs which are not specific to xenotransplantation. In particular we note here the use of **farrowing crates** (which are a means of restricting the sow's movement in labour with the aim of preventing harm to the piglets). There is currently no practical alternative available, although research by the Ministry of Agriculture, Fisheries and Food and others is being undertaken. We take the view that the use of farrowing crates is not desirable, and that in theory it may be possible to avoid their use in the future.

We recommend that research to establish appropriate alternatives to farrowing crates should be encouraged.

4.97   The issue of **wastage** of pigs arises at various points in the process of producing pigs for xenotransplantation.   At the initial stage of breeding the transgenic pigs, those pigs which do not express the gene in the desired way would be slaughtered, as they would be genetically modified, they could not be used for other purposes.   There is also the potential for producing pigs which are, ultimately, surplus to requirements. It is not possible to quantify exact wastage rates, but wastage constitutes a further harm to be considered.

We recommend that wastage rates be monitored closely during any future development of xenotransplantation.

4.98   **Continuing research and development**   It is worth noting that quite apart from the breeding and use of transgenic animals, research into aspects of xenotransplantation using primates is currently proceeding and will probably continue for some considerable time.   We have previously recommended that work be done to establish various aspects of the immunological and physiological status of recipient animals following transplants and the attendant immunosuppression and to investigate the potential for disease transfer.   This work may well involve large numbers of animals, including primates.   To the extent that primates are involved, we repeat our previous view, that this use be limited so far as is possible and that it should only be undertaken where no alternative methods are available.

We therefore take the view that further research involving primates should be kept to the minimum necessary, and that, wherever appropriate, other means of generating reliable information be used.   We also recommend that the welfare of the animals used should be closely monitored and supervised.

4.99   We take the view that some of the harm caused to animals in the procedures involved in xenotransplantation is more severe than those caused by good agricultural practice. We note, however, that there is existing legislation which justifies this harm (ASPA, see Chapter 8) provided that there is potential benefit to humans.

In conclusion; **we take the view, from the point of view of animal welfare, the use of pigs for xenotransplantation is ethically acceptable so long as continued efforts are made to avoid or minimise the harm caused.**

RESOURCES

4.100   We turn again from harm to animals to possible harm to people. Harm to the patients and to the wider population is not restricted to the issues relating to risks.   There is also the question of resources, which includes the allocation of resources (financial and human), the investment of resources, and any consequential opportunity costs. Inequitable allocations or unwise investments carry the potential for harm through other, potentially successful, therapies not receiving adequate investment.

4.101   Xenotransplantation has the potential to impose a large financial burden on the National Health Service. It is a fact that scientific and medical developments can often cost money rather than save it. A much greater (perhaps unlimited) supply of solid organs could mean that many people could receive transplants who otherwise would have received little more than palliative care and, who would have, as a consequence, a short life expectancy. Furthermore, new therapies are being developed based on xenotransplantation which are not commonly available as allotransplantation (for example, the transplantation of pancreatic islet cells to treat diabetes and the transplantation of fetal cells to treat Parkinson's disease). This could mean that a large number of people could receive new treatments.

4.102   The cost of xenotransplantation depends on the demand for tissue, its price and the cost of the procedure and aftercare set against any possible savings. The demand for hearts and lungs is potentially quite high as the conditions for which transplantation would be an effective treatment have a high incidence in the population eg heart failure and cardiomyopathy and chronic obstructive pulmonary disease. However, as these diseases particularly affect the elderly, who may not be able to tolerate the toxic effects of immunosuppression, this could serve to reduce demand. Conversely, if it were found that less immunosuppression is needed for xenotransplantation, demand would rise. As there are few alternative treatments for these conditions, the introduction of xenotransplantation would mean an increased cost. The initial demand for kidneys is high, due to the accumulated waiting list. However, once that waiting list had been cleared, there would be a relatively low level of demand as the incidence of end-stage renal failure is relatively low. As there is an alternative treatment (dialysis) for this condition which is more expensive than allotransplantation, an increase in transplants occasioned by xenotransplantation, assuming that it became a cheaper procedure than dialysis, could reduce costs. There are also two conditions which are currently the focus of research into the transplantation of cells and tissue – Parkinson's disease and diabetes. The incidence of both is relatively high.

4.103   Given the speculative nature of any calculations, not least as to the price to be paid for tissue and subsequent immunosuppressive drug treatment, we cannot begin to reach any plausible views on the impact which the development and introduction of xenotransplantation could have on the resources of the NHS. Furthermore, there are questions of cost-effectiveness as well as cost. A transplant may work but not provide a benefit commensurate with its cost. Clearly significant investment of money would be called for which may or may not be matched by savings, whether directly to the NHS or indirectly through having a healthier population. Equally clearly, while investment takes place, there would be opportunity costs elsewhere within the NHS.

4.104 We do not attempt here an analysis of the resource implications of xenotransplantation. It is a complex task which demands the consideration of a large volume of information, some of which exists only in the form of "guesstimates". Our concern at the level of ethical principle is that resources, including resources for xenotransplantation, are allocated fairly and justly. Justice in this context means in according with principles of social justice reflected by and explicit in the creation of the NHS. The difficulties arise, of course, in the detail.

4.105 Currently resources are allocated through health authorities at a local level to purchase services. There is an exception to this general rule. Certain services are not purchased at this local level but by the National Specialist Commissioning Advisory Group (NSCAG) (formerly the Supra-Regional Services Advisory Group). These services include the heart, heart-lung and lung transplant services (until the end of March 1997) and the liver transplant service. The NSCAG is responsible for advising the Secretary of State for Health on the identification of services to be funded supra-regionally and on the appropriate levels of provision. Since 1 April 1996, it has also been able to pay the treatment costs of developing services whilst they undergo clinical evaluation, but only where the services, should they become established, would themselves be likely to qualify for central purchasing. In coming to their recommendations about suitable services to be purchased in this way, they take into account a number of factors including the rarity of the condition, its cost, and the ability of the service to justify this cost when set against alternative uses for NHS funds. NSCAG does not purchase services which are provided widely across the NHS.

4.106 We consider that NSCAG would be well placed to consider the purchase of xenotransplantation. NSCAG purchases specific therapies for specific groups of patients and must consider whether the service being proposed is able to justify its costs when set against alternative uses for NHS funds. Going through this system as regards each proposed type of xenotransplantation programme would help to meet our concerns that resources for xenotransplantation be allocated fairly and justly and with regard to alternative services.

We recommend therefore that NSCAG consider the purchase of the various xenotransplantation services, should their development reach the stage at which central support for the treatment costs might be appropriate during clinical evaluation. NSCAG could also consider the purchase of xenotransplant services, should they become established, but not widely provided, services.

We further recommend that in its considerations, the NSCAG should take account of the various concerns which we have expressed in this Report (in particular, in paragraphs 4.102- 4.105).

EFFECT ON THE DEVELOPMENT OF ALLOTRANSPLANTATION AND OTHER THERAPIES

4.107   If xenotransplantation were thought to be ethically acceptable and if it were to proceed to clinical trials and then a full-scale transplantation programme, it could affect the development of other therapeutic responses (including allotransplantation) to the diseases which lead to the need for transplantation. This potential harm to possible patients is related to, but distinct from, the issue of resources.

ALLOTRANSPLANTATION

4.108   It will be recalled that a major problem with allotransplantation is a shortage of solid organs. It is possible that xenotransplantation could either increase or reduce the supply of human organs. The supply of human organs in this country depends largely on the supply of cadaveric organs. This depends on the extent of donation through donor cards, on the willingness of relatives to give permission for the use of the deceased's organs and on the willingness of doctors to request such permission. Our concern focuses on the possibility that the advent of xenotransplantation even at the clinical trial stage, could lead to a significant reduction in supply. This is important as it is thought that allotransplantation will, for some time, provide a more effective treatment than xenotransplantation. Such a decrease in supply could come about for several, opposing, reasons which depend largely on public perception:

   i   xenotransplantation could be perceived as providing successful treatment, even at the stage of clinical trials. Relatives may feel less inclined to consent to the removal of the potential donor's organs, and the public may decide not to register as organ donors, as an alternative is perceived to be available.

   ii   xenotransplantation could be perceived as not being successful, even at the stage of clinical trials. This could be accompanied by a perception of science being "pushed too far" and this, with the controversial nature of xenotransplantation, could make people less well inclined towards transplantation in general.

4.109   On the other hand, it is also possible that the advent of xenotransplantation could lead to an increase in the supply of human organs, again motivated either by the perception of xenotransplantation's success or lack of success.

   i   If xenotransplantation were perceived as successful, but perhaps not as successful nor as acceptable as allotransplantation, and were widely reported as such, the public could become more aware of the need for human organs and be more willing to agree to the removal of the organs of their relatives or to register their intention to donate their organs.

ii   If xenotransplantation were perceived as being unsuccessful, the public could be more aware of the need for human organs, now unlikely to be eased by using organs from animals.

4.110   As both possibilities, the success or failure of xenotransplantation, could conceivably give rise to both an increase and a reduction in the human organ supply, it might be possible to mitigate the risk of reducing the supply. The risk of reduction would seem to depend on an over-emphasis on the likely success or an over-emphasis on the novel and controversial nature of the procedure. Certain measures could be taken to lessen the impact of this emphasis, such as commitment to public education about the procedure and encouragement of balanced reporting about it and its likely success, particularly relative to the success of allotransplantation and other forms of therapy.

We accordingly recommend that consideration be given to means of educating the public about xenotransplantation.

OTHER THERAPIES

4.111   If xenotransplantation were to be the focus of increasing amounts of research and development and then introduced as a therapeutic procedure, this would clearly have implications for the use or development of therapies other than allotransplantation. The costs associated with xenotransplantation would, all things being equal, inevitably mean that resources would not be made available elsewhere. As a consequence, therapies or therapeutic strategies which could contribute a viable alternative might get less support. More importantly, research into therapies which might possibly constitute an alternative, and perhaps better, approach could be deleteriously affected.

4.112   Expressed in this way, it is clear that to some considerable extent, these are issues of resources. As such, we repeat our view expressed earlier that they should be considered by the NSCAG. But the issues go beyond questions of allocation of existing resources for treatment. They involve the direction of biomedical research and reflect a concern that too much may be invested in one activity to the exclusion of the consideration of others. In large part this is a concern which must be expressed to Government. Industry will make its decisions on commercial grounds and will direct its research accordingly. Government can and does seek to ensure that a wide range of research is pursued.

We take the view that Government, through the relevant mechanisms, should ensure that research into therapeutic responses for those whose conditions currently call for transplantation, in addition to xenotransplantation, is adequately supported.

SUMMARY

4.113   We have now considered the kinds of harm intrinsic in xenotransplantation.   We have concluded on the principal question regarding the use of animals, that we could not support the use of primates as source animals for xenotransplantation purposes.   We accepted, albeit with regret, their role as tissue recipients in the research process and noted that this is permitted under the Animals (Scientific Procedures) Act.   In the case of pigs, we considered that the ethical acceptability of their use depended on the harm caused to the pig weighed against the benefits to patients.   We also considered a range of possible harm which affected potential patients and the wider population. We note here that the minimisation of harm to the patient and the human population has the effect of increasing the harm to the animal.   For instance, reducing the risk of tissue rejection means that the pig might be genetically modified; reducing the risk of infection means that the circumstances in which the pig would be kept are more restrictive and involve undergoing monitoring tests and the sampling of tissue.

4.114   We described this weighing process as negotiating a series of gateways.   Each gateway has been examined.   We have identified conditions to be satisfied before the gateways may be satisfactorily negotiated and the harm mitigated so that any benefits outweigh it.   These conditions must be fulfilled if xenotransplantation is to be considered ethically acceptable.

CONFLICTS OF INTEREST

4.115   As a final point in our consideration of ethical concerns, we take this opportunity to make a point of general importance relevant to but going beyond the particular issues surrounding xenotransplantation. We have become aware of the changing environment in which scientific and medical research is conducted. For a number of complex reasons, particularly the manner in which an increasing proportion of research has come to be funded by industry, the researcher may also be an entrepreneur. The researcher occupies a position fraught with the possibility of tension as the research interacts with the investment which in turn reflects back on research.

4.116   Traditional thinking about the way in which science ought to be done is under challenge as a result of this changed environment. The convention is that research results are announced in the scientific literature and can thus be subjected to the critical gaze of peers and validated (or otherwise) by replication. Announcing results at a press conference clearly may affect the share performance of a company. It does not, however, invite the same exposure to peer review, particularly if it is plausibly stated that to go into greater detail would blunt the competitive edge of the research team.

4.117   Quite apart from questions concerning the ethics of scientific research which this changed environment poses, there are significant issues of public policy. Government requires the best and most reliable information on which to base its policy decisions. When knowledge becomes a commodity in the market place, the Government's task is made more difficult and the public interest harder to determine.

4.118   In making these points we must not be understood as in any way commenting adversely on any of those currently involved in xenotransplantation. We draw attention to the issue in general terms. We take the view that it warrants careful reflection by Government and those charged with making public policy.

CHAPTER FIVE:

SOLUTIONS OTHER THAN XENOTRANSPLANTATION

INTRODUCTION

5.1   We have identified (Chapter 3) the potential benefits of xenotransplantation and examined (Chapter 4) the ethical concerns which xenotransplantation raises. We must now turn to the second and third questions which we identified at the beginning of this report as being entailed in our terms of reference. These are:

> **2.**   Are there ways to improve the current programme for obtaining human tissue so as to meet all or a greater part of the demand for transplantation of tissue?

> **3.**   Are there currently no other procedures for responding to the needs of those whose conditions call for transplantation and are such procedures unlikely to be developed in the relevant timescale?

5.2   While apparently of a factual nature, both of these questions are fundamentally ethical. They touch upon such questions as the just distribution of resources as well as the need to avoid risks and harm, whether to humans or to animals. They are, of course, questions of a different nature from Question 1. It was concerned with issues inherent to or intrinsic in xenotransplantation itself. Questions 2 and 3 are concerned more with the proper place of xenotransplantation; what we have called the extrinsic arguments.

5.3   The answers to these two questions are critical in arriving at any final assessment of the benefits accruing from xenotransplantation. One view may be that xenotransplantation appears to have the advantage. Another may be that xenotransplantation should not be seen as the only or even the best way forward. Indeed, if the needs of patients can be fully met through other means it becomes more difficult ethically to make the case for xenotransplantation, as no *unique* benefit flows from it which would outweigh the ethical concerns which are intrinsic to it.

5.4   We have said already that to concentrate on xenotransplantation may be to run the risk of failing to recognise that there may be alternatives to xenotransplantation: this risk must be avoided. The costs, the attendant risks and the reliance on animals all make it essential to avoid seeing xenotransplantation as the only solution to those needing tissue transplants. Thus, appropriate resources must be deployed to allow the potential for development and application of alternative approaches to be properly assessed. Such assessment must proceed in parallel with the development of xenotransplantation. Furthermore if alternatives are found to be viable, the cost-benefit analysis of xenotransplantation in terms of the use of animals, of immunosuppression and the risk of infection could well be affected. This could, in turn, prompt a revaluation of the direction which public policy should take. We now examine these questions in detail.

ALLOTRANSPLANTATION

5.5   Question (2) raises the problem of the shortage of human tissue, both solid organs and other tissue. We examine here measures which aim to increase the numbers of cadaveric and living donors. They would have an effect both on the supply of solid organs and on the supply of certain human tissue; that is, bone, skin and, possibly, pancreatic islet cells.

IMPROVING THE SUPPLY OF ORGANS FROM CADAVERIC DONORS

5.6   Much attention has been given to improving allotransplantation and increasing the amount of tissue, particularly organs, which is available. This work has been carried out against the background of the decreasing number of people becoming available as potential donors (on the whole, those who die from road accidents or strokes) (see Chapter 3), the knowledge that not all who could become donors do so, and that not every organ which could be retrieved is, in fact, retrieved from those who become donors. There are, broadly, three options for improving this situation. They are:

❖   To improve the retrieval rates of organs from available cadavers.

❖   To increase the proportion of potential donors who become available as donors.

❖   To change the law.

IMPROVING RETRIEVAL RATES

5.7   It has not always been possible to retrieve all useable organs which have been offered from a cadaveric donor. **Multi-organ donor retrieval arrangements** were introduced in 1993. The primary aim was to co-ordinate retrieval activity across the UK more effectively. Other measures were also introduced. These require every potential donor to be examined by a clinician able to decide whether or not organs are useable. Formerly, this was left to transplant co-ordinators to decide and, not infrequently, organs were rejected that might have been viable. Further, as it is the same local retrieval team which usually visits the hospital each time a donor becomes available, there has been the opportunity to build up good relationships with the hospitals which they serve[69]. The effect of these new arrangements has been encouraging. Although a 4% increase in the number of cadaveric solid organ donors in 1995 failed to match the record year of 1990[70], a higher number of solid organs were subsequently used for transplant than in 1994 and the greatest average number of transplanted organs per donor was achieved. Particular increases were in liver transplants, in the separate use of liver lobes, and in the number of double lung transplants. Zonal multi-organ retrieval arrangements seem to be responsible. A contributory factor to this success has been improved surgical techniques. Some organs may require surgical repair before being implanted but this is often considered worthwhile in an attempt to reduce the waiting lists [See Table 4, Chapter 3].

INCREASING THE PROPORTION OF POTENTIAL DONORS WHO ACTUALLY BECOME AVAILABLE AS DONORS

5.8   As the numbers of potential donors fall, it becomes increasingly important to reach those who become available. A number of factors contribute to the effectiveness with which potential donors are identified and their organs retrieved and transplanted. The Hoffenburg Report[71] identified a range of reasons, which centred around: public attitudes to transplantation influencing the deceased or the deceased's family against donating organs; the inexperience of medical staff in requesting permission for the use of organs; and the organisation of organ retrieval systems, including cost.

5.9   Public attitudes can be influenced by a lack of awareness of the transplant programme and by doubts about its success and about the criteria for brain stem death. These contribute to the failure to obtain agreement for organ retrieval from relatives. A survey[72] by the British Association of Critical Care Nurses (BACCN) and the United Kingdom Transplant Co-ordinators Association (UKTCA) found that where the deceased's wishes are unknown, one in four families refuse permission to use organs. However, refusal by relatives is unusual when it is known that the deceased wished to donate.

5.10   Much work has been done, therefore, to **increase the public awareness and acceptance of organ donation and transplantation.** The aim has been to encourage individuals to register as organ donors and to discuss donation issues with members of their family. There have been a number of media campaigns, and these have been backed up by initiatives to make it easier to register as a donor, for example through inclusion of organ donor consent boxes on driving

---

69   Information provided by UKTSSA

70   United Kingdom Transplant Support Service Authority (UKTSSA) Annual Report 1995/96. Statistics for the United Kingdom & Republic of Ireland as notified to the UKTSSA.

71   Department of Health and Social Security: Report of the Working Party on the Supply of Donor Organs for Transplantation, 1987.

72   Mori: Organ Donation - Reasons for Relatives Refusal. Research study conducted for UKTCA/BACCN, funded by DH. July 1992 - June 1994.

licenses. The establishment of the computerised NHS Organ Donor Register in October 1994 may make it easier for transplant co-ordinators to ascertain whether an individual had registered a willingness to be a donor. By 31 May 1996 more than 3 million people had applied to go on the Register[73]. However, a pilot scheme in Wales[74] has shown that the level of registration is unlikely to be sufficient to influence donor numbers.

5.11 Educating and influencing medical staff are similarly important. The Hoffenburg Report[75] stressed that doctors may have little experience of the diagnosis of brain stem death and of requesting organs for donation from bereaved relatives. A programme of information and training for doctors and nurses working in Intensive Care Units, developed by the European Donor Hospital Education Programme, is currently being evaluated. This may reduce the number of relatives refusing permission for the retrieval of the deceased's organs.

5.12 Finally, the organisation of organ retrieval services, to ensure that potential donors are identified and properly managed is also important. In the UK, UKTSSA audits of organ transplantation have shown that rates of potential donor identification and of organ retrieval can vary between regions. This suggests that not all potential donors are identified. This variation is often due to the enthusiasm of the local transplant team. Another feature of areas with good donation rates is the pioneering status of the local transplant team. We are told that where transplants started in the early days, there are often good local co-operative arrangements[76]. There may be lessons which can be learned from these examples for regions with lower donation rates. A more extensive programme, the Donor Action Programme, which trains staff to identify and manage donors more successfully is being piloted in Birmingham.

5.13 The "Donor Action" programme is also being piloted in hospitals in several European countries. For example, Spain introduced a decentralised transplant co-ordinating network (the Organizacion Nacional de Transplantes) in 1989, with organ procurement as its main goal. A critical element of the scheme is that one person is responsible for identifying potential donors. Transplant co-ordinators are trained to identify donors at an early stage, to advise on how they should be maintained until their organs are retrieved, and to approach relatives and obtain their consent. The results are encouraging. In 1989, 14.3 donors per million population were available in Spain. This rate increased to 17.8 in 1990, 20.2 in 1991, 21.7 in 1992, 22.6 in 1993, 25.0 in 1994 and 27.0 in 1995[77]. This sustained increase in donation rates is impressive. It does, however, require considerable financial investment in personnel and intensive care facilities. The improvement is that much more significant in that it occurred

---

[73]   Source: Department of Health
[74]   Salaman J. et al. British Medical Journal 1994 308:30-31.
[75]   Department of Health and Social Security: Report of the Working Party on the Supply of Donor Organs for Transplantation, 1987 (available from Department of Health)
[76]   Information provided by UKTSSA
[77]   Council for Europe Transplant Newsletter, March 1996.

despite a decrease in the number of road traffic deaths (from 150 pmp in 1991 to 121 pmp in 1993). There was also an increase in the number of multi-organ retrievals, from 30% in 1989 to 70% in 1993[78].

5.14   It has been suggested that hospital administrators should be required to ensure that, whenever a patient dies and is clinically suitable as a donor, the attending doctors should be required to ask the relatives for permission for the organs to be removed for transplantation. This system, known as **required request**, operates in some States in the USA. However, we understand that since the legislation was introduced the number of donors has increased only slightly. In practice, in the UK, the number of cases where relatives of potential donors are not approached is small[79].

5.15   There is also a technique which would increase the number of people who could become donors. This procedure, which applies to kidney (and possibly, liver) transplantation only, is the use of **non-heart beating donors**. This technique can take place outside intensive care units and involves the insertion of catheters and the perfusion either of the kidneys, or the whole body, of a recently dead person until such time as permission (or otherwise) has been obtained from the next of kin. Organ removal then takes place if appropriate. One trial in Maastricht produced a 20% increase in kidneys for transplantation over a period of 10 years[80]. Patients who received transplants from non-heart beating donors were, however, more likely than recipients of kidneys obtained conventionally to need post-transplant dialysis before their kidneys functioned. Overall, survival was comparable. Other recent studies[81] have similarly shown overall transplant patient survival can be comparable.

CHANGING THE CURRENT LAW

5.16   Other means of increasing the supply of organs have been suggested, or indeed, are practised in other countries, but are not within the law in the UK.

5.17   Some countries operate an **"opt-out" (or "presumed consent") system** which allows doctors to remove organs for transplantation from deceased persons unless they have previously indicated that they do not wish their organs to be used. The rationale is that this increases the number of organs available but the evidence is not clear. One study[82], for example, was unable

---

78   Matesanz R, Miranda B, Felipe C. Organ Procurement and Renal Transplantation in Spain: The impact of transplant co-ordinations. Clin Trans 1994; 2:281-6.

79   Gore, S. et al. (1992). Organ donation from intensive care units in England and Wales: 2 Year confidential audit of deaths in intensive care. BMJ Vol304: 349-355.

80   Daemon JW. et al. "Organ procurement from non-heart-beating donors" - Organ shortage the solutions, ed Touraine et al (1995). Kluwer Academic Publishers. pp 55-60.

81   Kootstra, G & Daeman JW: Procurement of Organs for Transplantation from Non-heart-beating Cadaver Donors in Europe; Procuring Organs for Transplant (1995). Johns Hopkins UP.

82   Land W. & Cohen B: Post-mortem and living organ donation in Europe: transplantation laws and activities. Transplant Procedure 1992; 24(5) (October) 2165-7.

to find an obvious correlation between high organ removal rates and the existence of presumed consent laws.   There are also safety concerns.   If such a system were in place, care would have to be taken to ensure that relatives were always approached to give an adequate social history of the potential donor. This might reveal lifestyle factors which would mitigate against organ donation, for example, the risk of infection with, perhaps, HIV, Creutzfeldt-Jacob Disease or Hepatitis.   Moreover, the introduction of such a system would be in itself controversial and could run the risk of turning the public mind against transplantation.

5.18   A more radical proposal is the recourse to **elective ventilation**.   This contemplates that patients, close to the point of death, are put onto a ventilator to maintain their organs in a state suitable for transplantation until death takes place.   No benefit to the patient can be expected from this intervention.   A pilot scheme of an elective ventilation scheme took place in the Royal Devon and Exeter Hospital, under a locally written protocol[83].   Over a period of 19 months from May 1988, it was estimated that eight patients who would otherwise not have been identified became donors.   However, this donation rate was not maintained.   There are legal, ethical and clinical objections to this measure.   Elective ventilation is illegal, in that any intervention carried out on a patient without consent must be in the patient's best interests.   If an intervention is not in the patient's best interests (and elective ventilation is not) then it is unlawful.   There are additional ethical difficulties. In carrying out the procedure, there is a small, but as yet unquantified, risk of inducing a persistent vegetative state in the patient.   Finally, there is a clinical objection.   The procedure may require prolonged use of the limited supply of intensive care beds and, therefore, potentially prejudices the chances of treating other patients who could benefit from intensive care.

CONCLUSION

5.19   Thus, it seems that more organs, and other tissue, *could* be obtained from cadaveric donors.   This could be achieved primarily, through continued attention to improving management of the organ retrieval system and to training those involved.   **We recommend that due attention continue to be given to improving donation rates**. We consider that this is particularly important as current evidence suggests that, even if xenotransplantation were introduced, human organs will be more successful than xenotransplants for some time, such that obtaining organs from cadaveric donors would remain the most important method of meeting patients' needs.

5.20   We note the options which would become available, should there be suitable changes in UK law. **We do not, however, recommend such changes**. We are not convinced that they are justified on the basis of current evidence. **We recommend, however, they be kept under review.**

---

[83]   Feast TG, et al. (1990) Protocol for increasing organ donation after cerebrovascual death in a District General Hospital. The Lancet Vol 335: 1133-1135.

IMPROVING THE SUPPLY OF LIVING DONORS

5.21 Experience from other countries suggests that it may also be possible to increase the contribution made through live donation. This is regulated by the Human Organ Transplants Act 1989. Thus, amendment of the Act would be necessary to take forward some of the following measures (for example, the sale of organs). Most living donors are genetically related to the intended recipients. Where donation between unrelated persons is proposed, particular controls are applied through the Unrelated Live Transplant Regulatory Authority (ULTRA).

5.22 Live kidney donation is well-established and transplant survival rates exceed those for cadaver organs. In 1995, 8.5 % of transplants were from living donors[84] (2.6 per million population). Varying live donation rates across regions in Britain and internationally [noted by the UKTSSA] suggests that there may be some potential for increases in regions with lower rates. Norway, for example, performs far more live related or living donor transplants than any other country (17pmp)[85]. Even a small increase in live donation rates could have a considerable impact. However, live donation is not without problems. Adverse psychological effects have been reported in donors, some of whom may, for example, have felt pressured into donating an organ.

5.23 Live partial-liver donation is also possible for transplant into children and a limited programme has started in the UK. The US has also had some experience of live lung-lobe donation to children. This depends on two adult donors (usually parents) donating lobes for transplantation. However, there is the possibility of significant morbidity in the donors and this, combined with the knowledge that even with live lung-lobe donation, chronic rejection may well occur resulting in only medium term survival, mitigates against expansion of the programme.

5.24 Thirdly, there is, in principle, the option of a market in organs. Currently it is illegal to trade in organs (usually, this would involve the sale of someone's kidney). In 1989 it was found that some Turkish people had been brought to the UK and paid to have a kidney removed and transplanted into patients in a private London hospital. Legislation (the Human Organ Transplants Act 1989) was then enacted to make such trade in organs illegal. Doctors who become involved in such trade are also likely to be found guilty of serious professional misconduct and suffer censure.

5.25 Having reviewed the various options, we conclude that some expansion of the live related transplant programme is possible, although this would not be without its difficulties.

---

[84] Johnson RWG.(1996)Renal Donation: UKTSSA Users Bulletin, Issue 19
[85] Johnson RWG.(1996)Renal Donation: UKTSSA Users Bulletin, Issue 19

SUMMARY

5.26   We asked if there were means of improving the allotransplantion programme. We conclude that means do exist and that, indeed, some should be pursued; namely the continued improvement of the management of the programme and the training of the professionals involved.   Such improvements may go some way to meeting the needs of those patients detailed in Chapter 3.   However, it is unlikely that they could meet the total need identified.

5.27   We must emphasise also that improvements in the allotransplantation programme would not easily meet the needs of people with diabetes or with Parkinson's disease. The tissue required for islet cell transplantation cannot readily be prepared from cadaveric human donation and the tissue required for the latter must be obtained from aborted fetuses, which may not be available in sufficient numbers.

OTHER THERAPIES

5.28   We turn now to our third question; that is, are there no procedures, other than xenotransplantation, which can meet the needs of those who could benefit from tissue transplantation? To answer this question we must examine potential therapies which may become available in the relevant timescale.   The answer is of great importance. If there were alternative therapeutic procedures and if the investment now being made in xenotransplantation were put instead into them, new therapies might emerge which did not depend on the use of animals and which avoided the costs, the immunosuppression and the risk of infection associated with xenotransplantation.

SOMATIC CELL GENE THERAPY

5.29   This relatively recent form of therapy seeks to identify and then alleviate illness through the modification of body cells.   The modification may correct gene function by the introduction of genes or modify the properties of particular cells.   Currently, the technology involved in somatic cell gene therapy is at an early stage and has only had limited therapeutic success. Around 1,500 patients worldwide have participated in gene therapy trials, the majority of which investigated the possibilities of gene transfer and expression. The limited success is in part due to the complexities of the interactions between genes and the environment and to the need to improve aspects of the technology which, for example, targets and transfers the gene. That said, there is every likelihood that the next decade could see significant developments in the application of the results of the human genome project to the treatment of disease.

5.30   The majority of gene therapy trials so far approved have concentrated on cancer and AIDS, though a small but significant number have been aimed at inherited, single gene disorders such as cystic fibrosis. The rate of progress in the field is unlikely to be rapid and the possibility of its playing a therapeutic role in a wide range of illnesses, particularly those for which transplantation is currently a treatment, is uncertain. It is difficult to predict when gene therapy may become available: we are advised that it may be more than ten years before it has been developed and it could be much longer than that before it is widely available, particularly as regards conditions, which if gene therapy were successful, would no longer require transplantation.

5.31   We believe that the public interest would be best served if appropriate means were found which allowed the parallel research, development and evaluation of gene therapy.

ARTIFICIAL ORGANS

5.32   We begin with the same general point: interest in the potential for xenotransplantation should neither prevent or discourage continuing research and development in artificial organs. If such organs were a viable option, they could well prove to be preferable as regards solid organs to xenotransplantation. Again, they would avoid the use of animals and the risks associated with immunosuppression and infection. We now review developments.

ARTIFICIAL HEART

5.33   Artificial hearts come in two forms: ventricular assist devices (VADs) or totally artificial hearts. VADs support but do not replace the heart and are implanted in the abdomen. They are attached by a small lead to a power source carried outside the body. Implantable VADs have an, as yet, undefined role in UK cardiac practice, but successful bridging for transplantation has been undertaken. If successfully bridged to transplantation, patients can expect results comparable to transplant surgery. However, bridging with VADs is not without its problems. We are told that of 100 patients bridged, 40 will die of complications and 60 will be transplanted of whom 40-50 will survive. Further, bridging, in itself, cannot solve the organ transplant problem. Indeed its effect is to increase the number of people waiting for a donor organ. Without bridging, a patient may die awaiting a donor heart while bridging may divert scarce donor hearts away from another population of patients who might be expected to have a similar long-term outcome. We are told that only in rare cases can it be expected that the patient's heart will recover sufficiently for the VAD to be removed without concomitant heart transplant.

5.34   Long-term implantation of VADs has received much recent attention but biocompatability problems need to be overcome to achieve total "implantability". More research is required to determine the importance of this form of therapy. There are relatively few recipients of long term VADs world-wide who have a satisfactory quality of life and there have been no rigorously controlled studies comparing prognosis, functional result or quality of life in patients receiving medical therapy, transplant or VAD implantation. It is estimated, however, that implantable VAD technology will continue to improve over the next 5-10 years and that such devices will be an important therapeutic option in patients with rapidly deteriorating heart functions, eg those patients presenting with cardiogenic shock immediately following myocardial infarction, as a bridge to transplantation.

5.35 Totally artificial hearts are designed, by contrast, to carry out all of the main functions of the heart. The devices have a potential for short term use but are still in the early stages of clinical trials. There are also various problems to be overcome, particularly the problem of blood clotting inside the devices which could cause a stroke and the problem that the devices themselves tend to damage blood cells, causing anaemia and serious liver and kidney problems. The power packs can also be inconvenient to use. We are advised, however, that these technical problems may well be overcome and, in the next 5-10 years, these may become viable alternatives to transplantation.

ARTIFICIAL LUNG

5.36 Located outside the body, artificial lungs were initially developed in the 1950s to support patients during heart surgery. There remain extensive biocompatibility problems restricting the use of current devices to the very short term. Trials of implantable devices, designed to oxygenate the blood and remove carbon dioxide, are now in progress, but these are not as efficient as external artificial lungs. We are advised that it is very unlikely that successful long term artificial lung therapy will be in place in the next 10 years.

ARTIFICIAL KIDNEY

5.37 The artificial kidney was developed in the 1950s and has long been a standard form of therapy for those suffering renal failure. Initially renal dialysis involved a large amount of technical equipment and required patients to spend long hours in hospital attached to a machine. Research over the years has resulted in the development of a small pack which can be worn around the waist. With advances in micro computing it may be that the machine will become even smaller and less intrusive. However, we are told that there are no new techniques available or under detailed research which are likely to replace or radically alter the current situation. The fundamental problem, however, with renal dialysis is that it is undoubtedly a treatment of second choice. The patient must observe a strict dietary regimen and always feels less than well. By contrast, a successful kidney transplant restores the patient to a feeling of health and well being. Thus, while the artificial kidney has a place, it must be a matter of conjecture whether it could be developed in such a way, that it could be said to offer a patient a better prospect of a healthy life than a transplant.

ARTIFICIAL PANCREAS

5.38 Automatic delivery of insulin or insulin analogues by some device coupled to a blood glucose detection system might provide for the construction of an artificial pancreas. We are advised that this is probably achievable and that such a development could circumvent the need for islet transplantation altogether. However, biosensor technology still needs to be developed some way further.

ARTIFICIAL LIVER

5.39   The artificial liver again functions outside the body and has been used for short-term support in patients with acute liver failure. As with extra-corporeal support with human and animal organs, this allows a patient's own liver time to regenerate, avoiding the need for liver transplantation. Initial experiments have not been successful but newer models may prove satisfactory for short term support. This may reduce the need for liver transplantation in acute liver failure. It will not, however, help those with chronic disease. Bioengineered livers have also been developed, again with the aim of short-term use either allowing the organ a chance to regenerate or keeping patients alive for a short time. It appears, therefore that at least as a bridging or short term measure, the development of an artificial liver may be of significant value. Given the incidence of acute liver failure it is clearly important that further development of a procedure which obviates the need for a liver transplant should be pursued.

SUMMARY

5.40   The development of both somatic cell gene therapies and artificial organs is at the forefront of medical research, as is xenotransplantation. There appears to be a real potential for both forms of development to offer benefit to patients currently in need of transplantation. Accordingly, **we recommend that appropriate means be found to support and encourage continued research into the development and application of gene therapy and artificial organs**.

TRADITIONAL HEALTH CARE MEASURES

PREVENTIVE MEDICINE AND HEALTH PROMOTION

5.41   Much emphasis has been given in recent years to preventative medicine and health promotion, through, for example, initiatives such as, the *Health of the Nation*[86] strategy. Could such measures have an impact on the conditions which lead to a need for transplantation? If so, there would be a case for investing in such measures and avoiding the morbidity associated both with the condition and with any transplantation procedure. The relevance of health promotion measures, in terms of the medical conditions we are concerned with, is explored below.

---

[86]   Department of Health: A Strategy for Health in England. HMSO, 1992.

HEARTS

5.42   End-stage heart failure due to cardiomyopathy has a number of causes and some may be amenable to health promotion measures. Valvular cardiomyopathy is to an extent preventable by measures eliminating rheumatic fever and by timely correction of faulty valves. Hypertensive cardiomyopathy is preventable (secondary prevention) through early diagnosis and treatment of high blood pressure. Inflammatory cardiomyopathies related to HIV and Chagas' disease are preventable. Both are infectious diseases. Chagas' disease, however, while endemic in South America, does not occur in the UK. Some metabolic cardiomyopathies are preventable by early and adequate treatment of the underlying disorder and some of the familial storage diseases or infiltrations which affect the liver (eg haemochromatosis) may also respond to early intervention. But despite this, we are told that the cause of disease is not known for around 60% of these patients. These conditions, and conditions which are genetic or family related or which result from muscular and neuromuscular disorders, are not preventable.

5.43   End-stage heart failure due to coronary heart disease is the area where health promotion has the most to offer. In patients assessed for transplantation, we are told that around 55% suffer from cardiomyopathy secondary to ischaemic coronary heart disease. The incidence of this condition can be affected by health promotion measures, such as ceasing to smoke, reducing fat in the diet and increasing physical activity. Where heart failure is caused by hypertension this, again, can be prevented either by lifestyle changes or by proper treatment of the hypertension. In men with raised cholesterol levels, drugs which inhibit the production of cholesterol (eg HMG-CoA reductase inhibitors) are of benefit. Secondary preventive measures following myocardial infarction or in patients with known coronary artery disease have been shown to be of benefit. These involve treatment with, for example, aspirin, ACE inhibitors and HMG-CoA reductase inhibitors. It is not possible to predict how great an impact such measures could have. We are advised that health promotion exercises over the next 20 years are unlikely to have a great effect on the number of patients requiring cardiac transplant, although there might be some diminution in the proportion of patients presenting with severe coronary heart disease.

5.44   Complex congenital heart disease, the other indication for transplantation, is not amenable to preventive measures, unless better *in utero* diagnosis becomes available and pregnancies are terminated, which, of course, raises its own ethical issues.

LUNGS

5.45   Of those patients referred for lung transplantation with a diagnosis of emphysema (around 30%), around one third have a congenital biochemical abnormality that leads to chronic lung disease and around two thirds have a non-specific diagnosis which probably includes a significant number of patients with smoking related disease. Measures to reduce smoking may be supposed to have an impact on these latter patients but we are advised that it is anticipated that it would take 5-10 years for an effect to be observed.

KIDNEYS

5.46 End-stage renal failure is not generally amenable to health promotion measures, although, as with hearts, proper treatment of hypertension may have an impact on the small proportion of patients in which this leads to end-stage renal failure. This may be particularly significant in more elderly patients.

5.47 Work is also proceeding on understanding the way in which diabetes causes damage to the vasculature generally, and specifically renal changes. We are told that there is increasing evidence that the early and rigorous control of diabetes may result in delayed onset of complications or even prevent them happening. It may be that the impact of diabetic renal failure on renal replacement programmes will be lessened over the next one or two decades, although, we are told, the extent of this effect cannot be estimated.

LIVERS

5.48 Health promotion interventions to control alcohol intake may reduce the numbers of patients with chronic liver failure, although alcohol cirrhosis is not common and not a major reason for transplantation. Immunisation against some forms of hepatitis could also lead to a reduction of cirrhosis.

SUMMARY

5.49 There seems to be some potential for health promotion measures to make an impact on those suffering from conditions which lead to transplantation and for some effects to be observed over a similar timetable to the proposed development of xenotransplantation. Avoiding such morbidity, particularly at a premature age, would be a prized goal. However, we emphasise that some of the relevant medical conditions are not amenable to either primary or secondary preventive measures. We note also that many factors affect lifestyle choices and that lifestyle changes can be difficult to achieve. However, **we recommend that such measures should continue to be pursued**.

5.50 We note also the irony that health promotion measures also affect organ supply. Reducing the incidence of strokes, and to a far lesser extent, suicides and of death through accidents can be expected to reduce further the pool of organs available from those dying in these ways.

SURGERY AND DRUG THERAPY

5.51 Medical and surgical therapies are continually being developed for many conditions. Indeed, many patients (for example, with heart failure) are only considered for transplantation when drug therapies are no longer effective. New surgical techniques may similarly obviate the need for more invasive transplant surgery. We look at the current position below.

HEARTS

5.52 We are advised that drug therapies for heart failure have improved, but that it is likely that these could make only a small impact on the total need for heart transplantation. Significant reductions in heart failure-related mortality have been ascribed to the advent of vasodilator therapy and more recently there is debate that the introduction of betablockade may improve prognoses further. However, the impact of drug therapy on improving a patient's quality of life remains small and so, at the present time, although refinement of medical management is important, it is unlikely to have a significant impact on the need for heart transplantation.

5.53 Early clinical results of a pioneering form of heart surgery, which seeks to address problems of heart failure, have recently been reported[87]. Heart failure is almost always accompanied by a gradual enlargement of the size of the left ventricular chamber (cardiomyopathy). This is regarded as a compensatory mechanism to allow the diseased ventricle to pump the same volume of blood per heart beat into the circulation. Because of this ventricular dilatation the tension in the wall of the ventricle increases and this is thought by some to be in itself deleterious. The reported technique (developed by Dr Batista from Brazil) removes part of this wall, thus reducing the ventricular volume and the wall tension. Good clinical results are reported by Dr Batista in a population of patients predominantly afflicted with Chagas' disease. We are advised that there is as yet no evidence to suggest that this form of surgery can be transposed from the Chagas' disease population to the forms of cardiomyopathy found in the UK. Furthermore, we are not aware of any rigorous evaluation of this technique and its efficacy remains unproven, in both Chagas' disease cases and cardiomyopathy. We are further advised that it may provide only temporary benefit in a small minority of patients. It is likely that the tension in the ventricular wall, having been reduced, will increase again causing cardiac function to deteriorate. Trials are underway in the UK in Bristol. When the results of these trials are evaluated, a more informed judgment will be possible on the extent to which this form of surgery could offer an alternative to transplantation.

5.54 Over recent years, it has also been recognised that some left ventricular muscle appears not to function normally due to a chronic reduction in its blood supply. Restoration of this blood supply by coronary revascularisation has been shown to improve myocardial function. This reversible condition is termed "hibernation". Its prevalence in patients with heart failure due

---

[87]   Article: "Heart-shrink surgery offers alternative to transplants" The Sunday Times 19/5/96

to ischaemic heart disease is currently unknown. It is possible that detailed scrutiny of patients with this condition will reveal a small fraction in whom conventional cardiac surgery may be applicable.

LUNGS

5.55   Long term studies are underway on replacement therapy for those patients with lung disease due to α-1-antitrypsin deficiency. It is possible that this therapy may also be used in the treatment of those patients with lung disease not due to this specific deficiency. However, we are advised that it is unlikely that such replacement therapy will be available for several years.

5.56   The average life expectancy for people with cystic fibrosis has now risen to around 40 years. This improvement has been the result mainly of improved management of lung disease but also of improved management of nutrition and bowel problems. Further increases in life expectancy may be possible but for the foreseeable future these are likely to delay the age at which a transplant is required rather than remove the need for transplantation. There may also be some progress in the next 10 years in correcting the underlying biochemical defect through conventional medical therapies. However, it may be that different treatments are required for different forms of cystic fibrosis. This would mean it would be optimistic to think that there would be effective treatment for the majority of patients within ten years.

PARKINSON'S DISEASE

5.57   Drug treatment can achieve a considerable degree of relief from symptoms in many patients. Surgical treatments are being developed but remain in the experimental stage. Improvements in motor functions have been reported after surgical removal of the part of the brain (GPi pallidotomy), thought to be responsible for the major motor disturbances in Parkinson's disease. Clinical trials are also commencing using injections of a chemical which mimics the activity of dopamine.

DIABETES

5.58   Dietary restrictions, oral therapy (for type 2 diabetics) and insulin (for type 1 diabetics) can help to manage diabetes effectively. However, even with treatment complications can occur which can cause a great deal of morbidity and early mortality. We are told that better preparations of insulin or insulin analogues for injection may be possible but that there are currently no alternative medical or surgical therapies.

OTHER THERAPIES: SUMMARY

5.59   We must now consider our answer to Question 3. We conclude that there are indeed other procedures, either in existence (such as health promotion methods) or in development (such as artificial organs) which may provide alternatives to xenotransplantation. We repeat that such methods must be pursued in tandem with xenotransplantation. We do not consider that it is possible to predict, at the present time, which therapies are most likely to meet the needs of the patients whose conditions call for transplantation.

SUMMARY

5.60   We conclude that xenotransplantation is not the only way forward and that it is not possible to predict that it will be the best way. The needs of certain patients may be met through other methods and those methods could avoid some of the problems inherent in surgery in general and in xenotransplantation in particular. Not least, xenotransplantation is more likely to pose a threat to the public health. We draw particular attention to the possible alternatives for those patients in need of solid organ transplants (and, perhaps, particularly those who are in need of hearts), both through any improvement and extension of the allotransplantation programme and through the development of artificial organs. There appear to be fewer alternatives becoming available for those patients in need of isolated cell transplantation, that is, diabetics and those with Parkinson's disease.

5.61   The needs of patients whose conditions call for transplantation are of such a magnitude and variety that we consider it unlikely that any one development could attempt to meet them in full. We repeat our conclusion that those who have responsibility for funding developments in, for example, allotransplantation or health promotion programmes, or research into alternative procedures should seek to ensure that these alternatives to xenotransplantation are pursued with appropriate vigour.

CHAPTER SIX:

WEIGHING THE ARGUMENTS

6.1   We can now return to the questions we posed for ourselves in Chapter 1, namely:

1.   In the light of current scientific knowledge, does xenotransplantation offer an ethically acceptable solution to the problems associated with the shortage of tissue for transplantation and to the problems caused by other medical conditions?

2.   Are there ways to improve the current programme for obtaining human tissue so as to meet all or a greater part of the demand for transplantation of tissue?

3.   Are there currently other procedures for responding to the needs of those whose conditions call for transplantation and are such procedures unlikely to be developed in the relevant timescale?

6.2   In answer to the first question, we conclude that;

❖   benefits to patients and wider population may flow from the development and introduction of xenotransplantation;

❖   these benefits must be set against the possibility of harm arising;

❖   some, who regard all use of animals as wrong, would not accept such a weighing exercise;

❖   we do not adopt this position, but rather a weighing of benefit versus harm

on balance, **we conclude that only if the conditions which we have outlined are met could xenotransplantation be considered to be ethically acceptable**.

6.3   These conditions include the following:

❖   primates must not be used as a source animal for xenotransplantation. They may be used only in the limited circumstance of tissue recipients in research to develop xenotransplantation, and then only where no alternative method of obtaining the necessary information exists.

❖ the limits to which xenotransplantation can be developed, both in terms of the genetic modification of the animals and in terms of the tissue which may be transplanted, must be monitored to assess possible effects and harm caused. Those charged with these developments should bear in mind the concerns we have outlined.

❖ further evidence should be obtained on certain elements of risk to the potential tissue recipient and to the wider population. This would include further research on the risk relating to physiology, immunology, and infection. In the current state of knowledge it is not acceptable to move to clinical trials involving humans.

❖ measures to minimise the risk of infection to the human recipient and to the wider population should be designed and put in place. These relate to the methods in which the source animals would be kept, the monitoring source animals would undergo and the methods which would be used to remove the tissue (that is, the production methods of the tissue). Measures should also be put in place to monitor observance of these measures.

❖ systems designed to collect data on the source animals used and the human patients involved in xenotransplantation should be designed and put into operation. The data and, where relevant, tissue samples to be collected should be agreed, after appropriate consultation, to ensure consistency.

❖ the welfare of animals, compromised by the infection control measures which we consider to be necessary, should be protected so far as is possible.

❖ the sequential removal of tissue from source animals should be forbidden.

❖ given that any therapeutic programme of xenotransplantation would make demands on the resources available to the NHS, the National Specialist Commissioning Advisory Group should consider the purchase of the various xenotransplantation services.

❖ given the recognition that the effects of xenotransplantation could extend to other therapies which exist or are being developed, attention must continue to be given to allotransplantation and any other new or existing therapy which could meet the needs of patients.

6.4   In answer to the second question, we conclude that;

there do appear to be ways to improve the current allotransplantation programme and these should be fully explored. This is particularly important as human organs offer a better prospect for patients, at least in the shorter term. However, any improvement is unlikely to meet all or even a greater part of the demand for transplantation. We conclude that the claims for resources for xenotransplantation must be weighed in the balance against the competing claims of the maintenance and enhancement of the current allotransplantation programme.

6.5 In answer to the third question, we conclude that;

there are procedures being developed to meet the needs of those whose conditions call for transplantation. These will take some time to have an effect because, for example, health promotion measures cannot reverse damage already done and can only affect future need, or because the procedures are being developed on a similar timescale to xenotransplantation, for example, artificial organs.

Thus, research into and development of other medical procedures as alternatives to xenotransplantation must be pursued with equal vigour and the allocation of Government resources should take account of this.

6.6 Having reached these conclusions, we return now to the conditions stipulated in our answer to Question 1. We draw attention to what we said at the outset: ethical decisions may change in the light of new knowledge. Clearly, if infection control measures were shown to require further compromises to animal welfare, or if information from research were to emerge to indicate, for example, that certain physiological problems could not be overcome or that the risks of infection were considerable, the balance of argument would move away from the introduction of xenotransplantation (or certain applications of it). Equally the converse is true: research demonstrating that developments in genetic medicine or artificial organs held out little prospect of meeting patients' needs, or that certain perceived risks were not in fact likely to occur could shift the balance towards xenotransplantation.

6.7 What of those of our conditions which specifically refer to the state of scientific knowledge: where, in our view, does the balance of argument currently lie? Our conclusion, in effect, is that current knowledge is not yet such as to allow us to support the introduction of xenotransplantation at the present time. The research which we stipulate should serve to make it more clear where the balance lies. It has to be said, however, that the constantly changing nature of science is such that the conditions which we have established arise from what we currently know. New information may itself raise further questions and suggest further conditions. We are conscious that there must be limits to this process. For this reason, we regard it as a primary duty of those charged with overseeing developments that they should determine a point at which either enough is known and enough has been done to warrant taking the step of introducing xenotransplantation initially through clinical trials, or to insist that all or some development be discontinued.

6.8 It follows therefore that, for xenotransplantation to be considered ethically acceptable, the conditions which we have outlined are necessary but not sufficient. We further conclude that some mechanism should be put in place to ensure that these conditions and any other matters which arise are addressed. In particular, no xenotransplantation research involving humans should be carried out until there is evidence that the conditions relating to the state of scientific knowledge have been met. We also note that any approval of clinical trials would not presuppose a move to a therapeutic programme. The outcomes of clinical trials, for each proposed xenotransplant therapy, should be carefully assessed before any such move to a therapeutic programme is contemplated. There is also a clear need for the progress of clinical trials to be closely monitored and to be stopped, should it be thought appropriate in the light of adverse effects.

6.9   We therefore conclude that a Standing Committee on xenotransplantation is required to monitor and review these matters and accordingly **recommend the establishment of such a committee. We further recommend that such a Committee should have a national role and that it should be established by primary legislation.** We will discuss why we consider primary legislation to be essential in Chapter 8. We will discuss the establishment and responsibilities of such a Committee at greater length in Chapter 9.

6.10   This then concludes the first part of our enquiry; that which concerns the ethical acceptability of xenotransplantation. We now move on to the second part; that which involves a detailed consideration of the elements which would comprise an ethical framework within which xenotransplantation, were it to proceed, could be ethically undertaken. The satisfaction of the conditions we have outlined and creation of a National Standing Committee through primary legislation form the central basis of such a framework.

SECTION THREE

AN ETHICAL FRAMEWORK

CHAPTER SEVEN:
FURTHER ETHICAL CONCERNS

INTRODUCTION

7.1   We have concluded that only if the conditions which we have outlined were to be met could xenotransplantation be considered ethically acceptable and that the fulfilment of these conditions should be monitored by a national standing committee on xenotransplantation. The need to balance both the needs of patients and animals, and the needs of the individual patient and the wider population, form the basis of these conditions. We now move to consider the second element in our terms of reference: the nature of any ethical framework within which xenotransplantation, were it to proceed, could be undertaken. In this Chapter, as a first step in constructing such a framework, we examine any further ethical concerns which would arise if xenotransplantation were to proceed so as to involve humans, first in clinical trials and, potentially, thereafter in therapeutic programmes. In Chapter 8, we consider the form which the ethical framework should take. In Chapter 9, we consider in more detail the role and remit of the National Standing Committee which we have recommended, given its central role in our proposed ethical framework.

7.2   The concerns considered in this Chapter relate to the patient, the professionals who would be involved, and the clinical sites in which xenotransplantation procedures would take place. They also relate to our recognition of the ethical difficulties which xenotransplantation poses. We have already stated that we are aware that whatever view we take, there will be a responsible body of opinion which will oppose it. It is important that our ethical framework respects and protects the interests of individuals whatever views they hold. In this context we draw attention to Annex B, which includes an outline of the responses to xenotransplantation received from different faith groups.

7.3   We recognise that the concerns raised and our responses to them may differ as between the clinical trial stage and any therapeutic programme and we attempt to draw the necessary distinctions below. We should also point out that considerations involved in any move from clinical trials to a therapeutic programme are likely to differ between xenotransplant therapies; for example, it could be that the problems surrounding heart xenotransplantation could be resolved more readily than those surrounding kidney xenotransplantation.

THE INTERESTS OF PATIENTS

7.4 Any ethical framework must seek to preserve and protect the interests of patients should xenotransplantation proceed to clinical trials in humans and then become a therapeutic option. The concern for patients' interests will be greatest initially. As a consequence, vigilance must also be greatest at the outset. We concentrate here on the following: the selection of appropriate patients; the need for consent and the information any potential patient must be given before giving consent; arrangements for confidentiality and privacy; and patients who refuse xenotransplants.

PATIENT SELECTION

7.5 We emphasise that at the stage of clinical trials, we are talking about *therapeutic research*. No question arises of *non-therapeutic research* involving xenotransplantation, because the risks are potentially too great. Benefit to patients must be thought possible. If the research must be therapeutic, then the initial question which arises is who may be entered into the trial (patient selection). This may well vary from therapy to therapy.

7.6 As the clinical trial must involve a possibility of benefitting the patient involved (as well as producing generalisable information), we suggest that patients who are moribund or so ill as not to be able to benefit may not be appropriate. It is not in their interests to take part if they cannot benefit and it will not properly test the procedure. Some, of course, may wish to volunteer, despite the likely absence of benefit. It is a matter initially of professional medical judgment and then for those reviewing applications for research (see Chapter 9) whether such a patient should be accepted, given the effect it would have on trial data and generalisable knowledge.

7.7 One particular issue of general importance is whether children and those incapable of giving valid consent should be considered for inclusion in clinical trials. Although it is undoubtedly the case that children could be significant beneficiaries of xenotransplantation:

We recommend that children should not be included in trials, at least until all the initial concerns about safety and efficacy have been satisfactorily resolved. We take the same view as regards those incapable of giving valid consent.

We have considered, in this context, the recommendations of the Law Commission in its Report on Mental Incapacity[88].

---

[88]   The Law Commission, Law Com No 231 (1995): Mental Incapacity

7.8   Should xenotransplantation become a therapeutic option, questions of selection could still arise although these primarily will be a matter for the doctor and patient to discuss. If allotransplantation or other, developing, therapeutic interventions represent a more favourable option and are available, patients may seek to opt for them. It may well be that, as a consequence, xenotransplantation will initially be an option effectively for those unable to benefit from other therapies – a treatment of last resort.

7.9   Given the current state of knowledge, however, it is not possible to offer anything by way of useful analysis as to how such judgments about selection should be made. It may be that, by the time any programme of therapy were to be considered, general agreement would have been reached on the medical conditions most likely to benefit from xenotransplantation. If so, issues of selection would turn largely on medical facts. At that point, patient selection would perhaps, arise only in the case of novel uses of existing xenotransplant techniques (for example, their extension to new groups of patients). It would only be these that need review. It could be of course that such novel uses should themselves be considered as clinical trials.

CONSENT OF PATIENTS

7.10   Once a patient is accepted for admission into a trial, the well recognised ethical principles governing therapeutic research apply. We expect them to be observed. Here, we concentrate particularly on the need for proper consent, which we discuss below.

7.11   Consent is an exceptionally complex concept from both an ethical and legal standpoint. A Report such as this is not the place to attempt to set out a comprehensive analysis of consent as it applies to clinical trials and any subsequent therapeutic programme of xenotransplantation. We are content to conclude here that the principles ordinarily applied both in the context of therapeutic research and treatment should equally apply to xenotransplantation. That said, there are certain particular issues which are raised by xenotransplantation and which call for particular comment. They are of sufficient importance that **we recommend that they should be incorporated into any consent arrangements, so that the patient may be properly informed.** They include:

❖   given the wide variation of views as to the acceptability of xenotransplantation, which may or may not be derived from religious beliefs, consent should always be sought (or in the case of the adult incapable of making a valid decision, the views of those closest to the adult must be sought).

❖   the current status of xenotransplantation, both as regards the research undertaken and the procedures which had been carried out in humans; including information about how many procedures of the kind being proposed had taken place, what the potential difficulties are (in terms of immunology and physiology) and what the outcomes have been. This would be particularly relevant during the stage of clinical trials.

❖ the potential risks of infection, including: what is known and what is unknown; what is relevant from the outcomes of previous procedures; the form of monitoring that might be required following the procedure, the fact that this might be life-long and the importance of complying with monitoring arrangements; and the implications for patients' close contacts, in particular their partners. Consent should also be sought for access to and appropriate dissemination of certain medical information which would be needed for monitoring purposes.

❖ the alternatives to xenotransplantation; including (for solid organs) the likelihood of receiving an organ in the allotransplantation programme and information about any existing or potential therapies (perhaps, for example, artificial organs, in particular, hearts) and the outcomes of these therapies.

❖ the nature of the procedure; including such information as enables the patient to make a personal decision about the acceptability of xenotransplantation. This should include information which would enable people, including but not limited to those from different faith groups, to make their decision. As explored in Annex B, this would include information about the source of the tissue; the breeding, genetic modification and raising of animals; and the degree of suffering to which the animals would be exposed.

❖ the nature of the tissue to be transplanted, including information which addresses particular concerns about the transplantation of certain tissue; for example, that which might be thought to affect personality.

❖ the potential psychological and social effects that xenotransplantation could have. Allotransplantation has well-documented psychological effects. It is possible that xenotransplantation could also have psychological effects and this would have to be explained to any potential patient. Given the novel and controversial nature of xenotransplantation and the wide divergence of public views, it would be advisable to point out that people might react in a hostile or uncertain way to a xenotransplant recipient.

7.12 All of the information which we have referred to would have to include the latest scientific and other evidence available and arrangements would have to be made to update any information pack regularly.

7.13 The need of the patient to assimilate a considerable volume of information, as part of the consent process, must be taken account of in the procedures for obtaining consent. There may be a need both for information packs and for individual counselling. The counsellor would be independent of the transplant team and be able to guide the patient through the information and the process of reaching a decision.

We recommend that a system of counselling, independent of the transplant team, should be in place and that prospective xenotransplant recipients should have access to it, both before any clinical trial and if judged appropriate, subsequently, should any xenotransplant programme be established.

7.14 It will be noticed that we have not discussed in detail, as an issue of significance, the potential psychological and social effects of xenotransplantation. There is little evidence on which to take a view: very few people have undergone xenotransplantation procedures and few of these have survived for a sufficient length of time for the issue to be explored.

We recommend that the psychological effects of xenotransplantation should be kept under review and that consideration should be given to funding research into these effects. Any such information gained would have to be fed back into consent arrangements.

7.15 To ensure that consent can be freely given, proper arrangements would have to be made for those who choose not to opt for a xenotransplantation procedure. Such patients must retain their place on the waiting list, whether for solid organs or for other tissue, and retain their rights to treatment for their condition.

Accordingly, **we recommend that patients who choose not to opt for xenotransplantation should not be penalised in any way in their medical care.**

7.16 We consider that a similar system of consent arrangements will need to be in place for both clinical trials and for any therapeutic programme. However, there will be a great deal more uncertainty about possible outcomes at the clinical trial stage and this should be made clear.

CONFIDENTIALITY AND PRIVACY

7.17 We do not propose to discuss in detail the ethical principles relating to confidentiality and privacy. They are well recognised. We note only that the probable media interest (and potential adverse reaction from some sectors of the community) is likely both to increase the patient's desire for confidentiality and make it more difficult to secure. Further, for monitoring and public health reasons, certain medical information on any xenotransplant recipient would have to be made available to those responsible for monitoring. This should be made clear when consent to treatment is being sought (see paragraph 7.11, bullet point 3).

7.18 Confidentiality issues are not always clear and instances may arise when problematic claims of access to information are made and when the protection of patients' privacy may be in doubt. Should a national committee be established (see Chapters 8 and 9), they should have a role in advising on such issues.

THE INTERESTS OF RELATIVES

7.19   When a patient undergoes major surgery, any relatives are clearly affected.   In xenotransplantation, this might be particularly true. Relatives may be at risk of contracting some xenozoonotic infection and might therefore be affected by infection control measures and monitoring arrangements. They may also be affected by adverse social reactions towards xenotransplantation. Further, at least in the initial stages, they have the emotional burden on having a loved one undergoing major surgery with uncertain outcomes. Should the patient die, the relatives might wish to keep in touch with the outcomes of any clinical trial or programme which the patient was part of; such involvement and information may help them to feel that the death "was not in vain".

7.20   We draw attention to these matters and **recommend that the clinical site addresses the needs of relatives as well as the needs of patients**. Best practice already exists in the form of patients' associations and this should be drawn upon.

THE INTERESTS OF PROFESSIONALS

7.21   A wide range of professionals is likely to be involved in any xenotransplantation programme. They divide, broadly, into two groups – those concerned with the animals and those concerned with the human patients. In the former group are included animal technicians and veterinary surgeons, in the latter, nurses, doctors and all those who work in the health care establishments where xenotransplantation would take place. Given this wide range, certain issues warrant attention.

PROFESSIONAL ISSUES: BRIDGING THE GAP

7.22   Xenotransplantation demands that those who work with the source animals have regard to the needs of health care professionals and that health care professionals understand certain aspects of the source animals' breeding and raising. For example, veterinary surgeons (who might remove the tissue from the animal) would need to be aware of the tissue requirements of transplant surgeons. Equally, hospital staff, particularly doctors and nurses, would require knowledge of the pathogens to which the source animal is subject and about the samples taken from the animals. There may also be "boundary" issues which warrant discussion. For example, would medical staff have some role in determining the care of the source animals? Would veterinary or medical staff be primarily responsible for removing the tissue and preparing it for transplant? Communication between the various professional groups involved would be essential to ensure that the welfare of the animal and the human patient is not put at risk.

7.23   Veterinarians, and paraprofessional staff including animal technicians and veterinary nurses, would care for the source animals during production and thus would play a crucial role in safeguarding the welfare of the animals and ensuring their health status. The Royal College of Veterinary Surgeons produces its Guide to Professional Conduct which covers the majority of the issues for the veterinarian and provides for a disciplinary process under the Veterinary Surgeons Act, 1966.

7.24   The Institute of Animal Technology produces guidelines which apply to Registered Animal Technicians. The British Veterinary Nursing Association produces similar guidelines for Veterinary Nurses.

We consider that such guidelines (currently non-statutory) should apply to all animal technicians and veterinary nurses involved in xenotransplantation, together with an appropriate system of monitoring compliance with them.

7.25   A variety of other related issues need to be addressed, including needs and mechanisms for training and the various roles of the professions involved.

We recommend that these issues be addressed as a matter of priority, taking advice from interested professional groups.

Should a national standing committee be established, this would be an appropriate forum in which to take these matters forward.

CONSCIENTIOUS OBJECTION

7.26   We recognise that, as in the rest of the population, the views of the professionals in the veterinary and human health care worlds will vary. Participation in procedures related to xenotransplantation may be affected not only by ethical or religious viewpoints but also by concerns relating to the safety of the procedures and the risks of infection. Accordingly,

we consider that those whose work may involve them in xenotransplantation must be given information about xenotransplantation and its effects, so that they are able to make a personal decision. This information might, in many respects, be similar to that given to patients.

Further, we take the view that any person in such a situation, should have the right to "opt-out" of this work without prejudice to career or employment.
This right should be protected by legislation.

However, we understand that veterinarians have a professional obligation to provide treatment, at least in the form of first aid, to any animal in an emergency and that doctors and nurses have similar obligations to treat any person at risk in an emergency. We acknowledge that these obligations should be paramount.

CLINICAL SITE

7.27 Any clinical site in which xenotransplantation procedures could take place would have to be not only well equipped to deal with the various surgical interventions involved, through appropriate surgical and nursing expertise, but also well organised so as to have regard to and take account of the interests of both their patients and their staff. In summary, this would include the availability of appropriate counselling staff, the provision of information to ensure appropriate consent arrangements, and arrangements for confidentiality systems, media relations expertise and access to appropriate training. The clinical site might also wish to consider means of raising the general awareness of all staff about xenotransplantation as part of a general process of education.

7.28 The "designated site" system utilised by the National Specialist Commissioning Advisory Group outlines one way in which the competence of institutions to undertake particular procedures is assessed. Should any xenotransplantation therapy become a service which is purchased by the NSCAG (as is suggested in Chapter 4), the clinical site would come under such control. However, no such control would exist at the initial stages of clinical trials. **We recommend that those clinical sites in which it may be proposed that xenotransplantation should take place be assessed at the early clinical trial stage. We further recommend that any assessment should be based on the conditions outlined in Chapter 6 and in this section.** Should a National Standing Committee be established, it would be appropriate for them to take on such a role.

SUMMARY

7.29 We have identified a range of further concerns which are ethical in nature. They form the basis of an ethical framework within which xenotransplantation, if it were to proceed, could be carried out. They concern the patient and their relatives, the professionals involved in xenotransplantation and the clinical sites at which xenotransplantation may take place. We have made a number of recommendations and note that these would best be fulfilled by being part of the remit of our proposed National Standing Committee on xenotransplantation.

CHAPTER EIGHT:
REGULATION BY LAW

INTRODUCTION

8.1 We have concluded that only if the conditions which we outlined are met could xenotransplantation be considered ethically acceptable (Chapters 4 and 6). We have also discussed further ethical concerns which should properly be considered as part of an ethical framework (Chapter 7).

These conditions can be grouped into two main areas;

1. Those which relate to the animal and its welfare; including the use of animals in research, the welfare of source animals bred for xenotransplantation and developments in genetic modification.

2. Those which relate to the human recipient of animal tissue (and possibly to the wider population), including, the control of risks when moving to clinical trials, and with the uncertainty of outcome in terms of tissue function and possible rejection; the control of infection of the recipient (and potentially the wider population); and, generally, the preservation and protection of any actual or potential recipient's interests.

8.2 We have also noticed the impact any programme of xenotransplantation could have on allotransplantation and other therapeutic options and we have made recommendations accordingly. These do not constitute conditions to be satisfied. They are, nonetheless, part of our ethical analysis and should, therefore, inform any decisions on public policy.

8.3 We have further concluded that, to ensure that the conditions we set are met both before and during any clinical trial and continue to be met should any programme of xenotransplantation be contemplated and introduced, some form of regulatory system is essential. This system **must in our view be founded in law** as the nature of our concerns regarding the protection of animal welfare and the control of risk to humans through, in particular, infection, are such as to make legal regulation essential. Guidelines, Codes of Practice and other such forms of regulation have their place but would not, for xenotransplantation, give the assurance which we consider essential.

8.4   Having reached this conclusion, we asked ourselves whether there already exists a legal framework (whether in one law or a combination of laws) which could serve the needs which we have identified. If there is such a framework, this would obviate the need to recommend primary legislation. For the reasons which we set out below, we conclude that, although there are provisions in current legislation which answer many of our concerns, they do not entirely meet the needs we have identified. This is not surprising. Xenotransplantation is a novel procedure and existing law was designed for other things. As a consequence, **we recommend that a comprehensive statutory framework of regulation be put in place, taking account of and drawing upon existing law wherever it is relevant and appropriate**.

8.5   In paving the way for new legislation, it may be of assistance to draw attention to the range of existing laws which touch upon our concerns. The legislation and guidance we look at provide a complex, interconnected web of regulation and control that has been built up over time to meet the constantly changing nature of research and experimentation. Traditionally it has been formed within the context of UK legislation, but more recently the approach throughout Europe continues to be made more consistent through EEC Directives.

8.6   We consider these regulatory mechanisms under the two broad headings identified above, 'Animal Welfare' and 'Protection of the patient and the wider population'. We however, appreciate that the legislation does not reflect this distinction such that the areas overlap. It may be helpful to keep in mind a brief summary of the principal legislation and what it covers (see Table).

BRIEF SUMMARY OF SOME OF THE RELEVANT LEGISLATION

Genetically Modified Organisms (GMO)regulations

Implement European law. They address the human and environmental health and safety aspects of GMOs. Areas covered include the health and safety of those working with GMOs and any subsequent release into the environment, as by marketing.

Animals (Scientific Procedures) Act (ASPA)

Regulates the use of animals for experimental or other scientific or other purposes which may cause harm. It covers aspects of animal welfare and overlaps with GMO regulations as it includes the process of genetically modifying animals. It also provides for licensing which can specify where and how animals are kept or subsequently used.

The Protection of Animals Acts

A general law relating to cruelty to animals, making it an offence to cause unnecessary suffering to any domestic or captive animal. This may only be of relevance, perhaps with other legislation that regulates 'farm' animals, if a transgenic animal were to be discharged from ASPA regulation. The relevant Acts are the Protection of Animals Act 1911; Protection of Animals Act (Scotland) 1912; Protection of Animals (Anaesthetics) Act 1954; Protection of Animals Amendment Act 1954; Protection of Animals Amendment Act 1988; Protection of Animals Penalties Act 1987 (the last three amend the 1911 Act).

Medicines Act & Related EEC Directives

Regulates the process of bringing a medicinal product onto the market from initial research to eventual licensing. This includes consideration of a product's safety, quality and efficacy. it is a matter of conjecture whether tissue from animals could be classified as a medicinal product, but if it were to be, a comprehensive quality control system would be in place.

EEC Medical Devices Directives

Regulate the sale and use of medical devices and equipment, to ensure that they conform to acceptable standards of safety, quality and effectiveness. Non-viable animal tissue is covered under this directive; which in turn may apply to treated bone from transgenic animals.

ANIMAL WELFARE

8.7   The Animals (Scientific Procedures) Act 1986 may be relevant to our concern about animal welfare in the context of xenotransplantation. It regulates the breeding, raising and use of animals for scientific procedures.

ANIMAL WELFARE: THE ANIMALS (SCIENTIFIC PROCEDURES) ACT 1986 (ASPA)

8.8   Within the UK control of animals used for "experimental or other scientific purposes" is regulated by the Home Office in Great Britain and the Department of Health and Social Services in Northern Ireland under the **Animals (Scientific Procedures) Act 1986**. For the purposes of the Act a 'protected animal' means any living vertebrate, other than man, and includes immature forms of mammals from half way through their gestation period.

8.9   The procedures which the Act seeks to regulate include any "experimental or other scientific procedure which may have the effect of causing a protected animal pain, distress or lasting harm". These terms are considered by Home Office guidance to include death, disease, injury, physiological or psychological stress, significant discomfort or any disturbance to normal health, whether immediate or in the long term.

8.10   The Act specifically excludes some procedures from the definition of "regulated procedures". These include:

❖   recognised veterinary, agricultural or animal husbandry practice. Home Office guidance gives the following examples: taking of blood or other tissue for diagnosis and giving established medicines by injection, if done for the benefit of the animal, and husbandry practices such as castration.

❖   the ringing, tagging or marking of animals or other form of procedure for the purposes of identification which cause only momentary pain or distress and no lasting harm.

❖   a clinical test on animals for evaluating veterinary products in accordance with the Medicines Act 1968 or an Order made under it.

OPERATION OF THE ACT

8.11   Where the Act applies, certain controls are exerted on the **project** by reference to which **procedures** take place, the **people** who carry out those procedures and the **place** where they are performed.

8.12 A Project Licence is needed for any programme of work involving regulated procedures on animals. The work must be carried out in specified, designated places by those who have an appropriate Personal Licence. The Project Licence itself sets out the work involved and the justification for the work. It does not deal with the competence of licensees to carry out the procedures.

8.13 Personal licences are required by those people working on a project. They are issued individually to those who are deemed competent by the Home Office to perform the procedures it details, if necessary under supervision. These licences specify the place where procedures may be carried out but are not generally restricted to a specific project.

8.14 Apart from a small number of authorised exceptions, all places where regulated procedures are to be performed must be designated under the Act. A certificate of designation is issued to an individual person in a position of authority at the establishment. This certificate will specify a named individual responsible for day-to-day care of the animals and nominate at least one veterinary surgeon to provide advice on animal health and welfare. These individuals are responsible for ensuring that overall control of the care of animals and the conduct of scientific procedures meet the necessary legal and administrative requirements.

8.15 Section 5(4) of the Act provides that a project licence cannot be granted unless the likely adverse effects (pain, suffering, distress or lasting harm) of the procedures have been weighed against the benefit likely to accrue as a result of the proposed programme of work. This assessment is carried out by an Inspector based on information provided in the application for a licence. Considerations include the suitability of design of the project in relation to its stated objectives; the regard paid by the applicant to the need to use non-sentient alternatives whenever possible, to reducing the number of animals to be used and to minimising their suffering; the justification for using animals (and the special justification required for the use of certain species, notably primates); and the adequacy of facilities. Applications will include an estimate by the applicant of the "severity" of individual procedures (or series of procedures) and the overall severity of the project. Individual procedures within a project licence are assessed on a "worst case" basis, ie the maximum expected or intended severity of the adverse effects that may be encountered by an animal used in the procedure. All the procedures in a project licence are then considered together to arrive at an estimation of 'severity' (mild, moderate or substantial) for the programme as a whole.

8.16 The breeding of certain animals to be used in scientific procedures must also take place in establishments designated under the Act. This applies only to the breeding of animals listed under Schedule 2 of the Act - mouse, rat, guinea pig, hamster, rabbit, dog, cat, primate, and common quail (pigs are not included). Special protection is also afforded by the Act to some animals, including cats, dogs and primates, but not pigs. The Home Secretary may not grant a project licence authorising the use of these specified animals unless he is satisfied that no other species is suitable or practicably available for the purpose of the programme of work.

8.17 The Act also sets out the conditions under which protected animals may be used more than once for research purposes (re-use). In general, re-use of animals is prohibited after a series of regulated procedures for a particular purpose which involved general anaesthesia and recovery of consciousness. There are three circumstances in which re-use may be authorised, one of which could be of concern in xenotransplantation. An animal that received anaesthesia in the first series of procedures may be re-used if the further procedures are also conducted during this general anaesthesia and the animal is not allowed to recover consciousness. Under ASPA all re-use must be specifically authorised in advance and we have recommended (paragraph 4.93-4.94) that sequential removal of any tissues should not be allowed.

INTERPRETATION AND MONITORING OF THE ACT'S PROVISIONS

8.18 The Act provides for the publication of guidance on its operation and in particular the processes involved in the exercise of the power to grant licences and certificates, and the conditions that may be imposed. It also empowers the Secretary of State (Home Office) to issue codes of practice covering the care of protected animals and their use in regulated procedures and to approve codes issued by other bodies. While these codes do not themselves have the force of law they are admissible in evidence and noncompliance with them will be taken into account in any criminal or civil proceedings brought under the Act.

8.19 The Act further provides for the appointment and functions of Inspectors and the Animal Procedures Committee.

Home Office Inspectors

8.20 It is the responsibility and function of Inspectors to advise the Secretary of State (Home Office) on applications, variations, revocations and periodic review of personal and project licences and the certification of designated establishments. This involves visits to check compliance with the specific conditions of licences and certificates. All applications for certificates and licences are assessed by one or more inspectors, and in certain cases they may be referred to an external assessor, the Animal Procedures Committee or both.

The Animal Procedures Committee

8.21 The Animal Procedures Committee is charged with advising the Secretary of State (Home Office) on all matters concerned with the Act and functions under it. In considering any question the Committee must have regard to

❖ the legitimate requirements of science and industry, and

❖ the protection of animals against avoidable suffering and unnecessary use in scientific procedures.

8.22 The Committee considers all project licence applications involving cosmetics; tobacco or tobacco products (except where the animals are terminally anaesthetised); the acquisition or maintenance of manual skills for microsurgery; and work of substantial severity on primates. It will not usually consider other individual applications unless a general question about the permissibility of a certain procedure is at issue.

8.23 As regards proposed research on primates, the Animal Procedures Committee monitors this through a Primate Working Group which receives information on all applications for project licences that include the use of primates as well as being consulted on all those involving primates in procedures of "substantial severity".

PENALTIES UNDER THE ACT

8.24 The Act provides the Secretary of State (Home Office) with a range of administrative sanctions including variation or revocation of licences. In more serious cases, any person who undertakes a regulated procedure without the authority of the appropriate licences or other than at a designated establishment is guilty of an offence under the Act and liable to imprisonment, for up to two years in certain circumstances, or to a fine or both. A holder of a project licence who knowingly permits a person under his control to carry out a regulated procedure otherwise than as specified in the project licence or otherwise than in accordance with that person's personal licence will be liable to similar penalties.

8.25 In practice infringement can vary from the technical to the very serious. Guidance from the Home Office states that any breach of conditions will be regarded as a serious matter and the Act gives the Secretary of State powers to vary or revoke licences on specified grounds which include the breach of a condition of the licence.

RELEVANCE TO XENOTRANSPLANTATION

8.26 For our purposes, the Act is relevant to the following stages in the production of transgenic animals for use in xenotransplantation. We note here however that animals involved in xenotransplantation need not be genetically modified.

❖ the insertion of DNA into the germline,

❖ the subsequent breeding of animals carrying the desired characteristics,

❖ the removal of organs or tissue from the animal, and

❖ research involving the transplantation of organs or tissue into other animals (eg pig to primate).

8.27 All of these procedures must, therefore, be carried out under the appropriate authority of project licenses and personal licenses. Each project is considered individually. We are told that the Home Office's view, based on the issue of project licences for "procedures" involved in the current work on xenotransplantation, is that any programme to develop a transgenic animal for xenotransplantation might involve individual procedures of mild, moderate and substantial severity. As a whole the project is likely to be assessed as "moderate".

ASPA – WHERE PROCEDURES INHERENT IN XENOTRANSPLANTATION MAY NOT BE COVERED

8.28 Although **research** into xenotransplantation is currently regulated by the Animals (Scientific Procedures) Act, it is possible, particularly in the production stage of transgenic animals that they may be discharged from the controls of the Act.

8.29 Breeding of transgenic animals is regarded by the Home Office as a procedure regulated under the Act until it can be demonstrated that the offspring are not likely to suffer adverse effects (harm) as a consequence of the breeding. This would normally be regarded as having been demonstrated if no harm ensues over a lifespan of two generations, as the object has been to ensure that animals homozygous for the induced characteristic are not affected by any deleterious effects not present in the heterozygotes. However, due to the complexities of the genetic modification procedure, many lines of pig will be bred, which will differ in some genetic particulars. Each genetic line must be considered separately. This may mitigate against large-scale discharge from the control of the Act.

8.30 The genetic modification of pigs for use in xenotransplantation as detailed earlier, in Chapter 2, has not been significant in affecting the normal functions of animals. It could therefore be argued that the animals have not suffered any adverse effects and could therefore be discharged from the control of the Act. This has not yet happened and as noted, there may be technical difficulties in discharging a large number of animals from the Act. However, it is possible that the situation may arise where applications for discharge are made for a large number of transgenic animals.

8.31 If the pigs are discharged from the Act, would they fall back under the Act's control by virtue of the procedures carried out on them? Some activities could fall within the Act's definition of a regulated procedure, for example, the clipping of ears or tipping of tails for genetic testing, the taking of blood or other tissue and the carrying out of other tests for diagnosis undertaken otherwise than for the benefit of the animal. Other activities may not be so covered. This gives rise to the possibility that either the source animals for xenotransplantation would not be covered by the Act, until they are anaesthetised for tissue removal, or that the source animals would fall in and out of the control of the Act. The animal would, of course, fall within the control of ASPA at the time of the operation to remove any tissue.

OUR VIEW

8.32   We take the view that there are considerable advantages in ensuring that the breeding and keeping of animals for xenotransplantation purposes fall within, or remain within, the regulatory framework established by ASPA. It is important that animal welfare controls are backed by legislation and ASPA is clearly relevant. There is in place an effective and established infrastructure to apply the Act, ensure compliance, through, for example, monitoring licensed procedures, places and persons, and ultimately, to impose legal sanctions.

8.33   We are concerned, however, that at various times in the process of producing animals for xenotransplantation purposes, in particular at the point at which production may concentrate on a small number of stable germlines, it would currently be possible for the transgenic animals to be discharged from the control of ASPA. We are concerned that the animals involved in xenotransplantation could only sporadically fall under ASPA control. We consider that this could have significant implications for animal welfare.

8.34   We have noted also that it is possible that the use of non-genetically modified animals as a source of tissue may be proposed. These animals would not come under the control of the ASPA, until such time as they were anaesthetised for tissue removal, unless the procedures undertaken for monitoring purposes were considered to be scientific procedures. However, we would wish to ensure that these animals were kept within controlled, specific pathogen-free surroundings and that their welfare would be protected. We therefore recommend that legislative measures be taken to protect the welfare of these animals.

8.35   We therefore **recommend that these gaps be addressed through legislation. We further recommend that appropriate legislative means be taken to ensure that the animals involved in xenotransplantation are brought and remain within the provisions of the Act by appropriate amendments.**

8.36   We further note that the system of inspection requires Inspectors to make individual professional judgments.   We understand and respect this approach.   However, xenotransplantation raises particular concerns, by virtue of, for example, the conditions in which the animals would be kept and the tests to which they would be subjected. These are such that we consider a more unified approach to regulation, and to its interpretation and implementation, is important. We noted in paragraph 8.18 that ASPA enables codes of practice to be issued under ASPA. **We therefore recommend that an appropriate code of practice be issued under ASPA and that this should take into account the concerns we expressed in Chapter 4.**

PROTECTION OF THE PATIENT/WIDER POPULATION

8.37   Here, we consider the need to control any hazards relating to the release of transgenic animals and to minimise or control the risk of transmitting infection to patients (and potentially the wider population).   By ensuring that transgenic animals to be used in xenotransplantation procedures would remain within the control of ASPA and that appropriate guidance on aspects of animal welfare should be followed, these potential risks would already be subject to one level of control. The question we ask here is whether existing law meets the needs of protecting patients and the wider population. We consider the various potential risks in turn and examine the applicability of existing law.

GENETIC MODIFICATION

8.38   The protection of human health and the environment from the possible risks associated with genetically modified organisms (GMOs) while in containment and on deliberate release and marketing is covered by:

❖   **Genetically Modified Organisms (Contained Use) Regulations 1992**

❖   **Genetically Modified Organisms (Contained Use) (Amendment) Regulations 1996**

Made under the Health & Safety at Work Act 1974 and European Communities Act 1972

❖   **Genetically Modified Organisms (Contained Use) Regulations 1993**, superseded by the **Genetically Modified Organisms (Risk Assessment) (Records and Exemptions) Regulations 1996**

Made under Part VI of the Environmental Protection Act 1990.

❖   the **Genetically Modified Organisms (Deliberate Release) Regulations 1992 and 1995.**

Made under the European Communities Act 1972 and Part VI of the Environmental Protection Act 1990.

8.39   These Regulations implement European law[89]. The Contained Use Regulations are administered by the Health and Safety Executive, acting in conjunction with the Department

---

[89]   EC Directives 90/219/EEC and 90/220/EEC

of the Environment. The Deliberate Release Regulations are administered by the Department of the Environment, acting in conjunction with the Scottish Office, the Welsh Office and the Health and Safety Executive, and with the Ministry of Agriculture Fisheries and Food in matters of concern to them. Separate but similar Regulations apply to Northern Ireland.

RELEVANCE TO XENOTRANSPLANTATION

8.40   A genetically modified organism (GMO) is defined as a *"... biological entity capable of replication or of transferring genetic material"* (the GMO (Contained Use) Regulations). The transgenic pigs which would be used as breeders and sources for xenotransplantation would come under the definition of GMO, but would no longer be considered as such once killed, nor would the removed organs/tissue be considered as GMOs.

8.41   The Contained Use Regulations apply to activities in which organisms are genetically modified or in which GMOs are cultured, bred, stored, used, transported, destroyed, or disposed of, and where physical barriers (or physical barriers plus chemical or biological barriers) are used to limit contact with the general population and the environment. The Regulations impose duties to notify the Health and Safety Executive of the general intention to use premises for work involving genetic modification. The Deliberate Release Regulations are concerned with the human and environmental safety of the release of GMOs into the environment. They also cover the marketing of those GMO products which are not controlled by the relevant EC Directives. The breeding of GMOs is also regulated as a procedure under the Animals (Scientific Procedures) Act 1986 and therefore, as outlined earlier in paragraph 8.29, breeding establishments employing genetic modification techniques are required to be registered with the Home Office.

8.42   The Advisory Committee on Genetic Modification (ACGM) advises the Health and Safety Commission and Executive and Ministers across government on the human and environmental health and safety aspects of contained uses of genetically modified organisms. Advice is provided to the Secretary of State on the human and environmental safety aspects of deliberate releases of GMOs to the environment and the marketing of GMO products, by a statutory committee, the Advisory Committee on Releases to the Environment (ACRE).

8.43   The GMO Contained Use Regulations, the GMO (Risk Assessment) (Records and Exemptions) Regulations 1996 and the ACGM Guidance Notes address the human and environmental safety aspects of transgenic animals. We consider that they provide an effective safeguard as they are and have traditionally worked well, in conjunction with ASPA regulation. Thus, the primary legislation which we propose should take due account of them. We understand, further, that consideration is being given to the updating of the ACGM Guidance note (ACGM/HSE Note 9), Guidelines on Work with Transgenic Animals. We ask that it should take into account any relevant aspects of our Report.

MOVEMENT OF ANIMALS AND TISSUE

8.44 While under the control of ASPA, the regular movement of animals between establishments may be covered by the conditions of the project licence. Authority for the occasional movement of animals between project licences or establishments may be sought from the Home Office. Permission is contingent upon fitness of the animal for travel and appropriate attention to other aspects relevant to the animal's welfare (mode of transport, duration, procedures carried out, and any special husbandry or other requirements).

8.45 This control may have a role to play in containing any possible hazard from being transmitted to the environment from the transgenic animals while in transit. It may also assist in ensuring that the source animals are kept free from hazards in the environment which they could then transmit to tissue recipients. However, the movement of *tissue*, once removed from the animal, is not regulated. Thus protection from transmission of possible hazards to the environment and from possible contamination of the tissue are not ensured. **We therefore recommend that the movement of tissue be brought within regulatory control in the primary legislation which we propose.**

SURPLUS OF ANIMALS AND RELEASE

8.46 There may also be concern about the use of the carcasses of transgenic animals or the use of animals, bred for xenotransplantation purposes, but which are not themselves transgenic. In particular, concern about the possible entry of such animals into the food chain should not be limited only to matters of food safety.

8.47 Surpluses of transgenic pigs initially intended for xenotransplantation could be produced. The release of these animals would require notification and consent of the Department for the Environment, under the GMO Regulations. Animals being bred for use in xenotransplantation would also fall within the Animals (Scientific Procedures) Act 1986 and would require Home Office consent for discharge from the controls of the Act. We also understand that, as part of the administrative process of any release or discharge, the Ministry of Agriculture Fisheries and Food (MAFF) would be notified. These arrangements form the basis for consideration of food safety issues raised by transgenic animals.

8.48 In the case of both transgenic and genetically unmodified animals derived from transgenic breeding programmes, the Advisory Committee on Novel Foods and Processes (ACNFP) is currently consulted, on a voluntary basis, on food safety. It may be expected that any proposed use for food of animals involved in xenotransplantation would be submitted to the Committee. The ACNFP also consults with the Food Advisory Committee on the labelling of food obtained from such animals and on the wider issues raised. More important, however, the use in food of such surplus animals, whether modified or otherwise, is expected to fall within the provisions of the proposed EC Novel Foods and Novel Food Ingredients Regulation, likely to be in force by late 1996 or early 1997. The Regulation will be primarily concerned with food safety, but it is also a requirement that a novel food must not mislead the consumer. The proposed legislation stipulates that a food containing a novel ingredient which might give rise to ethical concerns should be labelled. Whether this requirement would be applied to unmodified animals derived from a xenotransplantation programme is unclear, but the Regulation as currently drafted, could be interpreted to include such a possibility. The extent of evidence needed to demonstrate that an animal is in fact unmodified would need to be defined. Detailed rules are still to be drawn up by the European Commission.

8.49 We consider that any proposed use for food of any animals derived from a xenotransplantation programme should be regulated. The proposed EC Novel Foods Regulation would be an appropriate way of achieving such regulation. The provision for the labelling of animals which are the product of a xenotransplantation programme but are not themselves genetically modified needs to be clarified. In addition, the extent of the evidence needed to demonstrate that the animal is indeed unmodified would also need to be defined. **We recommend that consideration should be given to whether such animals should be used as food and, if so, whether labelling of food produced from them is required.**

TISSUE AS A MEDICINE OR DEVICE

LAW RELATING TO MEDICINAL PRODUCTS

8.50 There are two regimes of law which warrant consideration. First, there is domestic law in the form of the Medicines Act 1968. Then there is European law, consisting of a series of EC Medicines Directives (EC Directives 65/65, 75/318, 75/319 etc.) which are given effect to in the UK by the Medicines for Human Use (Marketing Authorisations Etc.) Regulations 1994[90]. Both of these legislative frameworks are concerned with the safety, quality and efficacy of medicinal products.

8.51 The question to be asked is whether either of these frameworks could be said to apply to xenotransplantation. If it could, there would already be in place a highly regarded regulatory system which would address those concerns relating to safety and quality as they affect humans (whether patients or the wider public) from first clinical trial to any subsequent therapeutic programme. There would, therefore, be a regulatory system which would complement the ASPA system (as modified) relating to animals.

8.52 Our analysis must proceed in stages. First, we need to identify the areas of competence (that is, what is covered by) the two legal frameworks. Put shortly, the domestic Medicines Act applies only to matters not covered by the European law.

---

[90] S.I. 1994/3144 made under the European Community Act, 1972.

8.53   European law applies to "medicinal products". Can it be said that tissue taken from an animal for transplant into humans is a "medicinal product" within EC Directive 65/65?

8.54   EC Directive 65/65 defines a "medicinal product" in Article 1(3) as follows:

> "...Any substance or combination of substances presented for treatment or preventing disease in human beings or animals

> ...Any substance or combination of substances which may be administered to human beings with a view to making a medical diagnosis or to restoring, correcting or modifying physiological functions in human beings or in animals..."

"Substance" is defined as:

> "...any matter irrespective of origin which may be: human, e.g. human blood and human blood products; animal, e.g. micro-organisms, whole animals, parts of organs, animal secretions, extracts, etc..."

8.55   At first sight it may be possible to argue that tissue for use in xenotransplantation, being animal tissue could be classified as a "substance" within Article 1(3) and thus a "medicinal product". It is difficult, however, to sustain this view. First, it is the "origin" of the "substance" which may be animal tissue, rather than the substance itself. Of course, if the origin is animal tissue, it will be the case that the substance, on one reading, will also be. But it appears to be the intention that the reference to animal tissue relates to the origin of the substance rather than to the substance itself and thus, such tissue would not fall within the meaning of "medicinal product".

8.56   Secondly, the applicability of the Directives relates to a very large extent to what apparently they were intended to regulate. The wording of the various Medicines Directives suggests very strongly that the Directives were intended to regulate the pharmaceutical industry rather than be applied more widely to xenotransplantation. Indeed, xenotransplantation was barely contemplated in 1965 (the date of the first and "parent" Directive), such that it cannot have been the intention that the Directives should apply to it.

8.57   For these reasons we conclude that xenotransplantation does not fall within the regulatory system contained in EC Directive 65/65 and subsequent Medicines Directives. There are further complex arguments concerning whether the UK rather than the Community is, in fact, competent to legislate in the area which we do not expand upon here.

8.58   However, even if this view were wrong, there is another reason for taking the view that xenotransplantation would not currently be regulated at European level. This is because Article 3 (1) of EC Directive 65/65 specifically states that the Directive does not apply to "medicinal products intended for research and development trials". It is of course at the stage of research and development, of clinical trials, that the closest monitoring may be important. Thus, if xenotransplantation is to be regulated by any current legislative system at the stage, it can only be through the application of the UK Medicines Act 1968. This Act continues to apply in relation to medicinal products which fall outside the EC Directive's definition. Most significantly, it applies to products for use in clinical trials.

8.59   Thus, again we must ask whether animal tissue intended for xenotransplantation is a "medicinal product" under the Medicines Act. The definition of a "medicinal product" in Section 130 refers, as do the EC Medicines Directives, to a "substance". This in tern, is defined in Section 132 (1) as "...any natural or artificial substance, whether in solid or liquid form or in the form of a gas or vapour". Arguably, this definition, on its own, is sufficiently broad that it could be said to include animal tissue. But, again, this definition cannot be read in isolation from the clear intention and purpose of the Act. The structure of the Act, its references to the pharmaceutical industry, and the fact that, when it was passed, xenotransplantation cannot have been in the minds of the legislators, suggest that the Act is not appropriate. We conclude, therefore, that although the matter is not beyond doubt, it is at best unlikely that the provisions of the Medicines Act relating to the conduct of clinical trials apply so as to provide a regulatory framework within which research into and development of xenotransplantation involving humans must be conducted.

8.60   There is one final argument which could be made for the applicability of the Medicines Act. It relates to Sections 104 and 105. By Section 104, the relevant Ministers may

> " (1)......... by order specify any description or class or articles or substances appearing to them to be articles or substances which are not medical products but are manufactured, sold, supplied, imported or exported for use wholly or partly for a medicinal purpose, and may by that order direct that, subject to exceptions and modifications as may be specified in the order, such provisions of this Act as may be specified (including provisions so specified which relate to offenses or penalties) shall have effect in relation to articles or substances of that description or class as those provisions have effect in relation to medicinal products"

Even if it could be argued that transgenic tissue from an animal was an "article" or "substance" within the meaning of S.104(1), clearly there are limits to the class of such articles or substances which it is in the Ministers' powers to regulate. Given that the Medicines Act generally and S104 in particular was never intended by Parliament to regulate transgenic tissue, it is likely that any attempt to do so under S.104 could be challenged in law as being *ultra vires*.

8.61   Section 105 of the Medicines Act provides that

> "(1) The Minister may by order specify any substance appearing to the Minister to be a substance which is not itself a medicinal product but –
>
> > (b) if used without proper safeguards, is capable of causing danger to the health of the community, or of causing danger to the health of animals generally or of one or more species of animals,
>
> and direct that, subject to such exceptions and modifications as may be specified in the order, such provisions this Act as may be so specified (including any provisions so specified which relate to offenses or penalties) shall have effect in relation to that substance as those provisions have effect in relation to medicinal products."

Again, even if transgenic tissue were regarded as a "substance" within the meaning of S.105, the same objections concerning the limits of Ministers' powers would apply.

8.62   We conclude, therefore, that while there may be a case for saying that the regulation of xenotransplantation could fall within the ambit of the Medicines Act 1968 and the EC Medicines Directives, the case is not strong. Further, we repeat that neither the Medicines Act, 1968 nor the EC Medicines Directives, was passed with xenotransplantation in mind. Finally, we recognise that attempts to apply the Medicines Act to clinical trials or more generally or clarify its meaning in relation to xenotransplantation could result in lengthy legal argument before the Courts.

8.63   For all of these reasons, neither the Medicines Act nor the EC Medicines Directives in our view provide a legislative framework within which our concerns for the protection of patients and the wider population can be met.

MEDICAL DEVICES DIRECTIVE 93/42/EEC

8.64   The purpose of the Directive is to ensure that medical devices comply with the specified standards of safety, quality and efficacy and that devices which do conform can be marketed freely across the European Economic Area. The Medical Devices Agency is responsible for ensuring that medical devices and equipment for sale or use in the UK meet these standards. The Agency is also responsible for the evaluation of medical devices and for standards of good manufacturing practice in the field of medical devices. It is also responsible for the investigation of device related adverse incidents and the dissemination of safety information.

8.65   The current law, the Medical Devices Directive (93/42/EEC) states in Article 1 part 5 that:

> "This Directive does not apply to........

> > g) transplants or tissues or cells of animal origin, unless a device is manufactured utilising animal tissue which is rendered non-viable or non-viable products derived from animal tissue."

8.66   Thus, only in circumstances in which non-viable material from animals is transplanted would xenotransplantation be regulated under the current Medical Devices Directive. The Directive will not apply to organs and most tissue, which will be 'viable', though it may cover the use of treated bone from transgenic animals. Such use has been proposed in certain current research protocols. Aside however from this limited possible application, the Directive cannot play a role in regulating xenotransplantation in general.

SUMMARY

8.67   Our conclusions on the applicability of the Medicines Act and the Medical Devices Directive demonstrate that, currently, the existing legal framework (other than that which relates to GMOs) is inadequate to answer our concerns about risks to patients and to the wider population arising from tissue from animals which are part of a xenotransplantation programme. However, we have noted the highly regarded regulatory structures which exist and **we recommend that the legislation which we propose take account of these regulatory structures so as to ensure that a similar structure is put in place to regulate any procedure involving xenotransplantation.**

THE CONDUCT OF CLINICAL TRIALS

8.68   We move now to another area of concern. There is no legislation which provides for conditions to be satisfied before proceeding to clinical trials on humans. We have identified certain conditions which must be met if clinical trials are to proceed. We take the view that these conditions should be reflected in legislation through the establishment of a national standing committee charged with setting them and monitoring the extent to which they are met.

8.69   This is a quite separate exercise from that associated with the formal regulation of clinical trials. As regards such trials, we are aware of the various codes regulating research on humans. We would add to them certain recommendations specifically concerned with xenotransplantation.

8.70   Generally, research in humans is regulated by such Codes as the World Medical Association's Declaration of Helsinki (1989)[91] and those of the WHO and associated bodies (Council for International Organisation of Medical Sciences/WHO 1993). Recommendation R(90)3 of the Committee of Ministers of the Council of Europe on Medical Research on human beings has also been accepted by the UK.

8.71   Further, medical practitioners undertaking research are bound by the Code of professional conduct of the General Medical Council and may face disciplinary action for breach of the Code.

8.72   The ethical acceptability of clinical trials in humans is determined (within the NHS) through a system of approval from independent Local Research Ethics Committees. The Department of Health requires that every health district have a Local Research Ethics Committee (LREC) to advise NHS bodies on the ethical acceptability of research proposals involving human subjects[92]. However, there is no legal requirement for Research Ethics Committees to be set up, either within the NHS or outside it, and no legal requirement for the submission of research protocols to an Ethics Committee for approval. Without the force of law, control mechanisms on the ethical acceptability of research proposals operate at other levels, at which LREC advice is taken into account:

❖   the Medical Research Council makes LREC approval a condition for funding research projects;

❖   projects involving NHS patients, premises or facilities require LREC approval; and

❖   many journals will not publish research results if LREC approval has not been obtained.

8.73   The NHS guidance provides that LRECs should give special consideration to research on children, women, prisoners and mentally disordered people, and contains a code of practice on the use of a fetus and fetal material in research and treatment. There is a wealth of guidance available to LRECs which provides detailed analysis of all aspects of their duties and responsibilities, including the 1994 Standards Framework issued by the Department of Health.

8.74   We believe that clinical trials of xenotransplantation procedures should be considered as "medical research". As such, within the NHS, they come within the remit of LRECs. However, in view of the complexity of the issues presented by xenotransplantation, we are persuaded that trials should not be left only to local consideration and that proposals for clinical

---

[91]   World Medical Association Declaration of Helsinki. Recommendations guiding physicians in biomedical research involving human studies. Adopted by the 18th World Medical Assembly 1964, amended by the World Health Assembly 1975, 1983 & 1989.

[92]   Department of Health. Health Service Guidelines - HSG(91)5, 19 August 1991

trials of xenotransplantation should be considered by a national body. We propose, in Chapter 9, the creation of a National Standing Committee. We **recommend that the approval and monitoring of such trials should be conditional on the approval of and monitoring by the National Standing Committee**.

XENOTRANSPLANTATION DEVELOPMENTS

8.75 We have expressed the view that there are potential limits to the ethical acceptability of the genetic modification of animals for the purposes of xenotransplantation, particularly if harm is thereby caused to the animal, and to the animal tissue which may be transplanted into humans. **We recommend the National Standing Committee monitor developments and examine any which could cause public concern.** This is particularly important since no system currently exists to monitor developments in this fast-moving field.

PRIVATE HOSPITALS AND OTHER REGULATORY SYSTEMS

8.76 It is conceivable that the private sector may wish to undertake xenotransplantation, were it to become an acceptable and successful clinical procedure. All independent hospitals, clinics and nursing homes, apart from any instituted by special Act of Parliament or incorporated by Royal Charter, are subject to statutory control through a system of registration and inspection provided for by Part II of the Registered Homes Act 1984. All such independent facilities providing surgery under anaesthesia are required to be registered. The responsibilities for registration are delegated to Health Authorities which are empowered to approve the types of procedure the registered facility intends to carry out. Health Authorities are charged with inspecting each hospital at least twice per year. Ensuring that the level of care provided is sufficient and suitable to meet individual patients' needs is a primary concern of the registering authority, and standards are expected to be at least comparable to good standards in the NHS.

8.77 We **recommend that guidance be issued to the Health Authorities that the prior approval of xenotransplantation procedures by the National Standing Committee should be regarded as a condition for obtaining or remaining registration under Part II of the Registered Homes Act 1984. We further recommend that any new primary legislation on xenotransplantation should seek to ensure that similar conditions apply for independent facilities as for NHS hospitals.**

8.78 Should developments allow for xenotransplant procedures to be undertaken without the need for local or general anaesthetic the Registered Homes Act has powers allowing regulations to be made designating the need for treatments which are not covered by the general provisions of the Act as specially controlled techniques. At present, the only treatment so designated involves the use of certain types of laser.

THE INTERNATIONAL PERSPECTIVE.

8.79   Xenotransplantation is an international, not a national, issue. Developments in xenotransplantation are taking place around the world, notably at present in the USA, under the auspices of multinational organisations who may move their operations across national borders. We understand that these organisations would favour regulation which is consistent between countries.

8.80   Public health considerations are also international. If infections are transmitted from source animals to tissue recipients, it is possible that they may be transmitted to their contacts. Global travel means that, no matter where the procedure took place, infection risks could be posed to other populations. Again, consistent regulation concerning infection control methods would reduce these risks and any related concerns.

8.81   As we have said, should xenotransplantation proceed to clinical trials in this country, monitoring arrangements would be vital. Clinical trials of xenotransplantation have, of course, already occurred in other countries, again notably in the USA. In these early stages, while only a few procedures have taken place, we consider it important that knowledge about outcomes and adverse effects, especially infections, is shared. Monitoring on an international scale may be more effective as it would allow quicker accumulation of data, common and comparable data sets, and data sharing (particularly important, should problems arise). It is also desirable to minimise any duplication of effort by sharing knowledge so far as is possible. We note in particular current activity in the European Union, the USA and the World Health Organisation and mention these briefly.

THE EUROPEAN UNION

8.82   Xenotransplantation has been discussed and the view taken that further consideration will be needed. As detailed earlier in the chapter by reference to current EC legislation, the Community has an important role in the formation and development of the legislative and regulatory frameworks relevant to xenotransplantation.

THE USA

8.83   Guidelines on Xenotransplantation and Infectious Disease have been developed by a Consensus Panel and Working Groups, which included representatives from the Food and Drug Administration, the Centre for Disease Control, the National Institute of Health, the transplant community and animal ethics committees. They have been developed to safeguard public health. They are expected to cover such matters as the choice, source and keeping of animals, clinical protocols, infection control procedures and the subsequent keeping of records.★

★ These Guidelines are now available

THE WORLD HEALTH ORGANISATION (WHO)

8.84 The WHO are in the process of producing a first draft of guidelines on infection risks and are planning to hold an international meeting. The guidelines concentrate on examining, evaluating and controlling the possible risks of transmitting infectious disease.

8.85 We **recommend that appropriate account be taken of international developments and that there should be liaison with the EC and with other Member States and with appropriate international organisations, particularly in the framing of appropriate legislation and regulations.**

CONCLUSION

8.86 We began at the outset by recommending that a legal framework regulating xenotransplantation be established. We have since spent some time examining, in particular, two existing legislative frameworks only to conclude that they do not meet the needs we have identified. This examination was not, however, idle. What we have sought to show is that ASPA provides an appropriate basis for addressing our concerns relating to the animal. What may be needed are certain additional provisions. Equally, though it may not apply, the Medicines Act provides an appropriate model for tackling our concerns about patients and the wider population, in that it represents a highly-regarded quality control mechanism in a related area.

8.87 We take the view, therefore, that the legislation which we propose should, in particular, build upon and reflect these two legislative frameworks. With the creation of a National Standing Committee which we go on to consider in the next Chapter to monitor practices and keep developments under review, there should be in place an ethical framework in the form of a regulatory structure which will address satisfactorily the concerns which have occupied our attention.

CHAPTER NINE:

THE NATIONAL STANDING COMMITTEE

INTRODUCTION

9.1   We have outlined conditions which we consider form the basis of an ethical framework within which xenotransplantation can take place. We have concluded that they are best guaranteed by the establishment of a National Standing Committee which is itself backed by legislation.

9.2   We state here our view that new, specific, primary legislation to regulate xenotransplantation is required in the interests of patients, public health and animal welfare. However, we recognise that there is always pressure on Parliamentary timetables. **We therefore recommend, as an interim measure only, that our recommendations, particularly with regard to the National Standing Committee, are taken forward on a non-statutory basis until such time as legislation can be brought forward.** Such an interim body should not be regarded as a substitute for legislation not least because many of our recommendations are dependent on the existence of the National Standing Committee as well as the fact that, more obviously, such a body will only operate by consent.

THE NATIONAL STANDING COMMITTEE

9.3   **We recommend that the National Standing Committee should have overall national responsibility for overseeing the development of xenotransplantation; that is, the transplant of viable, replicating animal tissue into humans.** Its role would cover, broadly, the **setting of standards** for continued research into and, if appropriate, the introduction of xenotransplantation and **ensuring their implementation**. Given the range of expertise which would be represented on such a Committee it could additionally be responsible for a range of related, additional, functions (outlined in sub-paragraphs 11-14 below). The Committee would be charged with ensuring that the recommendations contained in this Report are implemented. Specifically, the Committee would have lead responsibility for:

SETTING THE STANDARDS

1.   advising on the research which needs to be carried out on infection risks, immunology and physiology; assessing the results of research with a view to determining whether further conditions should be stipulated or existing ones modified or withdrawn. It would decide, on the basis of scientific evidence submitted to it, whether conditions

had been met so as to permit clinical trials in xenotransplantation and, if appropriate, the introduction of a therapeutic programme.

2.   defining measures designed to minimise the risk of infection to the human recipient and to the wider population; the conditions in which the animals should be kept, the methods used to remove tissue and transport it to the clinical site, and infection control procedures at the clinical site. These measures will affect animal welfare.

3.   setting the standards, under which source animals and the herds providing these animals should be kept with regard to the welfare of the animals. In doing so, liaising with the Home Office and other interested organisations as appropriate.

4.   ensuring that there were arrangements for long term surveillance and follow-up of xenotransplant recipients and advising on the analysis of the surveillance results as they became available. This would include the development of "stopping rules" and their enforcement at the stage of clinical trials if necessary. Thereafter, there must be a mechanism to discontinue any therapeutic programme, if necessary.

5.   working with appropriate professional groups to take forward such matters as the complementary roles of various professionals, training and professional registration for animal technicians and veterinary nurses.

ENSURING IMPLEMENTATION

6.   liaising with the Home Office, concerning the research on animals, including pig to primate transplants.

7.   approving the clinical sites where xenotransplantation is proposed and in doing so, having regard to:

>   the establishment and implementation of effective infection control procedures;

>   the availability of appropriately trained support staff, including those with expertise in media relations.

Under legislation, this would be by means of a licensing system.

8.   approving the animal facilities which are used to breed and raise animals for use as sources for xenotransplantation and in doing so, having regard to:

>   the welfare of the animals in co-operation with the Home Office

appropriate infection control procedures

appropriate monitoring procedures

Under legislation, this would be by means of a licensing system. We note that the animal facilities would be designated under ASPA and that they would be inspected by the Home Office Inspectorate with regard to animal welfare considerations. They would also be notified under the GMO (Contained Use) Regulations operated by the Health and Safety Executive.

9.   considering in consultation with appropriate professional bodies, methods of approving those who propose to undertake xenotransplantation procedures involving humans. Inspection arrangements should also apply. Those removing tissue from animals would be required to have licenses under ASPA.

10.   approving applications to proceed with clinical trials in humans of xenotransplantation and in doing so, having regard to:

the need for granting prior approval of the animal facility, clinical site and transplant teams;

the source of the animal tissue. Applications under ASPA proposing the use of primates as a source animal for tissue to humans must be refused.

the scientific evidence presented on the infection risks posed by the transplant;

the procedure proposed, and its scientific and medical validity;

the tissue to be transplanted;

reviewing the appropriateness of the selection of any patient(s), having regard to the benefits and risks for that patient;

the arrangements for informing and gaining consent from patients;

procedures for monitoring the progress of clinical trials; in particular, agreeing in advance "stopping rules" for the trials.

Under legislation, this would be by means of a licensing system. Inspection arrangements should also apply.

ADDITIONAL FUNCTIONS

11. providing advice to Health Ministers on the safety and efficacy of developments in xenotransplantation.

12. keeping under review developments in xenotransplantation, nationally and internationally, with particular attention to work on infection risks.

13. advising on xenotransplant developments which may cause public concern, for example, because of the tissue being proposed for transplantation or because of the potential adverse effects on animals (again, ASPA monitors the effects of genetic modification). Advice may be given to Ministers or new proposals made for consultation procedures.

14. advising on such issues as arrangements for consent, confidentiality, appropriate groups of patients to be offered xenotransplantation and monitoring of the psychological effects of xenotransplantation. Advice may also be called for on issues related to the allocation of animal tissue relative to the allocation of human tissue. The Committee would be well-placed to advise on this in liaison with the UKTSSA.

9.4 A number of **executive functions** are assumed in the responsibilities of the National Committee. These would include, in addition to the organisation and administration of the Committee:

a maintaining a database of information on tissue recipients and databanks of tissue samples from both source animals and recipients.

b inspecting clinical sites and animal facilities, with regard to infection control (Under ASPA, the animal facilities would be regulated with regard to animal welfare by the Home Office Inspectorate).

It would be a matter for the Committee in liaison with the relevant UK Government Departments to determine how these functions should be carried out.

LIAISON

9.5 There are a number of other Committees which have responsibilities in areas related to xenotransplantation. We recognise the range of responsibilities and the expertise which exist in such bodies as the Animal Procedures Committee, the United Kingdom Transplant Support Service Authority, the Advisory Committee on Dangerous Pathogens, the Public Health Laboratory Service, the National Institute of Biological Standards and Control, the Advisory Committee on Releases to the Environment and the Advisory Committee on Genetic

Modification. There are undoubtedly other bodies which also have an interest in this area. However, xenotransplantation involves a wide range of issues and no existing body is constituted to address them all.

9.6 As regards overseeing the development of xenotransplantation, **we further recommend that in carrying out its responsibilities the National Standing Committee should work with these other interested bodies in an appropriate way so as to co-ordinate the work being undertaken, thus minimising duplication, and to call upon the skill and expertise necessary to undertake its role successfully.**

9.7 We draw particular attention to the Animal Procedures Committee and the legislative framework of ASPA. We described the operation of ASPA in some detail in Chapter 8 and have noted in paragraph 9.3 how it might interact with the responsibilities of the National Standing Committee. There is a clear relationship between the needs of humans and the interests of animals. There is also potential for confusion over where lead responsibilities might lie. For example, the Home Office Inspectorate have responsibility for inspecting sites licensed under ASPA with regard to animal welfare considerations. However, they are not responsible for monitoring the maintenance of infection-free conditions that would be required for xenotransplantation. It may be that separate inspection arrangements may need to apply to this. The National Standing Committee on Xenotransplantation would have an interest in ensuring that the programme of research was co-ordinated and directed towards filling specific gaps in scientific knowledge. They would also seek to ensure that the use of primates was kept to the necessary minimum.

9.8 We note that the Animal Procedures Committee does not directly consider each of the many licence applications made. **We recommend that the Home Secretary treat xenotransplantation as a special case, and request the APC to consider which mechanisms may be needed to deal in a co-ordinated manner with all applications which involve xenotransplantation.**

9.9 We see a need for close liaison between the National Standing Committee on Xenotransplantation and the Animal Procedures Committee. **We accordingly recommend that the National Standing Committee should act in co-ordination with the Animal Procedures Committee and measures to achieve this should be addressed as a matter of urgency.**

9.10 Particular attention should also be drawn to the role of Local Research Ethics Committees (LRECs) which advise NHS bodies on the ethical acceptability of research proposals involving human subjects in their health authority area. We recognise their valuable role in assessing the ethical acceptability of such research, particularly in the light of their knowledge of their local communities. However, as we have argued, we consider that the National Standing Committee should also approve applications for clinical research involving xenotransplantation, prior to local review. **We therefore recommend that the National Standing Committee should co-ordinate its activities with those of LRECs,** such that anyone wishing to conduct xenotransplantation research should submit proposals to both the national committee and to the appropriate LREC. **We further recommend that any proposal for research into xenotransplantation which involves humans must be approved by the National Standing Committee prior to approval by a properly constituted LREC.** We also recognise the need to make decisions promptly, and to keep bureaucracy for researchers to a minimum. **We therefore recommend that the arrangements for the co-ordinated working of the proposed National Standing Committee with LRECs should be addressed as a matter of urgency and further that these arrangements should seek to minimise the problems of delay and bureaucracy.**

MEMBERSHIP

9.11   The National Standing Committee must command the respect of the public at large, the animal welfare community and the medical scientific community and the confidence of UK Health Ministers. Its membership must, therefore, reflect an appropriate range of expertise and interests.

INDEPENDENCE

9.12   We **recommend that the proposed National Standing Committee should be funded by, and be under the aegis of the appropriate UK Government Departments** lest it be thought that the committee would not be sufficiently independent of medical research.

REGULATION

9.13   We have concluded that the regulation of xenotransplantation should take the form of primary legislation: a comprehensive statutory framework of regulation should be put in place, taking account of and drawing upon existing law wherever it is relevant and appropriate. There should be powers of enforcement under this legislation.

9.14   We have further concluded that until such time as primary legislation can be passed, a committee should be set up on an interim basis as a temporary measure. **We recommend that such a committee be supported by some means of control, through, for example, appropriate guidance to LRECs, and that the Committee should be empowered, where necessary, to bring matters of concern to the attention of Ministers.**

ANNEX A

GLOSSARY

ANNEX A:

GLOSSARY

ACE inhibitors

ACE inhibitor drugs are used to treat **hypertension** and heart failure caused by reduced pumping activity.

Acute cellular rejection

Occurs within a few weeks or months following **transplantation**. It is mainly caused by the action of **T cells** acting against graft **antigens**, leading to rejection.

Acute vascular rejection (AVR)

Foreign (xeno) **antigens** e.g. of the **endothelium** of the transplanted tissue (from the pig), stimulate the production of newly formed **antibodies** in the recipient. There may also be additional activity associated with various groups of recipient white blood cells. Acute vascular rejection (AVR) causes rejection within days (compare with Hyperacute rejection (HAR) where **rejection** occurs within minutes, due to the presence of preformed antibodies, present in the recipient before **transplantation**).

α-gal - See Gal epitope

Allotransplantation

The transplant of **organs** or **tissues** between genetically different members of the same species.

α1-antitrypsin

α1-antitrypsin is a protein which protects **tissues** from digestion by the enzyme elastase. A deficiency leads to destruction of lung tissue.

Analgesic Nephropathy

Kidney damage caused by long term use of pain-killing drugs.

Antibody

A protein that is produced in response to stimulation by **antigens**, and that reacts specifically with that antigen.

Antigen

A molecule that is recognised as foreign by the **immune system** and which may stimulate the production of a specific **antibody** and/or stimulate **T cells**.

Anti-microbial

An agent which kills or inhibits the growth of **micro-organisms**.

ASPA

Animals (Scientific Procedures) Act 1986.

Bacterium (pl. Bacteria)

Any of a group of single-celled **micro-organisms**. Some bacteria cause disease in humans and animals.

Betablockade

A state induced by a group of drugs (betablockers) that help to slow heart rate and reduce the force of contraction of heart muscle.

B cell

A class of **white blood cells** of the **immune system** that interact to produce **antibodies** and the 'antibody mediated' **immune response**.

Biliary Atresia

A congenital disease in which the bile ducts within the liver do not develop properly.

Blastomycosis

A disease caused by the fungus *Blastomyces*.

Bovine

Relating to cattle.

Brain Stem Death

Occurs when a person has irreversibly lost the capacity for consciousness combined with the irreversible loss of the capacity to breathe. It represents the point at which a person is accepted as being dead even though their heart is still beating. Diagnosis of Brain Stem Death is determined from detailed criteria

Cadaveric Organs

Organs for transplantation obtained from individuals who have died.

Campylobacter

A particular group of related **species** of **bacteria**.

Cardiogenic Shock

A state of acute circulatory failure caused by a heart malfunction.

Cardiomyopathy

Any disease of the heart muscle that causes a reduction in the force of heart contractions and a resultant decrease in the efficiency of circulation of blood.

CD8+ (see T cell)

Cell

The smallest component of life, capable of carrying out essential life processes. The molecules found within and on the surface of a cell will depend on the **species**, and in multi-cellular **organisms** the **tissue** from which the cell is derived, as well as the environmental conditions in which the cell is living.

Cerebrovascular

A term describing the brain's **vascular** system.

Chagas' disease

An inflammatory **cardiomyopathy** caused by the **parasite** *Trypanosoma cruzi.*

Chimerism (of tissue/organ)

A state in which two or more genetically different populations of **cells** co-exist.

Chronic rejection

Usually occurs many months or years after **transplantation**, and leads to scarring and loss of function in the transplanted **organ**. The immune mechanisms are poorly defined but are thought to involve **humoral** (antibodies) and cellular (including **T cell**) mechanisms.

Cirrhosis

A diseased condition in which healthy liver **tissue** becomes replaced by fibrous tissue similar to a scar.

Complement

A group of some 20 blood proteins which interact in sequence when activated, to bring about the immune destruction of invading **micro-organisms** and transplanted **tissues**.

Complement activation

Complement activation is the initial triggering of the **complement** cascade system. Many **antigen-antibody** complexes act as the trigger. The cascade system is checked or down-regulated by **Regulators of Complement Activity (RCAs)**.

Concordant (of species)

Genetically closely related **species**.

Crohn's Disease

A condition in which there is inflammation and fibrosis of the intestine (gut). Symptoms include colicky abdominal pains and irregularity of the bowels.

Cryopreservation

Preservation technique involving use of extreme cold.

DNA (Deoxyribonucleic Acid)

The chemical substance which encodes the genetic information required to determine the structure and function of an **organism**.

Dialysis

The process of blood detoxification using semi-permeable membranes, a treatment which is used for patients with kidney failure, who may be waiting for a kidney transplant.

Discordant (of species)

Genetically distantly related **species**.

Domino Donation

Occurs when a patient receives a multi-**organ** transplant and their healthy organ is donated to another patient; for example a patient receives a heart/lung transplant and donates his/her heart to another patient.

Dopamine

A chemical found in the brain and other **tissues**. There is good evidence that a dopamine deficiency is one of the causative factors in **Parkinson's Disease**.

Dura mater

The outermost and strongest of the three membranes which envelop the brain and spinal cord.

Endogenous retrovirus

A **retrovirus** which is incorporated within the DNA of host **cells**, often (apparently) without ill-effect. If the retrovirus infects **germline** cells (eggs or sperm), it may be passed down from parent to offspring. (See also Retrovirus)

Endothelial cells/Endothelium

Endothelial **cells** form the lining of blood vessels, the endothelium.

Extra-corporeal support (see *ex vivo support*)

Ex vivo support

A method of partially taking over the function of a failing **organ** by passing the patient's blood through a substitute organ placed outside the body.

FDA

Food and Drug Administration (USA)

Fungus (pl. fungi)

Any of a diverse group of single or multi-cellular **micro-organisms**. Some fungi cause disease in humans and animals.

Gal epitope

A sugar **antigen** (galactosyl α-1,3-galactose) present on the surface of the **cells** of some animal **species**. The antigen is recognised as foreign by human **xenoreactive antibodies** following **xenotransplantation** of **tissue** from **discordant species**, and this results in **hyperacute rejection**.

Gene

A functional unit of heritable **DNA** which contains the information required for a specific function, for example the synthesis of a particular protein.

Gene Therapy

The **genetic modification** of target **cells** of an individual patient to alleviate disease.

Genetic modification/manipulation

The process by which the **DNA** of an **organism** is changed by artificial means.

Genome

A term used to describe the genetic material of a particular **organism** in its entirety.

Germ Free

A common language term used to designate an animal raised in the absence of all **micro-organisms**. (See also Specific-Pathogen-Free)

Germ line

Pertaining to the **cells** from which eggs or sperm are derived. These cells contain **DNA** which will be inherited by offspring.

Haemophilia

An inherited blood clotting disorder which results in prolonged bleeding even after minor injury.

HEPA filtration

The filtration of air through a High Efficiency Particulate Absorption (HEPA) system to maintain a sterile environment.

Hepatitis virus

A **virus** causing inflammation of the liver. There are several different types of hepatitis-causing viruses.

Heterozygous (of transgenic animals)

An animal carrying one copy of a **transgene** in each **cell**.

Histoplasmosis

A disease caused by the **fungus** *Histoplasma*.

HMG-CoA reductase

An enzyme involved in the biochemical synthesis of cholesterol

Homozygous (of transgenic animals)

An animal carrying two copies of a **transgene** in each **cell**.

Horizontal transmission

The transmission of infection from individual to individual in a population rather than from parent to offspring.

Humoral

Involving circulating **antibodies**.

Hyperacute rejection (HAR)

This is the most rapid form of **organ** transplant **rejection**. It occurs between **discordant species** because of the effect of **xenoreactive natural antibodies** (XNA) in the host (as human) blood. In HAR host blood coagulates (clots) throughout the donor organ, commonly within minutes, causing dramatic failure of the organ. About 70 – 90% of human XNA reacting against pig **antigens** recognise a sugar antigen termed the **Gal epitope**.

Hypertension

High blood pressure.

IgG

Immunoglobulin G (IgG) is a family of **antibodies**. IgG may be used as a diagnostic tool or indicator in the laboratory.

Immune response

A selective response mounted by the **immune system** of humans and animals in which specific **antibodies** and/or **T cells** are produced as a defence against invading **micro-organisms**, transplanted **tissue** and other material recognised as foreign. There are two main types of immune response: the 'antibody-mediated (or **humoral**)' response, and the 'cellular' response (mediated by **T cells**).

Immune System

Collectively the **cells** and **tissues** which enable animals to mount a specific protective response to invading **micro-organisms**, transplanted tissues and other material recognised as foreign by the body.

Immunity

A state of resistance to the onset of disease caused by a specific infectious agent. Immunity may be conferred: by innate non-specific body defences such as the skin and mucosal surfaces; or through immunological 'memory' of a specific **immune response** which was mounted against the same (or similar) infectious agent during a previous exposure.

Immunodeficiency viruses

Viruses which adversely affect the body's **immune system**.

Immunohistochemistry

The use of **antibodies**, **antigens** and chemicals to stain **tissue** for examination.

Immunology

Science of the **immune system**.

Immunosuppression

The use of drugs or other agents to suppress the **immune system**. Immunosuppressive drugs are taken by transplant recipients to prevent **tissue rejection**.

in utero

Within the uterus (womb).

in vivo

Refers to processes which occur or experimental procedures performed inside living **organisms**.

in vitro

Refers to experimental procedures performed on material which has been removed from an **organism**.

Islet cells (see Pancreatic Islet Cells of Langerhans)

Keratinocytes

A type of skin **cell**.

Lymph

A body fluid that circulates within the **lymphatic system** of an animal.

Lymphatic System

A network of vessels that conveys salts, water, proteins etc. constituting **lymph** from the **tissue** fluids to the bloodstream.

Metabolism

A series of integrated networks of biochemical reactions in living **organisms**.

Micro-organism

Microscopic **organisms**, including **bacteria**, **viruses** and **fungi**. Some are capable of causing disease in humans and animals.

Molecular techniques

A wide variety of scientific techniques used for the manipulation and/or analysis of nucleic acids. For example, **DNA** can be purified and analysed to screen for certain genetic and infectious diseases.

Monoclonal Antibodies

Homogeneous **antibody** populations specific to a particular **antigen**, which have various potential applications in molecular biology and medicine, including their use as therapeutic agents.

Motor functions

Muscular activities which are controlled by the brain.

Mycobacterium tuberculosis

A **bacterium** causing tuberculosis.

Neurological

Referring to the nervous system and its diseases.

Neuropathy

A disease of the nervous system.

NSCAG

National Specialist Commissioning Advisory Group (formerly the Supra-Regional Services Advisory Group).

Oncogene

A **gene** capable of causing cancer.

Oncogenic

Describes a **gene** which is capable of causing cancer, or a **virus** (termed an oncovirus) carrying such a gene.

Organ

A collection of different **tissues** that form a distinct structural and functional entity in the body. Examples of solid organs include liver, heart, brain and kidney. In this report, the word tissue is used to refer to solid organs and other tissue

Organism

A living thing (animal, plant or **micro-organism**).

Pancreatic Islet Cells of Langerhans

Groups of **cells** scattered throughout the pancreas which secrete glucagon and insulin (hormones involved in regulating blood sugar levels).

Parasite

An **organism** that is able to live in or on and which may cause damage to another organism. Parasites include many **micro-organisms**.

Parkinson's Disease

A progressive disease which is due to degenerative **neurological** changes in the brain.

Pathogen

An infectious agent that has the capacity to cause disease.

Perfusion

The transfer of fluid (such as blood) through a **tissue** or an **organ**.

Polymerase Chain Reaction (PCR)

A **molecular technique** used to amplify specific sequences of **DNA**. This can be useful for the detection of certain **micro-organisms**, providing suitable DNA sequence information is available in order to "probe" for the micro-organism(s) of interest.

Porcine

Relating to pigs.

Prion

A modified form of a protein. Prions are thought to cause fatal neurodegenerative diseases collectively known as spongiform encephalopathies.

Prophylactic medication

The use of medicine to prevent disease.

Pulmonary

Relating to the lung.

Random Display Amplification (RDA)

A molecular biological means of looking for the appearance of novel banding in analytic gels which may indicate the presence of the genetic material of infectious agents. The technique is generally of low sensitivity so there is a risk of false positives.

Regulators of Complement Activity (RCAs)

RCAs check or down–regulate the **complement** cascade reaction to prevent unnecessary damage being done to the body's own **tissues**. They are found on the surfaces of the body's **cells**; examples include Decay Accelerating Factor (DAF), Cluster Differentiation 59 (CD59), and Membrane Cofactor Protein (MCP).
RCAs are **species**-specific, although they may be partially effective in moderating **complement activation** in **concordant species**. Human RCAs will not therefore prevent the rejection of xenotransplanted pig **organs** or tissues to humans; however **transgenic** pigs have been genetically modified to express a human RCA. (See 'Addition of a gene', para 2.66).

Rejection (see Transplant rejection)

Renal

Relating to the kidney.

Retrovirus

A family of **viruses** with a special replication mechanism which includes incorporation of its genetic material into the **DNA** of the **organism** it has infected. Examples of retroviruses include the Human Immunodeficiency Virus (HIV) and certain **oncogenic** viruses. (See also Endogenous retrovirus).

Salmonella

A particular group of related **species** of **bacteria.**

Sentinel animals

Animals which are not to be used as sources of **organs** or other **tissues**, but which are kept in similar conditions and killed periodically to enable full testing for known **pathogens** through post-mortem.

Serology

The clinical use and study of **serum** to characterise **antigens**, **antibodies** etc. as a means of detecting infection.

Serum

The fluid component of clotted blood that contains **antibodies** and other soluble material.

Source animal

In this report, the animal from which **tissues** and **organs** are taken.

Species

A group of **organisms** that have similar characteristics and can interbreed to produce fertile offspring.

Specific–Pathogen–Free (SPF)

The term designating animals which have been bred in captivity to exclude known **pathogens** and to keep them in conditions which reduce the risk associated with certain infectious agents, for example through feeding a sterile diet and controlled ventilation and by exclusion of contact with non–SPF animals. (See also Germ free)

Subclinical

A description of a disease that is suspected (or described retrospectively) but which has not developed sufficiently or is too mild in form to produce clear signs and symptoms of disease in an individual.

T cell (= T lymphocyte)

A class of **white blood cells** of the **immune system** that interact to produce the 'cellular' **immune response**. Mature T cells can be divided into two major subsets,"CD4+" and "CD8+" that differ in function. 'Killer' T cells (a subset of "CD8+") directly attack and kill **cells** bearing foreign **antigens**.

Thoracic

Referring to the chest.

Tissue

An organised aggregate of similar **cells** that perform a particular function, for example bone marrow, nerve tissue. In this report, the word tissue is used to refer also to **organs**.

T Lymphocyte (see T cell)

Toxoplasma gondii

A particular parasite.

Transfection

The incorporation of foreign **DNA** into cultured **cells**.

Transgene

A **gene** which has been transferred from one **species** to another.

Transgenic

This describes an **organism** which, through **genetic modification**, has a heritable foreign **gene** (known as a **transgene**).

Transplant rejection

The process where the host **immune response** recognises the transplanted **tissue** as foreign and acts against it leading to damage/destruction of the tissue. Various forms of rejection have been defined with respect to time to rejection and the elements of the immune response which are involved - see **Hyperacute, Acute vascular, Acute cellular** and **Chronic rejection**.

Transplantation

The removal and implantation of **organs**, **tissues** or **cells** from one **organism** into another.

UKTSSA

United Kingdom Transplant Support Services Authority.

ULTRA

Unrelated Live Transplant Regulatory Authority.

Uraemia

The clinical state which may arise as a result of kidney failure.

Vascular

Appertaining to blood vessels (arteries, capillaries and veins) and/or **lymph** vessels.

Vasodilator therapy

The use of drugs to widen the blood vessels and thereby lower blood pressure and strain on the heart.

Vertical transmission

The transmission of infection directly from parent to offspring. This can take place *in utero* via egg, sperm, placenta, or postnatally via milk, blood or contact etc.

Viable

Capable of living (through continued **metabolism**); this will apply to **organs** and most **tissues** which may be transplanted, but does not include sterilised bone, which is 'non-viable'.

Virus(es)

Minute **micro-organisms**, some of which can reside and replicate in human and animal **cells**. Some viruses cause disease.

White blood cells

Blood **cells**, including **T Cells** and **B cells**, which are involved in protecting the body against foreign substances and which constitute part of the **immune system**.

Xenoantigen

Antigens of transplants from **discordant species**, for example the **Gal epitope**.

Xenogeneic Transplant (see Xenotransplantation)

Xenoreactive natural antibodies (XNA)

Pre-existing natural **antibodies** that bind to **xenoantigens** on the surface of the **cells** of a **xenotransplant** from a **discordant species**.

Xenotransplant

The **tissue** or **organ** that has been transplanted between **species**.

Xenotransplantation (=Xenogeneic transplantation)

The **transplantation** of **tissue** and **organs** between **species**.

Xenozoonosis (pl. xenozoonoses)

A zoonotic infection which can be transmitted by the **xenotransplantation** of animal **tissues** or **organs**.

Yersinia

A particular group of related **species** of **bacteria**.

Zoonosis (pl. zoonoses)

Any infectious disease which can be transmitted from animals to humans.

ANNEX B

THE
CONSULTATION
EXERCISE

ANNEX B:

THE CONSULTATION EXERCISE

1. The Advisory Group decided to solicit information and views on the issues that xenotransplantation raises from both interested organisations and the general public through conducting a public consultation exercise. The exercise was announced through an advertising campaign in the national and specialist press. The Group also wrote direct to over 200 interested organisations

2. A copy of the consultation letter and the accompanying background note is at Appendix B. The consultation letter requested written responses and directed consultees' attention to a number of issues:

    (i)   Whether there is a need for Xenotransplantation ie whether the current and future needs for organ transplants can be met by other means.

    (ii)   Whether it is ethical to use, to modify genetically and to breed animals so that their organs may be used for transplant to humans. Whether the issues are different from those involved in the breeding of animals for food. Whether different issues apply for different animals.

    (iii) should xenotransplantation be thought ethically justifiable, the considerations that should be taken into account in breeding and caring for the involved animals.

    (iv)   whether there is a risk of transferring zoonotic or other important infections in the transplantation of organs from one species to another. If there is thought to be such a risk, what assessment can be made of its likely impact on the recipient of the organ and the wider population and how could such an impact be minimised.

    (v)   whether there is a need for licensing of the breeding of the animals and for regulation of the use of xenotransplants, for example, in their allocation to human patients and the need for consent of those patients.

    (vi)   Whether such transplants would be acceptable to the public at large.

    Responses were sought from a wide range of organisations, including patients' organisations, clinical organisations, religious groups, and animal rights and welfare groups. In addition to this mailing, an advertisement announcing the consultation exercise was placed in a number of journals and newspapers between 16 and 27 January 1996. These were The Daily Mail, The Daily Mirror, The Guardian, The Daily Telegraph, The British Medical Journal, Hospital Doctor, General Practitioner, Health Service Journal, Catholic Standard and Herald, Church Times, New Scientist, Nature, Jewish Chronicle, Daily Jang, and the Veterinary Record.

3. The Advisory Group received 333 responses. A list of the organisations and individuals who responded is at Appendix C. In addition to this over 500 postcards were sent to the Secretary of State for Health as part of a campaign against xenotransplantation.

4. The Group was stimulated and challenged by the submissions and were grateful to all those who had written. A summary of the main points raised under each issue is at Appendix A.

5. One Advisory Group meeting was dedicated specifically to discussion of the consultation exercise.

ANNEX B:

APPENDIX A

CONSULTATION EXERCISE:
SUMMARY OF MAIN POINTS MADE

i) Whether there is a need for Xenotransplantation ie whether the current and future needs for organ transplants can be met by other means.

1. There was general agreement that the current demand for organs far outweighs the number of human organs available for transplant and furthermore that the demand is likely to increase as more patients become suitable for transplantation with technological advances in patient care. It was also pointed out that as the UK population is ageing, the number of elderly people requiring transplants is likely to increase.

2. Views were mixed about whether xenotransplantation was the answer to meeting the long term demand for organs for transplant. Of those who felt that there was a need for xenotransplantation there was a general view that this should be the 'last resort' and that attempts should first be made to improve the retrieval rates of human organs. Whilst a number considered xenotransplantation an effective solution to the problem, others proposed alternatives as detailed in the following paragraphs.

3. A change in the law to presumed consent or "opting-out". This approach has been adopted by a number of other countries although one response reports that evidence from other countries on the effectiveness of this system is conflicting – some countries with an "opt-out" law have better donation rates than the UK others do not; further it was reported that a survey of over 1,000 members of the National Kidney Federation conducted in 1993 showed a desire to retain the gift element of organ donation. In addition some respondents did not consider it appropriate to have an "opting-out" system.

4. Several respondents referred to the important role that the medical/nursing professions play in recognising potential donors and in approaching their relatives to discuss donation. It was felt that there was room for improvement in their training with regards to organ donation. Additional efforts to educate staff regarding the need for organ donation may do more to enhance the donation of organs than an obligatory request system. The effectiveness of a medical education/awareness programme introduced in Spain was mentioned. This involves trained staff, including transplant co-ordinators, who are usually medically qualified, being dedicated to transplantation at every district hospital. It was also mentioned that some doctors

find it difficult to approach relatives of potential donors. The considerable extra work entailed in caring for potential donors prior to organ retrieval was also considered to be an impediment.

5. Elective ventilation, currently illegal in the UK, was considered to be another option for increasing donor rates. This technique is said to now be accepted by the BMA, the British Transplant Society and the National Kidney Federation.

6. Many respondents felt that more resources should be spent on preventive health care and health education to reduce the numbers of people developing conditions which would require transplant surgery. It was also thought that an unlimited supply of animal organs would generate an even greater demand for "spare part surgery", diminishing further the role of preventive medicine.

7. Some thought that a better promotion of the donor card system with an information policy on the benefits of organ transplants and the need for organ donors was needed to help overcome the donor shortage. It was also suggested that the Department of Health should develop an ethnically sensitive advertising campaign to provide information to both the public and professionals.

8. Suggested alternative techniques to transplant surgery included artificial devices; human cell, tissue and organ culture; quantum pharmacology (computer based) modelling, simulation of biological systems and visual aids and micro-engineering. Other approaches being investigated include the seeding of additional myocardial cells, stimulation of the growth of existing cells, seeding and metamorphosis of skeletal muscle cells, the stimulation of new vessel formation and homo-seeded passive graft (HSG) technology. There was an opinion amongst a number of respondents that more funds should be directed to research into producing artificial organs.

9. There was much concern that a side-effect of xenotransplantation would be that fewer people would carry donor cards and doctors might well come to prefer to use animal organs rather than go through the traumatic process of getting organs from cadaveric donors.

10. Reports of instances where organs from British and Irish donors were sent abroad were used to highlight the fact that it is essential to consider what supply of tissue and organs the service can sustain. It was considered important that any advance leading to improved availability of any organs for transplant is accompanied by an assurance of adequate specialist hospital infrastructure to permit effective use of all organs.

11. It was pointed out that the comfort that bereaved families can gain from organ donation should not be disregarded. This benefit is quite separate from the fact that human organs may remain the best option for recipients for some time yet.

(ii) Whether it is ethical to use, to modify genetically and to breed animals so that their organs may be used for transplant to humans. Whether the issues are different from those involved in the breeding of animals for food. Whether different issues apply for different animals.

1. Respondents who considered it ethically acceptable to use, modify and breed animals for xenotransplantation generally felt that this use was no different than breeding animals for consumption. Some referred to the fact that porcine insulin and porcine heart valves have been used for years and that other porcine substances are being developed for other therapeutic purposes. There was also a consensus of opinion that only animals which are already bred for consumption should be bred for xenotransplantation and no other animals should be used. In particular primates should not be used. Similarly, some respondents thought that this genetic modification was not dissimilar to the current practice of creating new breeds. Care would, though, have to be taken that such breeding and genetic modification would not, in itself, cause the animal suffering.

2. Many of the respondents who opposed xenotransplantation on ethical grounds were also opposed to the breeding of animals for consumption. On the other hand others thought it wrong to say that as animals are bred for food they can be 'exploited' in other ways. It was thought that the genetic engineering of animals for human use and xenotransplantation represented an assumption that human beings have the right to regard animals as objects which could be used for human benefit. This implied bias in favour of humans was questioned.

3. Considerable concern was expressed for the welfare of the animals involved. Even those who find xenotransplantation acceptable, consider it is only ethically justified if the animals are treated humanely and their suffering is minimised. The suffering inflicted on animals during the experimental stages of xenotransplantation was also recognised.

4. It was suggested that the ethical decision to proceed with xenotransplantation should follow the same route and basis as those for all other forms of animal experimentation, i.e. a cost/benefit analysis of the degree of animal suffering versus its potential benefit to humans. The principles and criteria of such a cost/benefit analysis are clearly established in the Project Licensing system under the Animals (Scientific Procedure) Act 1986 (ASPA).

5. It was thought that animals modified for this purpose should not enter the food chain and that they should be prevented from breeding with animals intended for the food chain.

6. Some respondents questioned the value placed on preserving human life at all costs.

7. The need for organs for transplantation would support the ethical justification of xenotransplantation, but this was not universally seen as a valid consideration when debating the ethical acceptability of xenotransplantation.

8.   Some respondents felt that a dying person and their relatives were unlikely to have ethical concerns about xenotransplantation, if it was known to be effective. There was also a view that in life and death situations human beings take priority over animals.

9.   One respondent makes the point that an organ given in the love of humanity, at a time of tragedy, without any profit motive is a noble thing. An organ forcibly removed, perhaps with the whole process based upon profit motive, and without any empathy, is not "a noble thing".

10. Responses from religious organisations are summarised separately later in this appendix.

(iii)   should xenotransplantation be thought ethically justifiable, the considerations that should be taken into account in breeding and caring for the involved animals

1.   The breeding of the animals was raised in the submissions. There was some concern about the extent of genetic modification proposed and whether it would create some kind of mythical "beast" or cross-species animal. There was also concern about the effects of even a small genetic modification. The animals should be monitored and if adverse effects were reported, i.e. if the animal was harmed, such breeding should be stopped.

2.   Concern was also expressed about the breeding programme and the possibility that it would produce animals who would not be needed for xenotransplant purposes: "a breeding programme should not be permitted if say only 25% of the animals born have the sought genetic alteration with the other 75% being destroyed as unsuitable".

3.   On animal care, the concern of the vast majority of respondents was that the animals should be allowed to live in as natural surroundings as possible (and that these should be sensitive to the needs of the specific species) and that any suffering to the animal should be kept to the absolute minimum. It was also noted that contented animals would also be healthier and would be less likely to be injured by self harm or by each other. However, it was recognised that maintaining animals in infection-free surroundings would have an impact on animal welfare. One view was that animal welfare should not be adversely affected by this requirement, but it was also pointed out that a sterile environment need not be monotonous or barren eg sterile straw can be used as bedding and play objects which have been autoclaved can be provided to reduce boredom.

4.   Many respondents made reference to existing standards as being either acceptable or a good basis for standards - eg the ASPA regulations. There was support for some form of statutory safeguard of animal welfare considerations, particularly as the developments were taking place in a commercial environment.

5.   Some respondents commented on the species of animal to be involved and suggested that only domesticated animals should be considered; ie primates should be excluded from such a breeding programme.

6.   On a specific point, it was recommended that sequential removal of organs or tissue should be prohibited.

7.   The importance of public perception of the conditions in which the animals were kept - for humane reasons, and for infection-free reasons - was also highlighted, as this would be influential in forming views about xenotransplantation.

(iv) whether there is a risk of transferring zoonotic or other important infections in the transplantation of organs from one species to another. If there is thought to be such a risk, what assessment can be made of its likely impact on the recipient of the organ and the wider population and how could such an impact be minimised.

1.   There was general agreement that there was a potential risk of transferring infections from animals to humans. The majority of responses commented that efforts should be made to minimise this risk, few suggested that the potential risk meant that xenotransplantation should not proceed at the present time - or at all. One view was that the long history of contact between pigs and humans meant that it was unlikely that any new diseases would emerge.

2.   There were several detailed responses which detailed the types of infectious agent which could be important in xenotransplantation.

3.   Several respondents distinguished between risk to the individual graft recipient and the risk to the wider population. It was stressed that the risk from zoonotic infections to the individual, who had a terminal disease, would have to be balanced against the possible benefit from the transplant. In this context, it was pointed out that the immunosuppressed state of the individual would create a favourable environment for infection transmission. However, it may be that the individual should not be allowed to take some risks which could impact on the wider population.

4.   It was thought essential that a full assessment was made of the risks - and of those that commented on the infectious agents, viruses were thought to pose the greatest risk to the wider population. One organisation suggested that a sub-group (of the Advisory Group) be set up to look at these risks.

5.   Some respondents distinguished between the risks associated with using different species; amongst these respondents, there was agreement that non-human primates posed greater risks than animals such as pigs, and that this therefore mitigated against their use. There was some

comment about the use of sheep and cows, given their susceptibility to prion-mediated diseases.

6.   There was also concern, that there might be a risk of transferring infections from humans to animals and that there might be a risk of transferring genetic disorders from animals to humans.

7.   Many respondents commented on public policy issues which might follow from a recognition of these risks. There was agreement that risks could be minimised by restricting the animals which could be used as a source for tissue and by maintaining the source animals in a specific-pathogen free environment. The health of these animals would be monitored and it was suggested that the ancestry of the animals was examined to rule out the risk of genetic disorder. The removal of organs/tissue could also take place in aseptic conditions.

8.   It was suggested that full and detailed pre-transplant counselling (and fully informed consent) would be needed on these risks, to ensure the individual patient understood them fully.

9.   It was also pointed out that clinicians would not have a full understanding about the animal pathogens likely to cause a risk of infection and that they might therefore benefit from information on these likely risks.

10.   It was further proposed that a monitoring system would be needed to monitor not only the animals but also the transplant recipients (and their offspring) following the xenotransplantation procedure.

11.   There was some thought given to the need for approval of these procedures. It was suggested that a national framework or guidelines were needed for this process as Local Research Ethics Committees (to whom such applications were currently made) may not have the resources or expertise to take such decisions.

12.   There was also concern that the source animals themselves might pose a risk to the wider population. It was felt that they should be contained within the unit where they were bred and that they should not be allowed to breed outside this. One organisation expressed concern that infection could result from the units where they were kept and pose a risk to the local human population.

13.   Several respondents made reference to the recent publicity on BSE and commented that it might be difficult for scientists to convince the public of the safety of these procedures.

(v) whether there is a need for licensing of the breeding of the animals and for regulation of the use of xenotransplants, for example, in their allocation to human patients and the need for consent of those patients.

1.   There was unanimity amongst those who commented on this issue that some form of regulation was needed on the xenotransplantation process.

2.   Regulation was thought particularly important in the breeding and use of the animals to ensure their welfare and to maintain an environment where infection risks would be minimised; indeed, it was thought that xenotransplantation should only take place under such circumstances.   Some form of "external policing" was also suggested. ASPA was commended and it was suggested, along the lines of the Nuffield Council Report, that its remit should be extended beyond two generations.   It was also pointed out that the care of transgenic animals is currently regulated by the Advisory Committee on Genetic Manipulation. Another response recommended that the convention by which the Animal Procedures Committee advises on project licenses in difficult areas should extend to applications for the use of animals in xenotransplantation.

3.   Some thought was given to restricting the places where animals could be bred and kept and to restricting the hospitals which could carry out the procedures (and whether these establishments should be licensed).   It was also suggested that the medical profession would also need to be subject to an ethical code on xenotransplantation (an analogy was drawn with the ethical code on embryo research). These establishments should also pay attention to security arrangements.

4.   Regulation should also control and prohibit the release of the animals.

5.   It was again considered essential that full consent be sought from prospective patients. Protocols should be developed. It was thought that patients must be told where the tissue is from, and that conscientious and religious objection must be allowed for. Patients should have access to counselling. Consideration was given to minimising any pressure on the patient, particularly during the development phase.   In this regard, a specified time for reflection was recommended. Thought should be given to making consent arrangements independent from the transplant team. There was also concern about seeking consent in "emergency situations" when the patient was not able to give consent for themselves.

6.   Organ allocation policy received less comment.   Some respondents commented that organ allocation should not be on the basis of the patient's ability to pay, nor on any particular health authority's ability to pay. The consideration of which patients to give human organs and which to give animal organs was raised as an issue of concern.   In the early stages, there was a suggestion that xenotransplantation should be confined to those for whom there was no other hope of a cure or improvement.

7.   Not many respondents commented on the need for a regulatory body. Of those who did, there was some divergence of opinion about whether one body should cover all aspects of xenotransplantation eg the "animal" end and the "human" angle. One respondent endorsed the Nuffield Council view but suggested that the proposed committee could be extended to monitor issues such as the number of animals being used (or wasted), to monitor research into xenotransplantation, to avoid duplication and to monitor the conditions in which animals were kept.

8.   One respondent was concerned about the possibility of the human patients reproducing and passing on "animal" genes to their offspring.

(vi) Whether such transplants would be acceptable to the public at large.

1.   There was a large body of opinion that felt that whilst xenotransplantation would initially be unacceptable to the public at large it would in time become acceptable to the majority if it was seen to be effective in saving, or improving the quality of, lives. It was compared with other initially controversial medical techniques e.g. in-vitro fertilisation, and human transplantation. However it was reiterated that animal suffering must be minimised in order to gain public acceptability.

2.   There were also a considerable number of respondents who considered that xenotransplantation is and will remain unacceptable to the public at large. The issue of religious acceptability of organs from certain animals for certain religions and of other groups with conscientious objections was also raised.

3.   Comment was made that in order for the public to make an informed decision they must be informed fully about all the facts. It would be important to include information about the way the source animals are kept, the extent of any genetic modification of the animal and about the possible risks of infection. However, it was felt that the Advisory Group should consider the most effective way of ensuring that the public are objectively informed, without any sensationalism.

4.   Reference was made to the public's dislike of animal cruelty as highlighted by the recent "live export campaign" - xenotransplantation could be seen under the same category of unnecessary animal suffering.

5.   It was felt that patients waiting for an organ transplant and their families were more likely to be in favour of xenotransplantation. It was reported that a survey of potential kidney recipients showed that 40% would have no objection to receiving a kidney from a pig. Reference was also made to a survey conducted in America of 2,000 kidney patients, recipients and non-

recipients, which revealed that 65% were in favour of research and 75% of transplant recipients said they would accept a xenotransplantation if they needed transplant and no human organ was available. Another poll (by show of hands) conducted at an organ donor convention in 1995 showed that about 80% of those present accepted xenotransplantation.

The response of religious organisations to the consultation exercise

There were a number of responses to the consultation exercise from various religious groups within the United Kingdom. Their responses to the various questions posed by the Advisory Group have been summarised under the various headings, but this section looks at their responses as a whole. Many individuals' beliefs derive from the faiths they hold. We hope that we do their submissions justice in this section. There are some common themes to their concerns, although there are different assessments of the acceptability of xenotransplantation.

❖ All religions express concern for the welfare of the animals involved. Without exception, even those which find xenotransplantation acceptable argue for the humane treatment of the animals and the minimisation of their suffering.

❖ There is concern that consent must be sought from patients and that full information should be given about the origin of the tissue involved.

❖ There is some concern about the genetic modification of animals and the possibility of "hybridisation".

Baha'i We understand that Baha'is believe that humankind is different and of a higher order than animals. It is therefore allowable to use animals for food and other purposes. Xenotransplantation therefore seems acceptable although unnecessary suffering to the animals should be avoided.

Buddhism It was represented to us that Buddhism would not consider xenotransplantation to be acceptable and that alternatives should be sought. The basis of this objection is that proper ethical conduct reduces hurt and compassion to others and that all beings including animals experience feeling within their consciousness. Therefore concern about hurt and compassion is relevant to both humans and animals. However, it is recognised that some Buddhists may choose to benefit from xenotransplantation as they do from other medical products derived from or tested on animals (this will depend on their "stage of perfection" in the Buddhist path).

Christianity Responses were received from various denominations of the Christian Church. We were told that generally Christians would accept the use of animals for xenotransplantation, and the consequent necessity for genetic modification of some of these animals. However it was thought important that unnecessary suffering or cruelty to be avoided. However, we understand that some fundamentalist Christians, do not currently accept pig valve transplants or pig insulin and may therefore be unlikely to accept xenotransplantation. We also understand that there are particular concerns about perceived "tinkering" with creation that genetic modification presupposes. There is likely to be a diversity of view amongst the Christian community and a significant number of Christians may take the view that, on theological grounds, xenotransplantation represents a denial of the sanctity of both human and non-human life and an excessively instrumental use of animals.

A number of particular concerns were expressed, namely:

(i) that the number of animals used should be kept to a minimum, with no unnecessary experiments being performed;

(ii) about the transplantation of cells or tissue into the brain, due to the perceived central importance of neural tissue to personality;

(iii) that xenotransplantation would come to be taken for granted – it must always be considered in terms of whether it is genuinely the best solution available; and

(iv) about the transplantation of material which might affect the human germ-line, about eugenics and about any transplantation of human tissue into animals. Such developments were not thought to be acceptable.

Hindu Hindus, we were told, do not believe in either accepting or donating organs for transplantation and they would not accept an animal organ for xenotransplantation. They believe that when a person dies the body must remain whole to pass on to the next life. However, this strict view may be relaxed to allow acceptance of an organ (and this would apply to either animal or human). It is left to individuals to make their own decisions. On the use of particular animals, the cow is sacred to Hindus but the use of pigs would be acceptable.

Judaism The over-riding value in Judaism, we were told, is the saving of life. This overrides certain other considerations or prohibitions; for example, the prohibition on the consumption of pig flesh. The use of animals is also permitted in Jewish Law if it is necessary to alleviate human suffering and provided their welfare is protected. A view was expressed, however, that if the development of animals for xenotransplantation would result in considerable suffering, this would tip the balance in favour of other methods of meeting the need for transplantation, but not necessarily exclude xenotransplantation if it were the best means available. The genetic modification of the animals raises certain concerns, due to a traditional objection to modifying the natural order of creation if this lead to hybridisation. It is acknowledged, however, that the genetic modification proposed for xenotransplantation is not likely to be such as to be considered hybridisation and that, if it were, such concerns would be overridden by the goal of saving life. Concerns were also raised about the safety of xenotransplantation

It was also pointed out that heart transplants from human donors is controversial in contemporary Jewish law due to (1) a concern about definitions of brain stem death and (2) the unnecessary desecration of human bodies.

Muslim The submissions we received from Muslim organisations reflected the diversity of opinion which can exist on xenotransplantation. On one view, although emphasis is placed in Islam on protecting the welfare of animals, God allows the use of animals to fulfil human needs. Unnecessary suffering should be avoided. Animal experimentation is permitted given certain conditions, which would not appear to prohibit xenotransplantation:

1   If such experiments are designed to discover the effect of a new drug for curing diseases in humans then they are *acceptable;*

2   If the aim is to discover if a particular disease afflicting animals is transferable from animals to humans, then it is *acceptable;*

3   If the experiment is part of scientific research which is for the general benefit of humanity in an area of study where it is really needed, then it is *acceptable;*

4   If experiments are done out of curiosity and for no apparent benefit, then they are *unacceptable;*

5   Experiments to test cosmetics, beautification products and for other nefarious purposes are also *unacceptable.*

On another view, breeding animals for food is different from breeding animals only to supply organs for humans. The latter would be immoral. The transference of human genes to animals is prohibited as it interferes with the natural order of creation. However, on the use of particular animals, it is considered that the organs of those animals which can be lawfully slaughtered for food, like lamb, cows, deer can be used for human transplants.

Sikh Our understanding is that Sikhs regard the use of animals as permitted for, for example, food, clothing and footwear and that the use of animal parts for transplant is an extension of this usage. However, the breeding and treatment of animals for xenotransplantation in a way that causes suffering or a marked diminution in quality of life would be contrary to Sikh teachings. Sikhs also have concern regarding the risks of infection and any possible risk to future generations and advise that xenotransplantation should be confined to those who are not of child-bearing age. Sikhism also teaches that what we make of life is more important than its length or span and that medical advance should not lead to an obsession with prolonging life at any ethical or physical cost.

ANNEX B:

APPENDIX B

To all interested organisations or individuals

25 January 1996

Dear Consultee

THE ADVISORY GROUP ON THE ETHICS OF XENOTRANSPLANTATION

The Secretary of State for Health has set up an Advisory Group to look at the ethical issues surrounding transplantation of animals organs to humans. The membership of the Group is set out at Annex A.

The terms of reference of the group are: In the light of recent and potential developments in xenotransplantation, to review the acceptability of and ethical framework within which xenotransplantation may be undertaken and to make recommendations. The Group will report to the Secretary of State by summer 1996.

Xenotransplantation is the transplantation of an organ from one species to another. The Advisory Group is looking at the ethical implications of the scientific developments which contemplate the transplantation of organs from animals to humans, in place of human organs. Their interest includes the work being done to supply organs from genetically modified pigs and that involving the use of primates and will take into account potential future developments.

The Group has identified a number of issues for consideration:

(i)   whether there is a need for xenotransplantation ie whether the current and future needs for organ transplants can be met by other means.

(ii)   whether it is ethical to use, to modify genetically and to breed animals so that their organs may be used for transplant to humans. Whether the issues are different than those involved in the breeding of animals for food. Whether different issues apply for different animals.

(iii)   Should xenotransplantation be thought ethically justifiable, the considerations that should be taken into account in breeding and caring for the genetically modified animals.

(iv)   whether there is a risk of transferring zoonotic infections in the transplantation of organs from one species to another. If there is thought to be such a risk, what assessment can be made of its likely impact on the recipient of the organ and the wider population and how could such an impact be minimised.

(v)   whether there is a need for licensing of the breeding of the animals and for regulation of the use of xenotransplants, for example, in their allocation to human patients and the need for consent of those patients.

(vi)   whether such transplants would be acceptable to the public at large.

The Advisory Group would be grateful to hear your comments as an interested party in order to assist in its consideration of these issues.

Written comments should be submitted **by 29 March 1996** at the latest. If you propose very substantial comments, the Group would be grateful for an early indication of the main points of your submission. These should be set to Mr Carl Evans, Advisory Group on the Ethics of Xenotransplantation, Department of Health, Room 508 Eileen House, 80-94 Newington Causeway, LONDON SE1 6EF (FAX 0171-972-2907).

Written comments to the Group will not be made public although it is, of course, open to each contributor to make their own comments available. It is likely that a list of those who participated in this consultation exercise will be included in the final report, which may be published. If you prefer your name not to be included in such a list, please indicate this in your response.

Yours faithfully

Rachel Arrundale
Secretary to the Advisory Group

ANNEX B:

APPENDIX C

ORGANISATIONS AND INDIVIDUALS WHO SUBMITTED RESPONSES TO THE CONSULTATION EXERCISE

Advocates for Animals

Alder Hey Children's Hospital – Paediatric Research Ethics Committee

Alderson, Lisa (Ms)

Allden, J. N.

Anglican Society for the Welfare of Animals

Animal Aid

Animal Concern

Archbold, Darren

Ashford Public Health Laboratory Service

Association of British Health-Care Industries

Association of Medical Microbiologists

Association of the British Pharmaceutical Industry

B & K Universal Ltd.

Baker, Amy (Miss)

Baker, Kathleen (Ms)

Barking and Havering Health Authority

Barkingside Progressive Synagogue

Barry, J. J.

Bartlett, A. J.

Baylis, P. J. (Mrs)

Beddeley, Maureen

Bell, D. M. (Miss)

Biotechnology and Biological Sciences Research Council

Blackburn, Hyndburn and Ribble Valley Local Research Ethics Committee

Blackpool, Wyre and Fylde Local Research Ethics Committee

Bolton, Emma

Bolton Research Ethics Committee

Boram, Pamela

Bowen, Tracey

Bray, M. A.

Brent Medical Ethics Committee

British Anti-Vivisection Association (London)

British Buddhist Association

British Laboratory Animals Veterinary Association, Institute of Animal Technology and
 Laboratory Animal Science Association Group (Joint Submission)

British Medical Association

British Organ Donor Society

British Society of Animal Science

British Transplantation Society and the British Society of Immunology (Joint Submission)

British Union for the Abolition of Vivisection

British Veterinary Association

Brown, O

Bryan, V. R.

Buddhist Priory

Burland, E. (Mr)

Burnley, Pendle and Rossendale Local Research Ethics Committee

Bury Local Research Ethics Committee

Busby, A.

Butcher, T. (Mrs)

Caddick, Jeremy (Reverend) – Emmanuel College, Cambridge

Calderon, R. D. (Mrs)

Campbell, Mairghneadh

Carbrick, Kay (Ms)

Catholic Study Circle for Animal Welfare

Catholic Union of Great Britain

Central Manchester Healthcare NHS Trust

Centre for Bioethics and Public Policy

Chappell, Phillip

Charles River U.K. Limited

Charlton, David (Reverend Canon Dr)

Cheeseman, D. (Miss)

Chester, June, T. H. (Mrs)

Chichester Priority Care Services

Chichester Research Ethics Committee

Christian Medical Fellowship

Church in Wales – Diocese of Monmouth

Church of England – The General Synod of the

Church of Ireland Board for Social Responsibility

Church of Scotland – Society, Religion and Technology Project

Ciruk, J. Z. (Miss)

City Hospital Birmingham Research Ethics Committee

Clark, Julie

Clwyd North Research Ethics Committee

Coates (Mr & Mrs)

Coffin, J.A. (Mrs)

Compassion in World Farming

Connor, L. (Ms)

Consumers for Ethics in Research

Cooper, Diane (Ms)

Council of Churches for Britain and Ireland

County Durham Local Research Ethics Committee

Coventry Research Ethics Committee

Crawley Horsham Local Research Ethics Committee

Crisp, R. J. (Miss)

Croydon Local Research Ethics Committee

Cullimore, Suzanne L.

Cystic Fibrosis Trust

Dack, D. (Mr)

Davison, June (Mrs)

Dean, J. (Mrs)

Derbyshire Ambulance Service NHS Trust

Diocese of Bradford, Medical Ethics Group

Doctors and Lawyers for Responsible Medicine

Downing P. J. (Mrs)

Dr Hadwen Trust

Dudley Priority Health NHS Trust

Duncalf, J. (Miss)

Dunne, Lynsey

Ealing Hospital Local Research Ethics Committee

East Kent Health Authority

East Lancashire Local Research Ethics Committee

Echlin, Edward (Dr)

Ellacott, L

Enfield and Haringey Health Agency

Evans, L. (Mrs)

Fells, C. (Mrs)

Foster, J.

Fosti, Anthea

Fox, Amy Jane (Miss)

Francis, Gladys (Mrs)

Free Church Federal Council

Freeman Hospital, Newcastle-upon-Tyne

Frewer, P. (Ms)

Friston, Gaynor

Frizzarin, Anita and Sutherland, Roger (Joint Submission)

Fund for the Replacement of Animals in Medical Experiments (FRAME)

Garnett (Mrs)

Genetics Forum

Goldie, F. (Miss)

Goodwin, D.P. (Dr)

Graham, S.D.

Grampian Health Board

Green, Janet

Green, Stephen

Gwent Research Ethics Committee

Hall, Linda (Mrs)

Hamilton, D. (Mr)

Hamilton, Paul

Hammond, D. E. (Miss)

Harefield Hospital

Harrogate Local Research Ethics Committee

Hart, Dyana

Head, K. (Miss)

Headley, L. W.

Henderson, L. (Mr)

Herefordshire Health Authority

Hertfordshire Health Agency

Highland Health Board

Hill, Christine

Hollingsbee, Veronica (Mrs)

Hollyhead, J. L.

Howman, Heather

Hubble, E (Mrs)

Huddersfield Local Research Ethics Committee

Humphreys, Michelle (Miss)

Humphries, E. R. (Ms)

Huntingdon Local Research Ethics Committee

Imutran Limited

Institute of Animal Technology

Institute of Biology

Islamic Shari'ah Council of the U.K.

Jeffs, Harry G.

Jenkins, Michelle (Miss)

Johnson, A. (Mrs)

Jones, B.

Jones, R. J. (Mr)

Jones (Mr & Mrs)

Kelgy, Dorothy

Kent and Canterbury Hospital Research Ethics Committee

King's College – Department of Theology and Religious Studies

Laboratory Animal Science Association

Leak, Alison

Lee-Cooper, Frankie

Lifecare NHS Trust

Lonsdale, Ingrid (Ms)

Lothian Health Board

Lynch, Kerry

Macfarlane, Fiona (Miss)

Maidstone Local Research Ethics Committee

Mair, L. H. (Dr)

Marshall, K.

Marshall (Dr)

May, Caroline

Maynard, F. J. (Mrs)

McConnell, A. A. (Dr)

McLanachan, B. (Mrs)

Meat and Livestock Commission

Medical Research Council

Medical Research Council – AIDS Secretariat

Melliard, Deborah

Metcalf, J. (Ms)

Methodist Church – Division of Social Responsibility

Mid Staffordshire Local Research Ethics Committee

Monksfield, S.

Morrow, Patricia (Mrs)

Mount Vernon and Watford Hospitals NHS Trust Local Research Ethics Committee

National Council of Hindu Temples (U.K.)

National Farmers Union

National Heart and Lung Institute, Imperial College

National Kidney Federation

National Spiritual Assembly of the Baha'is of the United Kingdom

Network of Sikh Organisations U.K.

Neurological Alliance

NHS Executive, West Midlands

NHS Executive, Northern and Yorkshire

North Herefordshire Ethical Review Committee

North Nottingham Health Authority Local Research Ethics Committee

North Tees Local Research Ethics Committee

Norwich District Ethics Committee

Nottingham City Hospital, Ethics of Clinical Practice Committee

Nuffield Council on Bioethics

Office of the Chief Rabbi

Owens, Jane

Palmer, L & J, and friends

Parker, E (Mrs)

Pennington, Sarah

Poulter, David

Powell, David. E. B.

Powell, Olive

Preston Acute Hospitals

Pudney (Miss J & Mrs)

Quaker Concern for Animals

Quaker Home Service

Quality Associates

Queen's Medical Centre, Nottingham

Randell, M. (Ms)

Rebon, Patricia

Reform Synagogues of Great Britain

Renshaw, S. (Mrs)

Research for Health Charities Group

Richardson, C. M. (Mrs)

Roach, Robert

Rochdale Local Research Ethics Committee

Roxburgh, Julie

Royal Brompton Hospital Ethics Committee

Royal College of General Practitioners

Royal College of General Practitioners, Clinical Research Ethics Committee

Royal College of Nursing

Royal College of Obstetricians and Gynaecologists

Royal College of Physicians, Edinburgh

Royal College of Physicians, London

Royal College of Physicians and Surgeons of Glasgow

Royal College of Physicians of the U.K., Faculty of Public Health Medicine

Royal College of Surgeons of Edinburgh

Royal College of Veterinary Surgeons

Royal National Orthopaedic Hospital Trust, Joint Research and Ethics Committee

Royal Pharmaceutical Society of Great Britain

Royal Postgraduate Medical School, Ethics Committee

Royal Society

Royal Society of Edinburgh

Royal Society of Health

Royal Society for the Prevention of Cruelty to Animals

Rushton, Verity (Miss)

Salisbury, Dorothy Joan (Mrs)

Sandoz Pharmaceuticals

Sandwell Local Research Ethics Committee

Savage, L (Mrs) and 21 Signature Petition

Sayer, S.

Scamats, Stephanie

Scottish Society for the Prevention of Cruelty to Animals

Seventh-Day Adventist Church

Sheddon, Rhea (Dr)

Sims, Christopher

Smale (Rev'd)

Smith, H. C. (Mrs)

Smith-Lyte J. (Ms)

Smorten I.

Snook, Ann (Miss)

South Bedfordshire Local Research Ethics Committee

South Birmingham Local Research Ethics Committee

South Glamorgan Local Research Ethics Committee

South Humber Local Research Ethics Committee

South Tees Local Research Ethics Committee

South Tyneside Local Research Ethics Committee

Southen, L. C. (Miss)

Southmead Medical Research Ethics Committee

Southport and Formby Local Research Ethics Committee

Spring, Natalie (Miss)

St George's Healthcare NHS Trust

St George's Local Research Ethics Committee

Stanley-Lainchbury, Paul

Starkey, Peter

Stephens, E. (Ms)

Sterling, Carol (Mrs)

Stokes, G. M.

Stoot, M.

Tague, Marian

Taylor, Rachel (Ms)

Tennant, C. E. (Mrs)

Thomas, E. (Ms)

Thomas, Vicky

Thomas, J. L. (Ms)

Thompson, A. E. (Mrs) and Family

Thorpe, T.C. (Rev'd)

Tomlins, F. G.

Tuffnell, Alison

Turner, Emma

Turp, C.

Union of Liberal and Progressive Synagogues - Rabbinic Conference of the

Union of Muslim Organisations of U.K. and Eire

Union of Orthodox Hebrew Congregations

United Bristol Healthcare NHS Trust Research Ethics Committee

United Kingdom Co-ordinating Committee on Cancer Research

United Kingdom Transplant Co-ordinators Association

United Kingdom Transplant Support Service Authority

Universities Federation for Animal Welfare (UFAW)

University of Cambridge, Department of Clinical Veterinary Medicine

University of Central Lancashire

University of Liverpool Local Research Ethics Committee

University of Luton, Faculty of Health Care and Social Studies

University of Nottingham, Centre for Applied Bioethics

University of Southampton, Department of Psychology

University of the Third Age in Brent

Valentine, Michelle (Ms)

Villar, Richard

Wakefield Healthcare

Walsall Local Research Ethics Committee

Walshe, S. K. (Miss)

Waring, D. (Miss)

Wells, Stefan

Welsh Consumer Council

West Berkshire Local Research Ethics Committee

West Lancashire Local Research Ethics Committee

White, Karen (Ms)

Whitehouse, L.

Wilkie, Lynette (Mrs)

Wilson, A. R.

Woods, Tania

Woodward, D (Mrs)

Yaxley, E. F. (Mrs)

Yaxley, E. H. (Mr)

Young, Shirley (Mrs)

ANNEX C

INFECTIOUS DISEASE
AND
XENOTRANSPLANTATION

A report of the Workshop held jointly by the
Advisory Group on the Ethics of
Xenotransplantation
and the
Advisory Committee on Dangerous Pathogens
on 25 April 1996

ANNEX C:

INTRODUCTION

The Advisory Group on the Ethics of Xenotransplantation was appointed by the Secretary of State for Health and charged as follows:

> In the light of recent and potential developments in xenotransplantation, to review the acceptability of and ethical framework within which xenotransplantation may be undertaken and to make recommendations.

One of the major ethical concerns which they identified early in their work was the possibility that infectious disease may be transmitted from the animals used as sources for xenotransplantation to the human recipients of their tissue and, possibly, to the wider population.

The Advisory Committee on Dangerous Pathogens (the ACDP) is a standing committee, with the remit

> "to advise the HSC, the HSE and the Health and Agriculture Ministers as required on all aspects of hazards and risks to workers and others from exposure to pathogens."

During the latter part of 1995, the Committee began to address the concerns which xenotransplantation raised for them.

In early 1996, the Advisory Group approached the ACDP for their advice on this issue. The discussions which took place culminated in the joint hosting of a Workshop, involving leading UK experts in both animal and human infection risks and in transplant surgery. The Workshop took place on 25 April at the King's Cross Holiday Inn. It was opened by the Chief Medical Officer, Sir Kenneth Calman, and both the Advisory Group and the ACDP are very grateful for his interest and participation.

The Workshop sought to combine short, focused talks on the main issues with the opportunity for open discussion between those attending. This Report covers the five presentations given at the workshop and records the main points made during a general discussion. Additional comments received from delegates are summarised in Appendix 1, the programme for the day is included as Appendix 2, and a list of participants is attached at Appendix 3.

THE PRESENTATIONS

Dr Phillip Minor: Allotransplantation

Dr Minor is Head of the Virology Department at the National Institute of Biological Standards and Control

My talk is about allotransplantation – that is, human to human transplantation. In allotransplantation, there are certain principles for infection control, which people try to follow, but, as you will see, it is not always possible to follow these, nor is it possible to be very precise about these principles.

First I will discuss the cultural background of the regulation of medicinal products and explain how this has been applied to human transplantation. I'm not a medical man and that will become clear as I go on. It does seem to me that medical men vary in their degree of heroism from what you might call, a deeply conservative approach to, what might be termed a First World War lieutenant type approach. You'll see what I mean in a moment.

Regulating medicinal products

All medicinal products, from the regulatory point of view, are judged on three criteria: **efficacy, safety and quality**.

Efficacy is the first criterion by which a product would be judged. There is probably nobody, except the most conservative regulatory authority, who would regard something that was safe, that could be reproduced, but was completely ineffective, as being a satisfactory medicinal product. Safety issues include adverse reactions to the drug and infections associated with the use of the material. Quality is essentially being able to ensure that the product is made in the same way each time. In other words, knowing that a particular medicinal treatment is safe and efficacious is of limited value if you cannot be sure that each product is the same and what the product given to the patient contains.

It is from the quality angle that I'm going to address transplantation. My Institute (the National Institute of Biological Standards and Control) is concerned with biological products. These are products which are either made or tested by a biological system, for example vaccines or hormones produced by recombinant DNA technology. There are some principles, developed over the years to address the virological aspects of this wide range of biological materials. Transplanted organs are not included. There are three stages:

1.   ensuring source material is reasonably clean, by screening donors, to make sure no viruses are present.

2.   ensuring that the production process is able to remove viral infectivity or any infectivity or undesirable materials which happen to be present.

3.   end–product testing: to see if it works or not.

These are principles which are applied across the board to biological products and, to a degree, this is the philosophical background from which the quality aspects of transplantation actually derive although they do not apply directly. There are certain aspects of human transplantations which may be applicable to xenotransplantation, but there are other aspects which, as you will see shortly, are not readily applicable.

Allotransplantation and infection risk

A wide range of tissues and organs are transplanted. There are instances of living donation - for example, kidneys, where the donor clearly can survive having one kidney removed - which gives an opportunity to examine the donor before organ retrieval. This is not possible in, for example heart transplants (except in the limited cases of domino transplants). Solid organs from cadavers have to be removed and used extremely rapidly. Again, it may be possible to examine other tissue to find out whether it has infectious materials associated with it and whether it is suitable for use. For example, bone and bone marrow can be stored for some time before they have to be used. Blood donation is a form of transplantation. With blood a far better constructed characterisation of the product is possible before it is given to the recipient.

The transplants can be categorised in several ways: into solid or non-solid; sterilisable or non-sterilisable; storable or non-storable; or from a cadaveric or living source.

Solid and non-solid: Solid tissue, for example bone, is more easily sterilised, although it is not possible to be certain that you have sterilised to the centre of the bone. There may also be organisms lurking in solid tissues that are not present in non-solid tissue.

Sterilisable and non-sterilisable: Bone, as I said, can be sterilised using, for example, ethylene oxide. There are also tissues which are non-sterilisable - it is not possible to sterilise a kidney, for example, without doing it serious damage.

Storable and non-storable: A complex organ such as a kidney or a heart is clearly not storable and therefore there are severe restrictions over the kind of tests and examination of the organ that can be undertaken before it has to be used (or discarded, if unsuitable). But other tissues, such as corneas, are storable which means there is a long period of time over which they may be tested.

Cadaveric or living source: Living donors, blood donors for example, can be questioned and examined - and even kept in quarantine. But the chances of getting any intelligent answers from cadavers are really quite limited!

One of the issues raised by xenotransplantation is that it may give more opportunity to characterise the tissue before transplantation into the patients than allotransplantation does.

Over the past 40-50 years, there have been numerous transmissions of bacterial, viral and other kinds of infection through transplantation. Most of the bacterial transmissions that have occurred are alleged to taken place because the material was contaminated as it was removed from the body, but there was a case where tuberculosis was transmitted by removing a piece of rib from a TB patient for use in a bone transplant. I am not sure that this is done any more! But nonetheless, there are cases where bacteria do appear to have been transmitted, probably because of contamination during the removal process rather from bacteria growing in the individual. Other transmission examples include the transmission of HIV and Hepatitis by bone. Rabies has clearly been transmitted by cornea transplant. Creutzfeldt Jakob Disease, bacteria, fungus and hepatitis B can also be transmitted by cornea. Dura mater is one of the classic examples where Creutzfeldt Jakob Disease has been transmitted, where tissue taken from a cadaveric brain was transplanted into the recipient's brain. This was despite the fact that you can, in principle, sterilise dura mater (and heart valves, skin and so on). A lot of viruses can be transmitted via bone marrow, and because the patients are quite severely immunosuppressed as part of the transplantation process, it may be more significant and serious than it would be for other kinds of tissues.

For many years, I was a member of the Medical Research Council's Vaccine Development Committee, and one of the sub-committees that I was involved with was the Herpes Virus Committee. I have some data presented by a member of that Committee on a number of different transplantation procedures and the risk of transmitting cytomegalovirus (CMV), in a certain London hospital. The procedures involved were bone marrow allografts, renal allografts and liver allografts. CMV, under normal circumstances in a normal healthy human being, is probably not a big problem. However, when the patient is immunosuppressed, it becomes a big problem. Many patients having these transplantation procedures could die of CMV-type pneumonias and so on if it was transmitted.

There are a number of different scenarios possible. There could be a recipient, who is sero-negative for CMV, so they have no immune status against it and can become infected. You can have a donor who is either sero-negative for CMV, that is to say uninfected, or you can have a donor who is infected. There are four possible combinations in transplantation - negative donor/negative recipient, positive donor/negative recipient, negative donor /positive recipient and positive donor/positive recipient. The question then arises - what is the worst possible outlook for the recipient?

The evidence from renal allografts is that:

❖ **Negative donor/negative recipient** - there is no infection present and no disease results - as you would expect.

❖ **Positive donor/negative recipient** - I have data on 14 recipients in that position - 11 of those 14 developed infection, and 10 of those infections actually produced disease. I am not sure what the severity of the disease produced was, but this, clearly, is a very bad combination.

❖   **Negative donor/positive recipient** - there are still some signs of infection, presumably because of reactivation of the CMV which is already present.

❖   **Positive donor/positive recipient** - this results in a very high level of infection, roughly speaking, the same level of infection if your donor is positive and your recipient is negative - but most of that does not get expressed as disease.

CMV is a good example. It shows that there is an infectious agent which you can screen for in both the donor and recipient - but it doesn't necessarily follow that, because your donor is positive, you don't use the material from the donor. It is possible to treat CMV with ganciclovir and other anti-cytomegalovirus type treatments. Whether to use tissue infected with CMV is an ongoing argument. Having said that, in the context of xenotransplantation, I don't think you would want your donor to be positive for anything. Human results may not actually help you very much as regards the animal tissue and type results.

Department of Health guidance on the microbiological safety of human tissues and organs used in transplantation[93]

A Department of Health note about guidance on how to deal with the virological aspects of human to human transplantation was published recently. This concentrates on donor selection and is not really relevant to xenotransplantation. The idea, here, was to try to avoid using as donors groups at risk of having an infection, which could possibly be transmitted by blood, tissue or by solid organs. The main concerns were HIV, hepatitis C and hepatitis B. So, the groups to exclude are males who have had sex with another male or with prostitutes, sufferers from Creutzfeldt Jakob Disease and so on. The idea is that, as regards the safety of the transplantation, a great deal of what you do is to do with selecting the donor carefully and making sure that the donor is in reasonably good shape in terms of : "Are they in a risk group or non-risk group for having blood-borne type infections?"; "Are they in a risk group or a non-risk group as regards things like Creutzfeldt Jakob Disease, for example?". If the potential donor has died of a neurological disease, I think it would be wise not to use organs from that cadaver for transplantation. You have to bear in mind, of course, that the human population is not specific-pathogen free, neither are they in-bred, neither are they transgenic, so there is a limited amount of control over the donor population. Further, given the shortage of human tissue, you can't afford to throw too much away. These conditions would not apply to transgenic pigs bred in particular surroundings and in large numbers, specifically for transplantation purposes.

If the material comes from a living donor and is storable and, especially if you can sterilise and store it, there are a number of options for ensuring its safety. It is possible: to question the donor to determine with some certainty whether or not they are in a risk group; to test the donor at the time of donation

---

93   Committee on Microbiological Safety of Blood and Tissues for Transplant. (March 1996). Guidance on the microbiological safety of human tissues and organs used in transplantation. Department of Health, London.

for viral infections – if you know which viruses to look for, for example, HIV and hepatitis C and if there is a specific test; to test the donor some time after donation in case they were in an incubation period, when infection didn't show, at the time of the first tests. If the material, however, is from a cadaver, then the scope for tests is really quite small. They can't, for example, be re-tested 90 days later or questioned. However, it is possible to talk to the relatives of the donor, though this is not necessarily an easy thing to do and it may not elicit a full range of satisfactory information. In essence, if the transplant material comes from a cadaver, the advice is "do what you can".

Even if there is opportunity to test tissue, an appropriate test is needed. If you have a specific test for a specific virus, you can pick it up. If you don't, you can't. And even when particular markers of infection or particular infections are considered, it may not necessarily be easy or straightforward to actually apply these tests.

With an antibody test such as a hepatitis C or HIV, if the individual has been infected recently, then the immune response which they make to the infection won't be picked up –and the antibody test is going to be negative. This is why we go back and look at living donors 90 days after their first test – there is a chance that they may have sero-converted by then. So, even when you have a test and apply it properly, it may not be 100% accurate – and there is some evidence that some of the tests are not applied properly.

Viral antigen tests (eg for hepatitis B) are slightly better, as these are more directly linked to the virus infection itself – that is to say the virus produces the antigen and the test picks up the antigen. However, again, they are not necessarily very sensitive and they do not necessarily indicate infection; that is to say, the antigen may be present for other reasons, not necessarily because infectious virus is present in great amounts.

It is also possible to look for infectivity itself, if there is a suitable assay for it. This is something which is done a great deal in vaccine production and in the biotechnology industry. I don't think there are any really adequate rapid infectivity assays (although I could be wrong) for most of the kind of infections of concern in transplantation. Genome detection (PCR) is the flavour of the month. There may be, many ways of using that, provided the system is actually going to pick up the viruses that you think it's going to pick up. Again, it may be very specific – or it may not – but it could be a good way of actually looking at infectivity – but only if you know what you're looking for.

To summarise, the key feature of all of these tests is that you really only find what you're looking for.

The Department of Health guidance document also lists what the indications for specific tests actually are. I think it may be that this document is trying to cover too wide a range and it may be better to distinguish between solid organs and tissue. This may be a message for regulatory authorities in approaching xenotransplantation. It might be best to identify the particular target and the particular organs and tissues you're interested in. However, if you have a solid organ you test for everything:

including, hepatitis B surface antigen, HIV, hepatitis C, CMV antibody and Toxoplasma. For tissues, you wouldn't worry about CMV and Toxoplasma because, so far as we know, CMV is not a problem in, for example, blood donation, whereas it is a problem with tissue such as kidneys and bone marrow.

There is also a section in this particular document on what you do if you have, or suspect, bacterial/fungal infections in the organ for transplantation. From the regulatory background I come from, I think a bacterial fungal infection would rule out use of a biological product. But in transplantation where solid organs are in very short supply, you can't afford to do that. In one of the appendices to the Department of Health document, the following strategy is suggested: consider whether it is a serious bacterial infection; and whether it is known and can be treated; and if so, can it be treated with antibiotics before there is a problem. Finally, there is a section within the document which discusses Good Laboratory Practice. It's something of a shock to me to think you need to describe good laboratory practice - but that's just my particular cultural background I guess! So, for example, the document recommends that the origin of the donor material must be positively identified and any samples that go with it must be tested. There should be good operating theatre practice to remove the donor material in such a way that it doesn't become contaminated in the process. There should also be validated control test procedures for contamination, appropriately maintained test and storage equipment, validated storage and transport systems, competent staff and so on. I would also suggest that somebody should be out there monitoring to see that these procedures are being followed, with a degree of competence.

Clearly, most of the people who receive a transplant are in a life-threatening situation, so it is possible to argue that anything done may help their condition. Quality and safety aspects would very definitely take second place to the possibility of keeping somebody alive. Nonetheless, there are practices which could be introduced.

The guidelines I have been discussing are regarded as being fairly general and I think they provide an overall framework, within which more specific guidelines can be fitted. I know that the Blood Transfusion Service are developing guidelines along tissue banking lines which may be rather more detailed, and in the end, I think, these may possibly be more useful than the current guidelines. However, these guidelines are a very good start. There will inevitably be more developments in this particular area.

Summary

I'll summarise briefly with four points about how the human allotransplantation business is, to some extent, controlled in order to reduce the associated problems.

❖   Choose and screen your donor properly.

❖   Under certain circumstances, select your recipient and at least characterise your recipient from the point of view of infectious diseases. This is particularly important in the context of CMV and other persistent virus type infections.

❖   If you can, devise a method for treating the patient should something go wrong. This applies both to bacterial infections and to CMV, for which ganciclovir may be given prophylactically.

❖   Implement a Good Laboratory Practice approach and adhere to guidelines.

So, in short, choose your donor, choose your recipient, sort out a fall-back position and make sure that, if you make rules, people stick to them.

Comments on Dr Minor's talk

Prof John Salaman: I enjoyed listening to your talk. Clearly the transplant community is very concerned about transmission of infection, particularly CMV, and a lot of the things you mentioned are already done. All patients who enter the transplant programme have a batch screening, and these samples are kept for ever as far as I know. Virology laboratories also follow up patients.

Further comments were made and points raised on Dr Minor's talk, These have been incorporated into the summary on the general discussion (page 233).

Dr Tom Alexander: Xenotransplantation - infection risks

Dr Alexander is Deputy Head of the Department of Clinical Veterinary Medicine at the University of Cambridge. He is also an adviser to Imutran.

I have worked on pigs and pig diseases most of my life. It is with that background that I approached xenotransplantation when Imutran asked me if I would advise them on two matters:

1.   What are the risks of putting pig organs into human beings? What diseases might they transmit?

2.   How do we set up production operations which are free from the organisms we are worried about?

Of all the domesticated animal species, the pig seems to offer the best option as a xenotransplant donor. It is a prolific breeder; it grows quickly to sizes commensurate with the patients; it has similar physiology to human beings; and its organs have a similar structure, size and function. Pigs have also been the subject of immense study, including studies of their diseases and their biology.

High health status breeding techniques

The other advantage of using pigs is that there has been a demand over the years for the production of high health-status pigs. This has been both for genetic improvement and for research purposes. So, there are already some sophisticated techniques to produce pigs relatively free from pathogens.

The first is the **gnotobiotic technique** - a strict technique - by which you can produce near germ-free pigs. They become gnotobiotic pigs – you know what organisms are in them. It is not, however, easy to maintain these conditions. There are people who advocate that, if we go to xenotransplantation from pigs, the pigs should be reared as gnotobiotic animals. But I have to say that anyone who has worked with germ-free techniques in pigs will know that although this would not be impossible, it would be extremely difficult and very costly. It would also defeat its own purpose, that of producing sufficient organs for transplant to meet the current shortage, because use of these strict techniques would produce a few donor pigs at a high price for a limited number of patients.

A pig, when it is born, is about the size of a man's fists. Within four to five months, it is the size of a full-grown man. It grows extremely rapidly. It has been bred for meat, which is muscle, so it is very strong. The greatest desire in a pig's life is to eat itself to death. It spends all its time looking for things to eat, and when it is full it sleeps, and then it gets up to eat again. The pig's method of finding food is to root and for this it has a powerful neck and a tough nose. The pig is an extremely destructive animal - it roots and it bites, and it roots and it bites. So, an animal of around 100 kilos, composed almost entirely of muscle, that wants to root all the time, is difficult to contain in a gnotobiotic unit. We tried it! I could tell you stories about it - how we found a pig outside the isolator and sitting on the feedbag! So, I would not use gnotobiotic techniques, but I would attempt to come as close to those conditions as possible.

The next method is **primary SPF (specific pathogen free) techniques or secondary SPF techniques**. The initial stages of these are the same as the initial stages of producing gnotobiotic animals. However, when the animal grows to a certain size it is allowed to roam around a biosecure room. The advantage here is that if you are going to produce pigs to supply xenograft organs, then those pigs should be healthy. It would be extremely difficult to maintain a 100 kilo animal in robust health in gnotobiotic circumstances. However, if you keep them free in a biosecure room, well monitored and screened properly, then the pigs will be both close to gnotobiotic and robust and healthy.

There are also other methods; for example, **classical medicated early weaning**. Piglets, when born, are mostly microbiologically sterile and do not pick up many infections from their mother or many infections at all in the first few days of life. They do become infected with coliforms, clostridia, bacteroides, staphococci and so on which can be identified. However, they do not become infected with the worst diseases of pigs because they are protected by maternal antibodies. So, if they are removed from their mothers at about 5 days of age they are almost as good as SPF animals. This is being practised in many parts of the world and is a recognised, established, technique.

This technique can be modified - **modified medicated early weaning**. This produces almost as clean an animal microbiologically. You can modify this technique still further by not using medication or by varying the age of the early weaning (from 5 days to 10 days) - this technique is called **Isowean** or **segregated early weaning**. These techniques are being applied on a large scale, particularly in the United States and in Mexico.

Finally, there is the **vaginal catch** technique. I would not, however, use this technique but would concentrate on SPF medicated early weaning, segregated early weaning and modified medicated early weaning, using them sequentially.

Pathogens of concern

When I was asked by Imutran to advise them on the infections that might be present in pigs and be damaging to a patient, I thought it would be an easy task, listing all the viruses, bacteria, and parasites known to infect pigs. I would then identify which are likely to be damaging and which ones can be excluded from the pig. Following from this, I would design the methods of producing "safe" pigs. How naive I was! It was a very difficult job and I consulted at length many colleagues in Cambridge – some of them are present today. We formed a panel of experts which met several times and examined every single organism that I could think of that might be in the pig.

It is also important to remember that techniques to exclude pathogens are not perfect. For example, a number of potential **pathogens** infect foetuses **congenitally** and none of these techniques can be guaranteed to eliminate them. So-called "germ-free" pigs are no more likely to be free from these than pigs produced by the other techniques. Examples of pathogens passed congenitally to pigs are:

Viruses: circovirus, cytomegalovirus, parvovirus, porcine reproductive and respiratory virus, porcine retrovirus, some enteroviruses

Bacteria: Eperythrozoon suis, Leptospira bratislava

Leptospira bratislava is present in the fallopian tubes of the sow and so piglets are born already infected. Circovirus is a common virus though we know nothing - or very little about it. It is thought to be the cause of delayed myelination in piglets and infects them before they are born. I was interested in the discussion earlier about dealing with cytomegalovirus (CMV). I am not quite so confident about being able to exclude it, although I hope we can. These are the viruses we know about - I have no doubt there are others that we do not know about.

There are some viruses that are not known to infect pigs, but may be perceived to present a risk. Examples are Borna Disease virus, hantavirus (bunyavirus) and sendai virus (parainfluenzavirus). Borna Disease virus was seen in horses in Germany and was found in other animals. It was later also discovered to be present in human beings where it seemed to cause depression. Experimental work to try to infect pigs, did not succeed (this work has not been published) - that is the only information I have.

We do not know whether there are prions in pigs, but we think there are not. The next talk will expand upon this.

Bacteria

There are at least a thousand species of bacteria in any given pig, and probably many more than that. We know about a very small percentage of them because, in places like the gut, they are very fastidious anaerobes with very fastidious nutrient requirements – examples are methanogenic bacteria, cellulolytic bacteria, lipolytic bacteria. They have not been isolated and they do not have names. The only solace we can take from this is that I do not think that they would ever be pathogenic.

However, an eminent virologist I respect in Harvard holds the view that any organism in a potential xenograft donor must be regarded as a potential pathogen in an immunosuppressed patient. I do not agree with that because all the work that has been done on, for example, methanogenic bacteria, shows that they survive in a very small niche and that they cannot survive in any other environment.

I have included here bacteria that I felt might possibly cause trouble in immunosuppressed xenograft patients. Bacteria that are not present in pigs in the UK are listed separately. I do not think we should consider pathogens which do not occur in the UK. Most of the viruses that occur in other countries in pigs are under regulatory control and are notifiable diseases. If they ever came into the UK they would be stamped out. If you had a biosecure isolated donor-herd producing pigs you could be confident that these organisms would not be present. (See Tables 1 to 4)

TABLE 1:

**POTENTIALLY* PATHOGENIC GRAM NEGATIVE BACTERIA
THAT INFECT PIGS IN THE UK**

SPIROCHAETES

Leptospira
> bratislava
> muenchen
> canicola
> icterohaemorrhagiae
> others – rarely

Serpulina (Treponema)
> hyodysenteriae
> innocens
> unnamed spp.

Borrelia
> burgdorferi

PASTEURELLACEAE

Pasteurella
> multocida

Haemophilus
> parasuis

Actinobacillus
> pleuropneumoniae
> suis
> equuli

BACTEROIDACEAE

Bacteroides
> melaninogenicus
> fragilis
> other species

Fusobacterium
Necrophorum

**AEROBIC MOTILE HELICAL
BACTERIA**

Campylobactor
> coli
> hyointestinalis
> jejuni

Lawsonia
> intracellularis

AEROBIC RODS AND COCCI

Pseudomonas
> pyocyanea

Bordetella
> bronchiseptica

ENTEROBACTERIACCAR

Escherichia
> coli

Salmonella
> cholerae suis
> derby
> typhimurium
> enteritidis
> other serovars

Klebsiella
> pneumoniae

Yersinia
> enterocolitica
> pseudotuberculosis

Other coliforms

(* Potentially pathogenic to immunosuppressed patients)

TABLE 2:

**POTENTIALLY★ PATHOGENIC GRAM POSITIVE BACTERIA
THAT INFECT PIGS IN THE UK**

GRAM + COLLI	NON SPORING RODS
Staphylococcus	Listeria
hyicus	monocytogenes
others	Erysipelothrix
Streptococcus	rhusiopathiae
suis	Corynebacterium (Eubacterium)
equisimilis	suis
others	Actinomyces
	pyogenes
SPORE FORMING RODS	Nocardia
	species
Clostridium	Dermatophilus
chauvoei	congolensis
novyi A, B, C, D	Mycobacterium
septicum	avium/intracellulare
perfringens types A, C	
tetani	

(★ Potentially pathogenic to immunosuppressed patients)

TABLE 3:

**MISCELLANEOUS★ POTENTIALLY PATHOGENICV BACTERIA
THAT INFECT PIGS IN THE UK**

RICKETTSIAS AND CHLAMYDIAS	MYCOPLASMAS
Clamydia	Mycoplasma
psittaci	hyopneumoniae
Eperythrozoon	hyosynoviae
suis	hyorrhinis
	flocculare
	Ureoplasma

(★ Potentially pathogenic to immunosuppressed patients)

TABLE 4:

**POTENTIALLY★ PATHOGENIC BACTERIA NOT
PRESENT IN PIGS IN THE UK**

Leptospira	Brucella
pomona	suis
grippotyphosa	
	Streptococcus
Bacillus	Group E
anthracis	

(★ Potentially pathogenic to immunosuppressed patients)

We can also list the parasites (Table 5) and fungi (Table 6) of the pig. Again these lists concentrate on those parasites which are present in the UK. In general, fungi are incidental to pigs. There are some fungi in the alimentary tract but they are likely to be non-pathogenic.

TABLE 5:

**POTENTIALLY ★ PATHOGENIC PARASITES
THAT INFECT PIGS IN THE UK**

Toxoplasma gondi	Ascaris suum
Neospora	Metastrongylus spp.
Sarcocystis suihominis	Oesophagostamum app.
Cryptosporidium	Trichuris spp.
Giardia	Hyostgylus rubidus
Isospora suis	Trichostrongylus axei
Eimeria spp.	Toxocara canis
Balantidium coli	(Trichinelle)★★
	(Strongyloides)★★
	(Macrocanthorrynchus)★★
Sarcoptes scabei	
Demodex	Taenia hydatigena
Haematopinus suis	Echinococcus grandulosus

★★ very rare in the UK

(★ Potentially pathogenic to immunosuppressed patients)

TABLE 6:	
POTENTIALLY* PATHOGENIC FUNGI THAT INFECT PIGS IN THE UK	
Aspergillus spp.	Microsporum spp.
Candida spp.	Trichophyton spp.
(* Potentially pathogenic to immunosuppressed patients)	

Risk Identification

Once these pathogens have been identified, the panels of experts we had established looked at them from the point of eight questions:

1.   Does the organism generalise in the pig

    a)   early in the infection

    b)   transiently

    c)   throughout the infection, or

    d)   for long periods?

This is quite important because if it does not generalise, and you are removing an organ which the organism does not infect, whether it is in the pig does not matter so much.

2.   Whether or not the pig develops a carrier state; and,

3.   If so, which is/are the carrier organ/s.

4.   Whether or not the organism is a zoonosis or is known to multiply in human tissues.

5.   Whether it can be excluded from the donor herd, reliably or unreliably. Of course there is a gradation between reliably and unreliably

6.   Whether it can be excluded from an individual or a small group of donor pigs (relevant if you are rearing cohorts of pigs for use) reliably or unreliably.

7.   If the pigs are infected with this organism, can it be excluded from an organ reliably or unreliably.

For example, an organism might be present in the gut but not in the kidney.

8   What special precautions will have to be taken? What are we going to have to do to ensure that an organism is not going to be present? Are there any tests available, and what tests should be done?

We found, at the end of our work, that the majority of the organisms that we had listed could be ruled out; in that, we could make sure that they were not in a xenograft organ. We were left with a short list of ones that could not be ruled out (see Table 7).

TABLE 7:

ORGANISMS OF CONCERN IN THE UK

VIRUSES - that are known to infect pigs	**BACTERIA**
Porcine retrovirus	Lepospira bratislava & muenchen (kidney)
Porcine polyomavirus	Pseudomonas pyocyanea
Porcine parvovirus	Bordetella bronhiseptica (lungs)
Porcine congenital tremor virus (porcine circovirus)	Salmonella spp.
Porcine cytomegalovirus	Pasteurella multocida (lungs)
Porcine reproductive & repiratory syndrome (PRRS) virus	Actinobacillus pleuropneumoniae (lungs)
Influenza virus	Mycoplasma hyopneumoniae (lungs)
VIRUSES - that are not known to infect pigs	**PARASITES**
Borna disease virus	Toxoplasma
Hantavirus (Bunyavirus)	Neospora
Senai virus (Parainfluenzavirus 1)	Crytosporidium

This list includes real concerns and also reflects the perceptions of other people of the organisms that they might be worried about. My opposite number at Harvard includes in this list things like HIV, which is extraordinary, because it does not infect pigs, However, he thinks it is important because people will ask the question.

The bacteria of concern are listed although I think they are of very much less concern than viruses. The risk attached to bacteria depends on the organ you are transplanting; for example, Leptospira bratislava could be in the kidney and I do not think you would want to transplant a kidney which was infected by it. Again, if you were transplanting lungs you would have to be sure that, for example, Mycoplasma hypopneumoniae, was not present. With regard to parasites, I am quite happy about including Toxoplasma and Neospora but less happy about including Cryptospoidium.

Risk Assessment

Prof David Onions from Glasgow has been very helpful in this exercise and we have worked closely with him. He suggested that we carried out a risk assessment based on the Brenner system.

In doing a risk assessment with the aim of ruling out individual organisms, it is first important to identify the ones of particular concern. There are two components to risk:

a)   Risk to the individual patient from viruses, bacteria and parasites

The decision is easier in cases where there is a desperately ill patient and an organ that might have an infection.

b)   Risk to the environment – really only from viruses.

However, if you give an organism to a desperately ill patient and the organism mutates to become a human epidemic, then this is much more problematic.

Risk to the individual patient is further divided into two components – access to the patient and then damage. Access is further divided into access into the donor organ and then ability to replicate in the human tissue. It is possible to assign probabilities to all of these but these probabilities are very much guess work.

There are also different levels of damage – life threatening, serious disease, mild disease, mild damage to the organ and minimal pathogenicity.

The environmental risk assessment was quite difficult. There are three components:

a)   The individual – this is based on exactly the same as the damage risk to the individual patient;

b)   access to the environment; and

c)   damage to the environment.

With the organisms we knew a lot about, and about which we could answer all the questions posed by this method of risk assessment, it was comforting to find that the odds were very long against them ever doing any damage to patients.

The work was much more difficult when considering viruses and damage to the environment because it was really based on guess work. In the end, I lost faith in this method of trying to assess the risk to the environment. Further, with some diseases, it is not really possible to even attempt a risk assessment. For example, circoviruses were only discovered a year or two ago and are widespread in the pig population, but we know nothing about them. Therefore, a risk assessment is not possible because it is not possible to answer any of the questions that you want to put.

Another way of looking at risk assessment is to group the organisms into five different categories.

1.   Potential pathogens (mainly viruses) which pose the greatest threat or are likely to be of major public concern. These include zoonotic organisms; organisms that are not known themselves to be pathogenic to people, but belong to those groups of organisms which are associated with zoonotic disease, immunosuppressive associated disease, or degenerative disease; organisms that may be latent in the xenograft that may flare up and severely damage the organ that you have just transplanted; organisms that have been multiplying in a transplanted organ which may change and become adapted to grow in human tissues, and thus pose a new threat, not only to the recipient but to other people; and organisms about which so little is known, that it is not possible to make any judgment (there are a number of organisms in this category and these are what we are really worried about).

2.   The (porcine) pathogens about which most concern has been voiced, but on available evidence are judged to pose much less of a threat.

3.   Human organisms present in the patient which adapt to multiply in the xenograft organ, damaging or destroying it, and which the immunosuppressed patient's defence cannot tackle.

4.   Porcine organisms that are likely to pose no threat to xenograft patients – most of the organisms I have been talking about today.

5.   Organisms which cause problems in patients following human organ transplantation but which do not occur in pigs and so pose no additional risk following xenotransplantation from pigs.

The viruses in Class 1 are: porcine retrovirus, porcine polyomavirus, porcine parvovirus, porcine circovirus, porcine CMV, porcine reproductive and respiratory syndrome virus, influenza virus, borna disease virus.

Conclusion

I would like to conclude by putting this discussion into perspective – it is all too easy to be alarmed. There are estimated to be about 7,000 million pigs in the world at any given time. In many parts of the world humans have, for many years, lived and worked closely to them. Pigs have also been used for various drugs and tissues, such as insulin and corneas. These contacts, as far as I know, have not caused any major epidemic, except perhaps influenza.

Based on our analyses at Cambridge and elsewhere, we think that there are very few known organisms of serious concern. The critical question is whether there are many organisms that we don't know about.

Risks must be balanced against the known benefits - and the known benefits are large. They include the adequate availability of organs, tissues and cells to suit all needs; organs which are available at optimum pre-planned times; organs sourced from healthy microbiologically-monitored donors (not human donors, about whom little may be known).

However, there are some organisms about which we are ignorant. More research definitely needs to be directed towards xenografting. We know a lot about porcine organisms, but only about those organisms which cause damage to the pig, which are economically damaging for the farmer, or which are known zoonoses. We don't know anything about the organisms which don't damage the pig. Some of these are potential pathogens to immunosuppressed patients.

I would like to conclude by saying that I am a messenger today. My message is that Imutran have recognised the difficulties of our ignorance, particularly in relation to retroviruses, and they are sponsoring research into it. This research has already gone quite a long way although it hasn't been going for very long. We continue to be advised on this by Prof David Onions. The research has involved the development of porcine retroviral probes; a series of co-cultural experiments with human cells and porcine cells, and an analysis of primate tissues in which these transplants have been put.

Comments on Dr Alexander's presentation have been incorporated into the general discussion, reported on page 233.

Dr David Taylor: Prions

Dr Taylor is a microbiologist from the Institute for Animal Health in Edinburgh. He has worked on prions for some time and is particularly interested in prion inactivation.

Thank you very much for the invitation to speak here. I have attempted to make my talk as relevant as possible for this specialised audience.

Range of disease

The group of diseases I am going to discuss come under various nomenclatures, such as **transmissible degenerative** and **transmissible spongiform encephalopathies** (TSEs). The diseases which form the group include scrapie, which has been known to occur in sheep and goats for centuries. TSEs have also affected cows and various zoo species.

There is also a relatively rare disease which occurs in farmed mink (transmissible mink encephalopathy), which is putatively associated with feeding, but there is no direct evidence of this. There have only been a handful of outbreaks around the world. In elk and mule-deer in the United States there is also what they call chronic wasting disease – but, again, this is not terribly common. Another example, feline spongiform encephalopathy is almost entirely confined to domestic cats in the UK – this has only emerged since BSE was discovered in our cattle population and there is pretty strong evidence that it represents BSE in cats.

TSE diseases in the human population are the historic disease Kuru, which was confined to a tribal population of New Guinea and is now almost extinct, Creutzfelt Jakob Disease (CJD) and Gerstmann-Straussler-Scheinker Syndrome (GSS).

Additionally there are zoo species which we presume have been infected by BSE:

> **Ungulates:** Arabian oryx (1 case), scimitar-horned oryx (1), greater kudu (6), eland (5), gemsbok (1), ankole (1).

> **Felids:** puma (3), cheetah (4), ocelot (1).

These show pathological features of the diseases, but in only a very few cases have transmission studies taken place. A common feature of these diseases is the spongiform vascular change which occurs in the brain. However, this feature is not always present so these diseases *may* be termed transmissible degenerative rather than spongiform encephalopathies.

Transmission: the prion theory

In terms of the nature of the transmissible agents, the predominant theory developed in the early 1980s, is that the transmissible agent is the prion, a polymerised abnormal form of a normal host protein. If this modified protein gets into a naive host it acts as a template for the conversion of the naive PrP in the new host, into spongiform encephalopathy form.

These prions, now generically called scrapie-associated, can be seen under the microscope, for example in detergent extracts of brains of affected individuals. Brown staining evident around the circular cells is the abnormal form of this host PrP protein; there is also staining around the neurons in the brain. As the pathological process proceeds, and the protein builds up, it is quite common to find extra-cellular plaques of this protein. The chemical composition of the modified form of the PrP protein is the same as for the normal host protein. It is therefore thought that the change in structure involves some post-translation structural modification which enables it to build up and resist the normal biodegradation processes in the body.

The prion theory has one slight difficulty; scrapie is used as the example only because it has been studied the longest. At least 20 different strains of scrapie are known in mice, each with classical phenotypic characteristics - for example, the incubation period and the pattern of lesions and distribution in the brain. So, there is some difficulty in the protein-only model, in thinking that a modified protein could have that many different structural configurations. There are therefore number of individuals who still believe that there may be an informational molecule like a small nucleic acid although one has not, as yet, been identified.

Nature of the diseases: infectivity and transmissibility

The best understanding of the nature of these diseases has been through the use of laboratory animal models. Typically in these diseases there are long silent periods during which there is absolutely no clue that the individual is infected. In one mouse model it took up to 100 days (after injection with infected material) for any signs of disease to show in the brain of the animal and up to 280 days for clinical signs of disease to be evident. In other words, with the first deposition of abnormal PrP, and then with vacuolation starting at 150 days, there are long silent periods before any signs of disease are detectable. However, infectivity is building up over this period. There is an early stage not long after the infecting event, when tissues like spleen, lymph nodes and other particular tissues become infected, although the brain itself does not become infected for some time after either natural infection or an experimental challenge.

The infectivity titre has been measured in a whole variety of organs, in very well designed studies, in sheep, goats and cattle. Central nervous system tissue (that is, brain and spinal cord) has the highest infectivity titre; then the next category of infectivity is largely representative of the lymphoreticular system; then a miscellany of tissues - sciatic nerve, bone marrow, liver and lung, in which infectivity has been found. Tissues in which no trace of infectivity has been found include heart muscle, skeletal muscle and mammary gland (see Table 1).

Table 1:

TISSUES	Titre (mean ± SEM (M) samples)		Titre
	SCRAPIE SHEEP	SCRAPIE GOATS	BSE CATTLE
Category I			
Brain	5.6 ± 0.2 (51)	6.5 ± 0.2 (18)	5.3
Spinal cord	5.4 ± 0.3 (9)	6.1 ± 0.2 (6)	+ve
Category II			
Ileum	4.7 ± 0.1 (9)	4.6 ± 0.3 (3)	‹ 2.0
Lymph nodes	4.2 ± 0.1 (45)	4.8 ± 0.1 (3)	‹ 2.0
Proximal colon	4.5 ± 0.2 (9)	4.7 ± 0.2 (3)	‹ 2.0
Spleen	4.5 ± 0.3 (9)	4.5 ± 0.1 (3)	‹ 2.0
Tonsil	4.2 ± 0.4 (9)	5.1 ± 0.1 (3)	‹ 2.0
Category III			
Sciatic Nerve	3.1 ± 0.3 (9)	3.6 ± 0.3 (3)	‹ 2.0
Distal colon	‹ 2.7 ± 0.2 (9)	3.3 ± 0.5 (3)	‹ 2.0
Thymus	2.2 ± 0.2 (9)	‹ 2.3 ± 0.2 (3)	?.?
Bone Marrow	‹ 2.0 ± 0.1 (9)	‹ 2.0 (3)	‹ 2.0
Liver	‹ 2.0 ± 0.1 (9)	—	‹ 2.0
Lung	‹ 2.0 (9)	‹ 2.1 ± 0.1 (2)	‹ 2.0
Pancreas	‹ 2.1 ± 0.1 (9)	—	
Category IV			
Blood clot	‹ 1.0 (9)	‹ 1.0 (3)	‹ 1.0
Heart muscle	‹ 2.0 (9)	—	‹ 2.0
Kidney	‹ 2.0 (9)	‹ 2.0 (3)	‹ 2.0
Mammary gland	‹ 2.0 (7)	‹ 2.0 (3)	‹ 2.0
Milk	—	‹ 1.0 (3)	?.?
Serum	—	‹ 1.0 (3)	‹ 1.0
Skeletal muscle	‹ 2.0 (9)	‹ 2.0 (1)	‹ 2.0
Testis	‹ 2.0 (1)	—	‹ 2.0

With BSE, being a scrapie-like disease, it came as a very great surprise to us, when all these tissues were tested by bioassay, and mice were tested as the sheep and goats' tissues had been. There wasn't a trace of infectivity. The agent has also been found in retina, but all these major organs including lymphoreticular tissues have been totally negative. This is the work of Hugh Fraser at our unit - a very carefully conducted and well done study.

Implications for xenotransplantation

What is the relevance of these diseases to the xenografting situation?

(i)   Transmission

The crucial question is whether the **efficiency of transmission** can be reduced by **crossing a species barrier**. At the present moment we don't know. However, there are experiments underway at the Central Veterinary Laboratory at Weybridge which are looking at the effectiveness of transmission of BSE infectivity to calves compared with mice.

In terms of the human health risks from BSE, some reassurance was provided at the end of last year by data from John Collinge's laboratory at St Mary's (Collinge J *et al* (1995) Nature 378, 779). Normal laboratory mice, challenged with the brain from a CJD infected patient, produced no disease. However, when these mice were challenged with BSE, they produced disease. This was not a surprise as it was known that BSE brain did transmit to mice. The more interesting aspect is that transgenic mice (which have had their own PrP gene removed and replaced entirely with human PrP genes so that they express human PrP protein) did go down with disease when they were challenged with CJD agent (average incubation period: 196 days). However, when they were challenged with BSE, nothing had happened to the date of the report (268 days post-injection).

Unfortunately, as you all know, within the last couple of weeks the report from the CJD Surveillance Unit in Edinburgh has undermined this reassurance. Bob Will and his colleagues have described ten cases of CJD in a relatively young cohort, under the age of 42 (Will R G *et al* (1996) Lancet 347,921). The mean age of sporadic CJD development is usually about 57 years of age. Cases of CJD have occurred in relatively young people in the past, but not in this sudden high occurrence of ten cases within about 15 or 18 months. Furthermore, the cases share clinical features, and neurohistopathological features, which had not been previously described in sporadic CJD.

(ii)   Pigs

Pigs are being developed as a source animal for xenotransplantation. A natural spongiform encephalopathy has never been described in the pig. I would, however, add a slight caveat that the vast majority of pigs are killed at a relatively young age - and SE diseases are silent for long periods of time. Nevertheless, if there was a true spongiform encephalopathy of pigs, it would very probably have been picked up at some point previously.

However, in experiments conducted at Weybridge, pigs have been challenged with BSE agent and infection has resulted. In an oral challenge, ten piglets received a total of 4 kilos of BSE infected brain on three occasions, at one to two weekly intervals. This weight was calculated to be the equivalent of the meat and bonemeal (the vehicle for BSE infectivity into cattle) which could have been fed to these pigs over the same period. None of these animals developed the disease. However, in parenteral challenge, another 10 pigs were given 10% homogenates of infected brain - this is a fairly massive challenge - $^1/_2$ ml IC, 1-2mls intravenously and 8-9 mls IP. Seven of these pigs did go down with the disease and two died of early unrelated inter-current illness. Essentially this means that 7 out of 8 pigs went down in that study.

(iii)   **Analogies with allotransplantation**

There have been examples of iatrogenic transmission from human to human, through one case of corneal grafting and in a fairly significant number of cases involving dura mater grafts (23; 6 of which were in the UK). There are some known risk factors which one would use as exclusion criteria for transplant donors; that is, having had a prion disease, previous receipt of corneal or dura mater grafts, treatment with human pituitary derived growth hormone, gonadotrophin, and being a member of a family in which familial CJD has occurred. Most cases of classical CJD are sporadic and share no obvious patterns, but there is a small group which do have a familial distribution.

It was, and still is, unknown, whether the dura mater cases represented true infectivity in the dura mater or whether it was the consequence of advantitious contamination by brain tissue on removal. The question is slightly answered by Heino Diringer in Berlin, who showed in a hamster scrapie model, that dura mater does actually become intrinsically infected at a level of just 2 logs less than the level found in brain. Some of our own studies, just about to be published, have shown that the same is true for the dura mater of mice infected with scrapie agent. This titration table gives one a figure of about 10^6 ID so per gramme, which is about 2 logs lower than the level found in brain in this particular model (see Table 2 and Table 3).

TABLE 2:

UNCONVENTIONAL TRANSMISSIBLE AGENTS IN DURA MATER: SIGNIFICANCE FOR IATROGENIC CREUTZFELDT-JAKOB DISEASE

(DM Taylor and I. McConnell, Neuropathology and Applied Neurobiology 1996)

Dilution of dura mater	No. mice affected / no. mice injected	Mean incubation period in days (S.E.)
10^{-2}	12/12	214 (3)
10^{-3}	12/12	232 (6)
10^{-4}	10/12	284 (9)
10^{-5}	1/6	518

Mice injected intracerebrally with dura mater from scrapie–affected mice

Table 3:

TITRATION OF 263K (II) INFECTIVITY AGENT IN 10% BRAIN HOMOGENATE FOLLOWING EXPOSURE TO SODIUM HYDROXIDE: BIOASSAY IN LVG HAMSTERS

Group	Log dilution No. injected	No. infected/	Mean incubation period in days (SE)	Infectivity titre as ID $_{50}$/g
Saline/120 min	10^{-6}	10/10	112 (6)	
	10^{-7}	7/10	134 (19)	$\geq 10^{9.3}$
	10^{-8}	7/9	174 (48)	
1M/60 min	10^{-1}	3/4	139 (8)	
	10^{-2}	13/17	243 (38)	
	10^{-3}	6/17	293 (73)	$\leq 10^{3.8}$
	10^{-4}	2.20	198 (45)	
2M/120 min	10^{-1}	6/6	140 (16)	
	10^{-2}	22/23	182 (160)	$10^{4.2}$
	10^{-3}	11/23	185 (24)	
	10^{-4}	0/20		

During the manufacture of dura mater the manufacturers originally thought they had taken care of all microbiological concerns, by irradiating the materials. Unfortunately these types of unconventional agents are somewhat resistant to gamma irradiation. With hindsight, and recognising the potential for prion-type diseases, they have introduced in some cases, steps which involved the use of sodium hydroxide as a proposed method of inactivation. Unfortunately our own studies have shown that with the hamster scrapie agent, which can reach levels of about 10^9 ID so per gramme of tissue, was only reduced to about 10^4 by treatment with one molar hydroxide for an hour or 2 molar hydroxide for 2 hours. So there might still be a question mark about the manufacturing procedures which were introduced after the first emergence of iatrogenic cases.

(iv)   **Infectivity of human tissue**

There is some knowledge about infectivity in the non-cerebral tissues in CJD patients. Table 4 shows tissues with early reports of absence of infectivity in them, including heart, skeletal muscle and diaphragm. Table 5 shows the tissues reported to carry infectivity and includes brain, eye, spinal cord, and less obviously, the lung, kidney and liver. It is however important to remember that, with CJD studies, this table represents a composite of many small individual bits of work around the world, of varying quality. The information presented is not bang up-to-date, but it serves a purpose. It is important to note that, even with brain, only 74% of specimens actually transmitted infection to laboratory animals. I think that this is not an indication that the other 26% were improperly diagnosed but representative of the fact that going across the species barrier into rodents means that transmission does not always take place. This is our experience with scrapie going into mice. There are cases of sheep scrapie, where the symptoms are classical and the brain pathology is absolutely fine, and yet it does not transmit to rodents.

Table 4:	
HUMAN TISSUE NOT DEMONSTRATED TO CONTAIN CJD AGENT	
TISSUES	**No. STUDIED**
Peripheral nerve	1
Diaphragm	1
Heart	4
Skeletal muscle	2
Adrenal	3
Testes	1
Thyroid	1

Table 5:

HUMAN TISSUE CONTAINING CJD AGENT

TISSUE	No. OF SPECIMENS TESTED	PERCENTAGE OF SPECIMENS POSITIVE
Brain	329	74
Spinal cord	6	50
Eye	2	100
Lung	6	33
Lymph node	8	25
Kidney	23	17
Liver	28	11
Spleen	23	4

There has also been some recent debate in the medical literature about whether CJD infectivity could be present in blood. The balance of opinion in this debate is that experience with transfusion suggests that this is unlikely. Further, at an FDA meeting in January, Paul Brown, who is a renowned authority on CJD and these types of disease, reviewed the complete world literature and came to the conclusion that, on balance, the evidence seemed to suggest that CJD was not present in blood. There have been reports of infectivity being transmitted to rodents – but in some cases these have come from laboratories where there has historically been an acknowledged difficulty in their interpretation of the brain pathology of experimental animals; and in another case, from a laboratory whose other transmission claims have been shown by repeat studies elsewhere to have been incorrect.

However, as these composite results do represent rather sporadic efforts, rather than the concerted effort put into the scrapie and BSE situation to determine infected organs, interpretation of the literature has to be done in a rather guarded fashion.

Questions/comments on Dr Taylor's talk

Some of the comments and discussion on Dr Taylor's presentation have been incorporated into the general discussion, reported on pages 233 and following.

Q: **Prof Walport**: The number of cases of CJD transmission through dura mater graft seems high, given the low incidence of CJD itself – any explanation?

Dr Taylor: There are some doubts about the quality of the sourcing.

Q: **Dr Crumpton:** What is the possibility of transmitting a transmissible spongiform encephalopathy from primate to human?

Dr Taylor: Primates are known to be susceptible to successful experimental challenge with these types of agent.   Sporadic CJD is postulated to be, perhaps, the result of spontaneous somatic mutation in the PrP gene. There is therefore, theoretically, no reason why the primate PrP gene might not also spontaneously mutate. There is no reason to suspect that a spontaneous disease might not occasionally occur in primates. It is important to emphasise that these are rare diseases, affecting one in a million of the human population.

Q: **Dr Bangham:** Are pigs fed to pigs? Would we know about a pig prion or the transmittable agent if it were there?

Dr Taylor: They were until very recently. Part of the package of measures taken several weeks ago as a result of the human health concerns, was to ban meat and bonemeal from being fed to all farmed animal species. Up until that time, although it had been banned from use in cattle feed, pigs and poultry were the main recipients of meat and bonemeal feed.

On a point about the nature of the diseases in most species, they don't seem to pass horizontally or maternally in most species, except in sheep. This is thought to happen in sheep because the placenta is actually infected, and therefore has a potential for causing perinatal contact infection. I have to say that is theoretical. It is known that the placenta is infected, but the mode of transmission is somewhat theoretical.

Dr Christopher Preston: Herpesviruses

Dr Preston is a specialist in herpesviruses from the Medical Research Council Virology Unit in Glasgow

Herpesviruses are large complex DNA containing viruses and one of their important properties is the ability to establish latency. With herpesviruses you have "a friend for life"; after primary infection the virus is not eliminated from the body it remains latent and it can reactivate at various times through the lifetime of an individual to cause recurrent disease. One of the best ways of reactivating herpesviruses is to take a suspect organ and culture it in the laboratory - this can't be too dissimilar from explanting it into an immunosuppressed individual.

The range of herpesviruses

We classify herpesviruses into alpha, beta and gamma sub families. The **alpha herpesviruses** are latent in neurological tissues. In human form we recognise herpes simplex types 1 and 2 and varicella zoster virus. There are homologues of virtually all of the alpha herpesviruses probably in all animal species. In Old World Monkeys we recognise herpes B Virus and SA8 (a baboon virus). In the pig the homologue of herpes simplex viruses is confusingly called **pseudorabiesvirus**. This virus does not cause any major disease in the adult pig but it is deadly in piglets. Crucially, when it infects a related species such as cattle it then causes a very serious disease and probably sometimes death. So, in a related species pseudorabies is a problem. It can infect human cells in culture but I know of no reports of serious human infection with pseudorabiesvirus.

The worse case scenario for herpesviruses is exemplified by **B virus**. This is the monkey equivalent of Herpes Simplex Virus (HSV) and so its biology is very similar to that of HSV in humans. However, if humans are infected with B virus, the consequences are disastrous. There are 22 reported human fatalities, most of which have arisen from a bite by infected rhesus monkeys. Human to human transmission is possible – one victim managed to transfer the virus to his wife. The similarity of the reaction in monkeys to that in humans leads to the suggestion that B virus may be able to establish latency in humans. If this were the case, there is the possibility of introducing into the population a potentially deadly form of HSV. This would clearly be very undesirable. The similarity of B virus to HSV and the equivalence of the tissues in which it replicates and establishes latency leads us to worry that recombination with HSV could occur. Again, this would be an extremely undesirable outcome.

The **beta herpesviruses** include human **cytomegalovirus** (CMV), which causes problems in allotransplantation. These viruses are latent in blood cells so they present different problems. We know there is both a simian and a porcine CMV. Herpesviruses such as CMV cause problems in allotransplants due to the immunosuppression of the recipient.   The virus can be reactivated either from the recipient or from the donated organ to cause disease and rejection.

The **gamma herpesviruses** include Epstein-Barr Virus (in humans) and herpesvirus papio (in baboons). There are two groups of gamma herpesviruses, the B cell tropic group, which is exemplified by Epstein Barr virus, and the T-cell tropic group, which includes **herpesvirus saimiri** of New World Monkeys. Again, this virus is essentially harmless in its natural host but, if injected into a related animal, can very rapidly cause the death of that animal. Herpesvirus saimiri can also immortalise human T cells in culture. This emphasises potential problems from these viruses.

The hazards from herpesviruses

So, based on current knowledge, there are definable hazards from herpesviruses.

❖ *increased pathogenicity of a herpesvirus in a related host*. For this reason, when considering herpesviruses, pigs would seem to be a better source material than any monkeys.

❖ *reactivation of latent viruses*. This could be exacerbated by interactions with other infectious agents, either released from the recipient to reactivate viruses in the donated organ, or vice versa. These agents could be herpesviruses or other viruses. In turn, viruses other than herpesviruses could be reactivated by these mechanisms.

❖ the *immunosuppression* of any organ recipient will exacerbate these problems.

❖ There clearly are a great number of *unknown animal herpesviruses*. Three new human herpesviruses have been discovered in the last ten years and it is fully expected that more will be revealed in the next ten years. We know more about human herpesviruses than about any animal systems. There is a serious problem of the great unknown.

❖ *recombination*. Although the hazard of generating a new recombinant herpesvirus would clearly be considerable, there is only a small probability of this occurring. There are no reports of related herpesviruses recombining with each other, except when they are very closely related; for example, HSV1 and HSV2. When genes have been exchanged between herpesviruses by genetic manipulation, the normal outcome is to create a virus which is equally or less pathogenic than the starting material. It should be noted, however, that responsible virologists do not tend to do this type of experiment very frequently - again, there is an element of the unknown.

Summary and conclusion

I want to end with three comments.

One, I have put recombination as the least of the hazards in this list. In fact, if such an experiment was proposed to a biological safety committee, it would be regarded as somewhat risky and would require stringent containment – if indeed it were permitted at all. So, in a different context, even the lowest risk can be considered to be quite severe.

Two, although I believe that the hazard from the various potential problems of herpesviruses that I have gone through are severe, I do believe that the risk is difficult to identify. Even in the case of B virus infection, it is possible to think of ways in which a bad outcome, in population terms, could have arisen and it didn't. Perhaps the risks of adverse infections and reactivation of herpesviruses might not be as great as we might have supposed.

Finally, the use of pathogen-free animals would eliminate many, but not all, of the problems associated with herpesvirus infections. CMV can be transferred to the fetus in utero. It is possible to imagine a situation, even in pathogen-free animals, where a CMV infection could be maintained without our knowing about it.

Some questions and comments relating to Dr Preston's talk

Some comments on Dr Preston's presentation have been incorporated into the general discussion, reported on page 233 and following.

Q: **Prof Weber:** Which animals can be infected by pseudorabiesvirus? Can humans be infected?

Dr Preston: Dogs, sheep, mice and rats can be infected, but as far as I am aware humans cannot be infected – although in the coffee break this morning, I heard that there had been some odd reports of possible infection of humans with pseudorabies virus.

Q :   What was the route of transmission of **herpes B virus** in the man to wife case

Dr Preston: The wife was tending one of the victims and she had been infected with B virus. She didn't die as she was treated with a large dose of acyclivir. It is thought that you need definite transmission from skin abrasions in order to infect people with this virus. In one outbreak, casual contacts have been followed up and have not been found to be infected – so casual transmission hasn't been the problem.

Professor Robin Weiss: Retroviruses

Professor Weiss is from the Institute of Cancer Research, London

Over 20 years ago, I was invited to give some evidence before a committee similar to the Nuffield Council's Working Group on Xenotransplantation to discuss whether any experimental work should proceed on genetic manipulation. I was asked to discuss what is different about genetic manipulation from our usual exposure to DNA and to develop the idea that organ transplants take their DNA with them. Just because DNA is wrapped up in chromatin and the cells of nuclein doesn't mean it isn't there. This led on to discussion about retroviruses. A little over 20 years later, there are some more sensitive probes for retroviruses, but our knowledge and concerns about trans-species transmission are much the same as they were in the mid 1970s. What's new is that human xenotransplantation is now being actively discussed as a possibility.

We tend to think about retroviruses as "nasties". HIV, which is a retrovirus, gives us AIDS. HTLV1 can cause both a form of leukaemia and neurological disease. However, to medical researchers, retroviruses have also been a great boon. The whole concept of oncogenes came out of retrovirus research before we discovered them in the human genome. The enzyme reverse transcriptase that allows retroviruses to replicate is widely used both in experimental labs and in biotechnology - we wouldn't have cDNA if we didn't have reverse transcriptase. Of course retroviruses are also convenient gene vectors, which are used in almost every molecular cell biology lab as experimental vectors in culture, and also in about 50% of the human gene therapy trials underway. So they are not only pathogens. Incidentally a lot of our own DNA is retroviruses too. During evolution we have acquired retroviral genomes and passed them on in the germ line from one generation to another.

They are called retroviruses because they go backwards in biological information flow. Once the virus particle gets into a cell its RNA genome is turned into a DNA provirus by the enzyme reverse transcriptase. This is unusual, although it is not unique to retroviruses. The DNA provirus becomes inserted into chromosomal DNA. In that sense, as with herpesviruses, once it's there, it's there for life. Not only is it there for life but it is in our own chromosomal DNA. That is a cause for worry, because if it inserts in the wrong place, it might activate adjacent proto-oncogenes or disrupt an essential gene. It's also getting a "free ride", in that when the cell divides, and the daughter cells will also inherit a copy of that viral genome.

The main types of retroviruses

There are three main sub families of retroviruses, all of which replicate in roughly the same way.

❖ **Oncoviruses** include those which cause cancer and other diseases such as autoimmune disease, AIDS-like diseases, or they may cause no disease at all. C-type oncoviruses, related to leukaemia viruses, occur in baboons (and also in pigs) and will infect human cells in culture. D-type retroviruses, common in macaques, are exogenous infectious virus that cause severe immunodeficiency.

❖ **Spumaviruses** (Foamy viruses) are very common in apes and in Old World monkeys, including baboons. They also occur in cats. I don't think anyone's looked for them in pigs. They are not known to be pathogenic in their natural host or in others. We do know that there are some genuine human infections with foamy viruses that have recently come to light. These are zoonoses from Old World primates. There is evidence that some monkey handlers have become infected. So we are susceptible to infection. However, none of these people have become ill yet. It will be important that these individuals to be followed up long term.

❖ **Lentiviruses** include HIV. Where did HIV come from? It's quite clear in my mind that HIV-2, which is endemic in West Africa and has become epidemic in India, is very closely related to a naturally occurring simian immunodeficiency virus (SIV) of the sooty Mangabey, but the monkeys seem to remain well. Contrary to the Nuffield report, I don't think it is yet clear where HIV-1 came from. It probably is a zoonosis and it probably came from a primate, possibly from chimpanzees because there are two isolates of HIV-1-like viruses from chimps. But, we are not absolutely sure which way round the virus was transmitted, from chimpanzee to human or human to chimpanzee. However, it is reasonable to assume that HIV-1, which is responsible for the major wide world pandemic of AIDS, started as a zoonosis, recently transferred across from some animal host or other, and then became a human to human epidemic.

The transmission of retroviruses

Retroviruses can be transmitted horizontally (from adult to adult or from adult to child); vertically, as a congenital infection, or vertically, by genetic transmission. In molecular terms, genetic transmission is a different phenomenon. In this case, the integrated DNA provirus in the chromosomes can be inherited from one generation to the next as a set of mendelian genes. This could go on for millions of years – and has done. We know that this has happened in chickens, mice and cats. The pig's C-type retrovirus is also inherited genetically. When we know more accurately how many endogenous genomes there are in pigs, it might be possible to breed "knock-out" pigs which lack these viruses. However more work is needed. Domestic pigs have a polyphyletic origin – pigs originally domesticated in China are not from exactly the same origin as pigs domesticated in Europe.

What virus transmission has occurred in the past? Baboons have genetically transmitted retroviruses going from one generation to the other and these viruses have jumped species, to cats for instance. In the case of retroviruses, I think the more closely species are related, the less likely the virus is to jump, which appears to contradict the Nuffield Report in this particular case. Baboons themselves are not susceptible to their own virus and trying to infect cells of a closely related species, for example the gelada, doesn't work. However, it is possible to infect cats and humans. This is because this class of genetically transmitted retroviruses are xenotropic. The retroviruses are inherited as a set of genes from one generation to the next in one host. It can become activated as an infectious, complete replicating virus, but it will only replicate in other hosts. Generally speaking, this is done experimentally or done with cells and culture. But historically, at some time, a virus very closely related to that of baboon species was transmitted to cats; that is, from an Old World primate into an unrelated carnivore. We know this got into cats after the divergence of cat species (Felis catus) into the spotted and tabby species of cats. The virus somehow transferred from baboons into the germ line of the cats. So, that is an example of one germ line adopting a virus from another germ line. We imagine that it has got across through an infectious event; for example, cats scavenging placentae of baboons, which carry millions of retrovirus particles.

The human placenta also expresses retrovirus particles – so maybe it doesn't matter because they are there already. In one case, humans have preserved an open reading frame for the envelope of a retrovirus all the way through primate evolution. Therefore, it is reasonable to assume that this viral protein plays a functional role in the primate placenta.

So, do we know, in an experimental transplantation situation, whether these endogenous viruses can transfer to the xenotransplanted tissue? The answer is yes – there is plenty of evidence for this. Human cancer xenografts in immunodeficient mice pick up a xenotropic replicating retrovirus from the host mouse by the time they have been serially passaged through three mice. That means that a xenograft can pick up a virus in the host. The question that is posed to us today is the converse, can the xenograft donate a virus to the host? I don't see why it shouldn't go either way around when you have this intimate relationship of living tissues derived from two different species. In the case cited, a mouse virus very easily transfers into human tissue – and rodents are not closely related to humans. In fact, most medical researchers who grow cell lines that have ever been passaged as xenografts probably have retroviruses in them. However, unless you are working in a retrovirus lab and assay for them, ignorance is bliss. Furthermore, lots of mouse hydridomas secreting monoclonal antibodies are also providing these viruses, including xenotropic viruses that can infect human cells. That has been known for some time, so care is taken if monoclonal antibodies are used for clinical use to clean them up.

Can a virus that is transmitted genetically in one species transfer to another one to cause a disease epidemic? This may have happened with the C-type retrovirus which causes acute myoloid leukaemia in gibbons and apes. Again, we have known about this for about 20 years. This virus will travel from gibbon to gibbon and they will develop an incurable acute leukaemia. This virus is closely related to an inherited virus in the genome of a species of mouse that lives in South East Asia, where the gibbons live. They are in the same geographical area but not in the same ecological niche as the gibbons live in the forest canopy about 50 meters above the mice. The virus probably transferred from the mouse to the gibbon, in artificial conditions when these gibbons were caught for medical research and were kept in compounds. We are not aware that gibbons in the wild have this virus, but it is known as the gibbon ape leukaemia virus.

Why can this virus become epidemic and disease causing in gibbons when it is apparently kept under strict control in the mice? I think that the animal hosts which find they have retroviral genomes as Mendelian genomes or traits, go to some lengths to keep that virus under control. In the case of this particular virus, we think we have the answer - that it is to do with receptors. If the inherited virus is activated in mouse cells, it cannot enter neighbouring mouse cells, but it can infect gibbon or human cells.

Thus, I would be suspicious of the non-pathogenic, inherited retroviruses in species like pigs. I don't want to be a scaremonger, but the question as to whether we could get an epidemic starting from individual rare events such as xenotransplanted patients has to be raised and thought through.

Retroviruses and complement activation

It has been said, again since the late 1970s, that we humans are protected from animal retroviruses because human complement destroys them. We have readdressed this question and have come up with some answers that were not quite the same as the conventional wisdom. The dogma was that the envelope of the retrovirus will bind the C1Q component of complement and trigger the classical pathway and indeed it does. But, this is supposed to happen in the absence of antibody. Many animal retroviruses, for example, mouse viruses, are destroyed when treated with human complement. What we found was that if you transfer the retrovirus for a single passage of propagation into human cells they become much more resistant to human complement. It now turns out that the sensitivity of retroviruses to human complement is largely an antibody mediated phenomenon, just like classical complement reactions. That has come from studies of xenotransplantation. Old world primates, including humans, are genetic "knock-outs" for an α (1-3) galactose sugar epitope. This means that we don't put this α-gal group on our carbohydrate branches of glycoproteins and glycolipids. All humans make antibodies, naturally occurring, heterophile antibodies, to this carbohydrate group. However, other non-primate species including pigs and mice, have this enzyme. When you grow retrovirus in those cells they include this carbohydrate group. Since we all have antibodies to it, the antibody binds to the virus envelope and the complement destroys the virus. This is exactly the same mechanism as the hyper-acute rejection of endothelial cells in, for example, transplants from the pig into the baboon. We proposed therefore, that instead of putting human genes into pigs that down-regulate complement reactions, it would be better to knock out the gene encoding the enzyme for the α-gal epitope. I am sure the companies involved in xenotransplantation will do it both ways round. It is curious how studying complement sensitivity retroviruses has joined forces with the field of xenotransplantation, just when we were beginning to worry about retroviruses.

Recombination of retroviruses

Related but distinct retroviral genomes can undergo genetic recombination. But I am not sure that I am more worried about recombination between retroviruses, which can certainly occur, than about retroviruses transferring across species. We should certainly look out for it but I think retroviruses that haven't recombined are a sufficient cause for concern and should be monitored and eliminated where possible.

Questions relating to Professor Weiss's talk

Some comments on Professor Weiss's presentation have been incorporated into the general discussion, reported on page 233 and following.

Q:	**Dr Minor:** What pig retroviruses are there?
Prof Weiss:	I understand that at least two laboratories have sequenced them, but the work is not published yet and some of it is tied up with companies so it is not public. Currently, there is more private knowledge than public knowledge. The ones we know about are C-type retroviruses that are related to the mouse and cat leukaemia family. They are frequently released by porcine cell lines in culture but not by fresh porcine tissue. We have observed that one porcine retrovirus infects certain human cells in culture, but this is a one off result and bearing in mind how many false positive results you can get in virus labs, it really does need analysing a bit further. Suffice it to say that I would not be confident that some of these pig retroviruses cannot infect human cells.
Q:	Do you get pig leukaemias?
Prof Weiss:	There is no porcine retroviral leukaemia I am aware of (Answer confirmed also by Dr Alexander).
Q:	**Dr Waldmann:** I tried to follow your argument about the complement restriction factors. The implication is that if natural immunity or natural protection to retroviruses from pig were due to antibodies against α (1-3 -gal epitope), if you remove the complement restriction factors then these viruses will no longer be eliminated so you might then increase the chance of infection.
Prof Weiss:	That's a very good point, yes. That's one step further than I was trying to say. It's perfectly true, maybe leaving them there would make it much more likely that any viruses that leaked out would get zapped before they could get into human cells. But let's consider, if one or two virus particles, with cells in close contact, managed to get across into the human cell, they would replicate to produce the same genetic envelope

but without this particular glycosylation modification and could then re-infect through human cells. The likelihood of that happening in a xenotransplant is quite high.

Q: **Dr Grey**: You say that if you grow human cells in tissue culture, you will see a large number of these viruses potentially being produced. For years, people have been culturing human cells in other animal products. So we have had systems which have been producing potentially disastrous levels of virus around humans for years. This is doing exactly what you are saying – taking animal products containing viruses and putting them through human cell systems.

Prof Weiss: Yes we have. A number of serially passaged human cell lines have become productively and persistently infected with animal retroviruses – interestingly not of bovine sources as far as we know – so calf serum has not apparently been a source of contamination. But there are monkey viruses floating around in human cell lines, and there are any number of papers that announced the discovery of a new human retrovirus that turned out to have an animal origin. So far there have been no problems of transmitted diseases from retroviruses that you can see have come to humans from very distant species.

Q: **Dr Grey:** The scientists or technicians working in labs with these might have been open to infection?

Prof Weiss: People of my generation have clearly been exposed. Nowadays we treat our cells as well as ourselves with more care and create better safety barriers in laboratories. I think it is true that there could have been some disaster, but it has not happened that way. I think that's a positive point to bring up. One can write these big disaster scenarios but in fact there have been a lot of opportunities for these viruses to come up and they haven't. However, handling animal retroviruses in the laboratory is not as intimate as actually growing organs or cells of one species inside another.

Q: **Prof Griffin:** You seem to be raising really quite serious question marks about porcine retroviruses that do need answering. Is primer technology sufficiently advanced to provide a specific diagnostic technique and probability of a given kidney having a retrovirus in? Would it be possible to biopsy donor kidneys before transplantation to see if the retrovirus was present?

Prof Weiss: If you had a known retrovirus which was exogenous and of infectious origin then with appropriate PCR primers, you could take a small biopsy and have a pretty good idea whether the kidney was clean or not, unless there was focal growth in some other part of the kidney. The C type viruses of pigs that we are talking about at the moment are genetically transmitted so they are represented in the genome of every pig cell. It is very easy to make primers for those and we have them. Then, of course, the tissue will be positive every time, if it is coming from the same species or strain of pig. If we are worried about genetically transmitted xenotropic viruses we would have to breed them out of the pigs used for xenotransplantation.

Further Reading:

R.A. Weiss. (1976) Why cell biologists should be aware of genetically transmitted viruses. Nat. Cancer Inst. Monoq. 48, 183-189.

Weiss RA, Teich NM, Varmus HE, Coffin J (Eds) (1985). 'RNA Tumor Viruses'. Cold Spring Harbor Laboratory Press, New York, 2 volumes, pp 1396 & 1233.

Takeuchi Y, Porter CD, Strahan KM, Preece AF, Gustafsson K, Cosset F-L, Weiss RA & Collins MKL. (1996). Sensitisation of cells and retroviruses to human serum by alpha (1-3) galactosyltransferase. Nature 379; 85-88.

REPORT ON GENERAL DISCUSSION

Unlike the rest of the report, this section does not repeat more or less verbatim the discussion at the Workshop, but organises the discussion thematically. Most of this section is drawn from the discussion session which took place in the afternoon of the Workshop; however, earlier discussion, which did not directly relate to the presentations it followed, is also recorded here. Contributions are attributed. This should not be taken to mean that those who are not mentioned did not participate in the day. Often points were repeated, or were made in different ways, and these may be recorded once only.

There were several themes to the discussion:

❖ the potential efficacy of the procedure: related to the physiology and immunology of xenotransplantation;

❖ specific information about parasites, bacteria and viruses and the current ability to detect and identify these reliably;

❖ discussion about the overall risk or concern about the procedure and the relevance of certain analogies and experience;

❖ the controls which could be instituted; and

❖ further work which should be done.

The physiology and immunology of xenotransplantation

There was general recognition that the risks attached to potential infection had to be balanced against the potential benefits of xenotransplantation.

"If you come to the conclusion that you are going to cross the barrier to get most of the information [about infection], then you want to have a strong sense that xenotransplantation has significant benefit as a procedure." (Prof Waldmann).

Various concerns were expressed during the day about whether there was yet sufficient evidence on the physiology and immunology of xenotransplantation to be able to say there was likely to be benefit from the procedure.

On immunological rejection, although there was some evidence relating to hyperacute rejection, there were likely to be further problems associated with, for example, chronic rejection (Prof Waldmann). Questions also remained about the amount of immunosuppression which would be required for xenotransplant recipients, and whether this would be stronger or weaker than that currently required in allotransplantation. There was general agreement that, in the short term at least, more immunosuppression would probably be required. This was important as any immunosuppression would be likely to amplify any infectious agent which was present (Prof Simpson). Other methods of overcoming hyper–acute rejection (such as tolerance induction) may eventually become available. These would be preferable, as they would avoid the problems of long term immunosuppression. However they were unlikely to be available for some time (Dr Gray).

Questions were also raised about the function of the recipient's immune system once the organ or tissue had been transplanted. The ability of the organ/tissue to fight any infection within it is dependent on the recipient's immune system. For the immune system to function in the transplant, the white cells from the recipient must be able to bind to, and cross, the endothelium and be functional in the transplanted tissue or organ (Prof Griffin). The ability of the human recipient to recognise infection in pig transplants was also thought to be a problem. This may not be a problem for bacteria, which are recognised by polymorphs, macrophages and antibodies. However, viruses require a T cell response and porcine MHC molecules may not be able to trigger this, which will leave the porcine tissue/organ open to infection (Prof Simpson). However, many fully HLA mismatched, organs have been transplanted over the past three decades without evidence of fulminant infection of the graft (Prof Fabre). This could be because allo-restricted T cells have some ability, albeit limited, to see foreign peptides (Prof Simpson).

Questions of organ and tissue function were also raised. It was thought that, due to the physiological differences (and the fact that there is not such a large shortage of livers) that livers were unlikely to be transplanted from pigs (Prof Fabre). The use of kidneys was more likely but, again, not without problems. For example, there was as yet no data to show whether pig kidneys will be able to filter the concentration of uric acid in human circulation (Prof Walport) or whether a pig kidney would produce soluble factors (such as erythropoietin). Also, these might be antigenically different to human counterparts and which may therefore trigger a response from the human system (Dr Schild). However, it was thought there was evidence, from experience of islet transplantation in mice, that such tissues can function correctly. If the immune reaction to the transplanted organ or tissue is controlled, then the immune reaction to the products of the organ/tissue is also controlled (Dr Gray).

Pathogens of concern: Viruses

The presentations on viruses focused on herpesviruses and retroviruses and consequently so did the discussion. One question focused attention on the presence of herpesviruses and retroviruses in pigs and in primates. Prof Weiss confirmed that there were retroviruses in pigs, which were *probably* endogenous. There is no veterinary evidence to suggest that any retroviruses are causing disease in pigs, which suggests that there may be no exogenous viruses (in sheep, an exogenous virus which causes severe disease is closely related to an endogenous virus which does not cause disease). The pig C-type retrovirus which has been identified is equivalent to human HTLV1, which is difficult to identify, and requires life-time follow up. However, there is no published evidence yet to suggest that the pig C-type retrovirus can infect human cells. Prof Weiss reported that the baboons' most common endogenous retrovirus does infect human cells in culture, that D-type retroviruses and foamy viruses in baboons or other monkeys will also infect human cells in culture, and that foamy viruses of other primates besides baboons have transferred into animal handlers. However, Professor Weiss did not think it was appropriate to assess relative risks of viruses from pigs or primates, but recommended a "case-by-case" approach – the animals or tissue should be tested for all identified viruses. He also felt that the potential for onward transmission from the initial tissue recipient was important.

Dr Preston reported that, on the basis of current knowledge, it appeared that herpesviruses posed a greater problem in closely related species than in distantly related species; that is, in terms of the transplantation of tissue into humans, primates are likely to present greater problems than pigs. Dr Field pointed out that although animal herpesviruses have transferred to different species and caused severe disease, the virus did not - either in experimental or natural conditions - transmit naturally in the new species. Dr Preston responded that this was generally so, but if herpesviruses can jump the species barrier they tend to cause disease, and if they are transmitted, they are ineradicable from the individual.

The potential for initial transmission from an animal to a human transplanted recipient could be increased by the particular circumstances contemplated in xenotransplantation. Xenotransplantation proposes the transplant of organs/tissue, which are potentially chronically infected or which carry proviral genomes. The transplantation process breaks the normal barriers to infection and, if the transplant recipient survives for some time, the organs/tissue have a good opportunity, over an extended period of time, to infect the recipient (Dr Minor).

The herpesvirus cytomegalovirus (CMV) excited a substantial amount of comment. It was thought desirable that CMV should be excluded from the source pigs (Dr Minor). Dr Alexander thought that this would be difficult as CMV is very common in British pig herds. This was particularly problematic as it was not possible to say that pig CMV could not be transmissible to human cells (Dr Preston). As far as was known, co-culture experiments had not been carried out to determine this.

The workshop was reminded that other viruses might also be a problem, perhaps particularly those which did not cause disease in the pig (Dr Skehel). For example, pseudorabies virus (commonly known as Aujeszky's virus in pigs) had been mentioned during Dr Preston's presentation, although this disease was not present in pigs in the UK (Dr Alexander). Porcine circovirus could prove to cause problems as it had only recently been identified (Dr Alexander).

Human viruses might also infect the transplanted pig tissue (particularly as it would be modified to contain human genes) and so act to destroy it (Dr Tyrrell).

Pathogens of concern: Identification

During the presentations and discussion, a number of pathogens had been identified as being potentially problematic and it was recognised that there could be a number of pathogens which had not yet been identified. Could the known pathogens be detected and reliably detected and identified in the source herd, animal or tissue before any potential transplant took place; and how could novel, potentially pathogenic, organisms be identified?

Bacteria and parasites were also raised in discussion. There was general agreement that they would be easier to identify than viruses. It was suggested that, in terms of parasites, xenotransplantation was potentially safer than allotransplantation. Most parasites were identified in the pig and it was possible to block most of the routes of infection. Immunosuppression of human recipients of a xenotransplant could have two effects; (i) the outbreak of parasitic infection already present in the human and (ii) multiplication of parasites introduced from the source animal (pig). A good example is infection with Toxoplasma where both humans and pigs are infected but control the infection. In the case of introduction of Toxoplasma from the pig, a source of infection (cat faeces) could be readily controlled so that "Toxoplasma free" pigs could be reared. Thus, the main concern may be the human parasitic infections as immunosuppression could readily lead to outbreaks of disease (Prof Tait). Prof Griffin confirmed that it was easy to screen for known intra-cellular parasites, such as toxoplasma and mycobacteria.

On bacteria, Prof Weiss said that it would be feasible to identify bacterial infections using a generic PCR (polymerase chain reaction) amplification approach for ribosomal genes. This had been carried out over the past two years with soil samples and swabs from the human mouth. However, this work has shown that around 90% of the sequences identified come from species of bacteria that have never been described before – only around 10% of bacteria have been catalogued. Prof Griffin said that, from a clinical point of view, bacteria were unlikely to pose a great problem, as the infections could be diagnosed easily and good agents existed to treat them. Dr Farrington agreed, but emphasised that the process of management of the potential problem was very important and must take each stage in the production process into account, including animal husbandry and tissue removal. The implications of bacterial infection would affect only the graft recipient and not the wider population. Dr Crumpton suggested that, although good antibiotics existed, it might not be sensible to use them in the source animals. Antibiotics act to suppress infection rather than eliminate it. It may be better to allow any infection to be expressed so that it could be identified, and to eliminate the infected animal as a source for xenotransplantation, if that is necessary.

The situation was more difficult with viruses. New PCR techniques had been developed by the genome project to look for new genomes present in the DNA. This meant that DNA of, for example, transplanted tissue could be examined for the presence of proviral responses. In fact, HHV8 was identified in this way using RDA (Random Display Amplification) (Dr Stoye). However, RDA was not a sensitive technique and fairly high virus loads were required for it to be useful (Dr Schulz). Further, negative results using RDA did not mean that no virus was present (Prof Weiss). Viruses also caused particular difficulties as there were no generic PCR primers available. It might be possible to identify a proportion of herpesviruses and retroviruses, but this would mean using many different sets of primers specific to many different families of viruses – including unknown virus families or virus families in which the viruses differ quite widely. PCR may therefore not be practicable for identification of all viruses (Prof Weiss).

For a known exogenous retrovirus, identifiable by tissue culture or PCR, it would be possible to take a small biopsy from the tissue to be transplanted and test for the virus. This should be accurate unless the virus was only present in selected parts of the tissue. The porcine C-type retroviruses under exploration are thought to be genetically transmitted and if so would therefore be represented in the genome of each pig cell. It would be easy to make primers for those – but if the same strain of pig were being tested, the tissue would be positive each time. A characterisation of a method to deal with unidentified viruses, was to "approach it non-specifically and keep your fingers crossed". But the paradox was that you "can only find what you look for and clearly you can only look for what you know" (Dr Minor).

These problems have been seen in the history of human transplantation and blood transfusion. Some important viruses eg hepatitis B and C have only been identified through experience of blood transfusion. Even in humans, where most investigation has been done, new agents were still being identified when transplantation took place (Prof Minson).

Discussion of overall risk

It proved difficult throughout the day to reach an assessment of the overall risk of transmitting infectious disease associated with xenotransplantation. The risk assessment presented by Dr Alexander was considered to be problematic. Quantitative methods had attractions for their precision but were not easily applied to microbiological risks. Such systems had not been designed for this use and were therefore meaningless (Dr Kinderlerer) and the detailed information which would be needed to use such systems was not available (Dr Crumpton). Dr Tyrrell reported that the Advisory Committee on Dangerous Pathogens had, under his chairmanship, tried to establish quantitative methods for microbiological risk assessment but this had not proved possible. Dr Crumpton, the current chairman of the Committee reinforced this view, saying that recently the ACDP had reviewed this again and had prepared a report on microbiological risk assessment. He noted that quantitation could also be misleading as numerical data implied precision and authority. The alternative to numerical assessment was characterised as the use of "experience, perception, insight, analogy" and, from these, deriving a "gut feeling" (Drs Crumpton and Tyrrell).

Some distinctions were important. It was possible to distinguish between risks to the transplant recipient and risks to others (the recipients contacts and potentially the wider population). It was the latter which caused most concern (Prof Waldmann) although it was important to recognise that hazard (how intrinsically dangerous the infection is) is separate from risk (how likely that hazard is to materialise). There was general agreement that there was a "very, very low probability" of a severe disease being spread rapidly through the population. but it was important to emphasise that this conclusion is speculative and not known with certainty.

If the risk to the public health was low, as agreed, then the key question could be said to be whether it was acceptable to take this risk (Dr Crumpton). There was, not surprisingly, a variety of views on this. Those who believed that it was acceptable to "move to the human experiment", with appropriate controls, drew analogies with allotransplantation, where controls on tissue (particularly, organ) safety were limited and all known viruses were not tested for. It was also recognised that some infections (opportunistic and transmitted) which arose could be treated (Prof Griffin). In some respects (for known pathogens) xenotransplantation might, in fact, be safer than allotransplantation as the breeding process and planned nature of the procedure enabled more testing to take place (Prof Beringer). Questions were raised on the dangers attached to unknown pathogens. All pathogens had the potential to change and become harmful in different circumstances (Dr Caraday).

If xenotransplantation were to be attempted, appropriate controls were essential, partly as insurance against the risk assessment being wrong (Dr Minor). However, the assessment of the public health risk as "very, very low" has implications for the introduction and maintenance of appropriate controls. That is, in monitoring, "you will only see those things that are likely to happen" (Prof Beringer). Conversely, risks with a low probability may not materialise until many thousands of procedures have taken place. This meant that it could be meaningless to impose containment or monitoring conditions for only the first patients, when the procedure was unfamiliar (Dr Kinderlerer). However, it was important not to interpret the "very, very low" risk purely in terms of a rare infection manifesting itself in the long term – more frequent infections in the shorter term were also a possibility (Prof Fabre). But, as with HIV, these may initially not cause disease and therefore may not be identified for some time.

It was pointed out that there were analogous situations. Humans had been in contact with 'normal' cultured animal cells in the laboratory but no documented cases of laboratory workers becoming infected (Dr Gray). A number of serially passaged cell lines have come up containing animal retroviruses and, in particular, there were monkey viruses in human cell lines but, as far as it was known, there were no problems of actual diseases being transmitted from such sources, to scientists or technicians in the lab who might have been open to infection. Therefore it was fair to say that there had been opportunities for a "disaster" to happen, but it had not occurred. However, such contact was not as intimate as growing organs or disperse cells of one species inside another. Prof Weiss added that laboratory practice over recent years had lessened the risk of infection.

Allotransplantation also offered an analogy. Although infections had been transferred from donor organs to recipients these had not transferred to the recipient's close contacts (as far as it was known).

The point made by Dr Alexander during his talk, regarding the close contact between pigs and humans in rural areas, excited a good deal of discussion about whether or not it could be regarded as truly analogous to the contact between pig and human tissue proposed in xenotransplantation. Prof Beringer thought the fact that there had been no known epidemic, despite the close contact, was a forceful argument which indicated the low probability of a latent organism mutating to cause harm to humans. However, Prof Walport questioned the validity of the analogy – Could living with pigs be considered similar to living with a pig inside you, while you were taking strong immunosuppressive drugs? It was also pointed out that there had been no monitoring of the relevant populations, either in terms of death rates or of causes of death. Further, the fact that people had survived despite living in what may be considered unhygienic conditions could indicate that they had developed some immunity to the diseases to which they were exposed. In fact, in the Far East, there was an example of infection being passed from pigs to humans. The most common cause of meningitis in China and Hong Kong is Streptococcus

Suis from pigs (Dr Farrington). An example was also cited to illustrate the difference between living in close contact and exchange of tissue/fluids. Two species (ducks and chickens) live closely together without harm, but when there is iatrogenic transfer of fluids between the animals, an epidemic can result which is fatal to the chicken population (Dr Bartlett). For example, adenovirus had also been transmitted from ducks to chickens via a contaminated vaccine.

Controlling infection risks

There was a general view that, should xenotransplantation proceed, it would only be acceptable to take the risk of transmitting infection if appropriate controls were in place. There were two main methods of control, through the conditions in which the source animals were kept or through monitoring systems.

Dr Alexander had highlighted in his talk the range of systems which were available to raise pigs in as "clean" a condition as possible. Some such system was generally considered to be essential, should xenotransplantation proceed, and to offer certain advantages over human (particularly, cadaveric) donors. It would be possible to test not only the animal to be used as a source of tissue, but also the "mother and grandmother" of the animal. This would help to ascertain whether congenital infections (such as CMV) could be present (Dr Jones). It was noted that hysterectomy was a particularly important feature of the proposed systems. Experience suggested that although, theoretically, certain micro-organisms can cross the placental barrier this tended not to happen (Dr Taylor).

Monitoring systems were important to ensure that any new infections which emerged were identified and that such information was disseminated quickly to those involved in xenotransplantation. It was noted that, as the risk of new infections causing disease was low, there was a danger of assuming that because no problems came to light in the first xenotransplant procedures there was no risk in the future. Experience counselled otherwise; one early strain of the rubella vaccine was found to produce arthritis only after substantial early trials were over and many thousands of people had been vaccinated (Dr Tyrrell). It was said that the existing monitoring for transplant patients with allotransplants was inadequate, in that opportunist infections, or novel infections and tumours were not monitored and the data collected centrally as part of any current data base. In addition, monitoring is frequently carried out in specialist renal units, where the concern is frequently more on the renal function than on the nature of infection. If xenotransplantation is undertaken it would be extremely important to undertake life long follow-up of recipients, with close attention being paid to the development of all infectious complications, so that they are properly pursued, identified, characterised and reported. It was suggested that centrally tagging notes at the Department of Health might be useful, so that the causes of death for patients undergoing xenotransplantation could be readily identified. Great clinical vigilance would also be required, with respect to looking at unknown sequelae from xenotransplantation, rather than recording known phenomena (Prof Weber)

A number of essential components of any monitoring system were identified:

❖ A surveillance system. This would involve national and international databases about incidents of infection, established by people with relevant experience, and the wherewithal to feed back information speedily so that appropriate action may be taken. (Dr Gross)

❖ Storage of an agreed range of biological material (eg blood samples separating serum and cells) from both the source animal and the human recipient.

❖ A national protocol for monitoring and advice for patients.

❖ The ability and flexibility to the protocol to include any new infections which emerged (similarly, SPF conditions should be geared to respond to new infections).

❖ "Fall-back" positions were important should some disease emerge – in terms of treatment, monitoring and reconsidering work.

❖ A list of the types of investigation to be carried out on xenotransplant recipients should be drawn up before xenotransplantation should proceed.

Research to be carried out before xenotransplantation could proceed

As there remained significant unknowns about the risk posed by xenotransplantation, Workshop participants were invited to identify research which ought to be undertaken and completed before any xenotransplant procedure could take place in this country.

A number of suggestions were made, but it was recognised that whatever research was done, the problems of pathogens which had not been identified would remain. It was also recognised that it might not be possible to provide all the answers without proceeding to clinical trials.

The research recommended was as follows:

❖ The immunosuppression of tissue recipients was considered likely to amplify any sort of infectious agent. Similarly, the immunosuppression of the source animals may amplify pathogens which are present but which are usually controlled by their immune system and should be investigated (Prof Simpson/Dr Skehel). NB: in any experimental work on immunosuppression in this context, it would be important to use the pigs being bred for use in xenotransplantation as they differed from normal pigs.

❖ Pigs had been immunosuppressed for other experiments – a literature search to see if pathogens had been identified in these pigs might be worthwhile (Dr Jones).

❖ Consideration should be given to not using antibiotics on source animals, as this also would act to suppress infection (Dr Crumpton).

❖ (Immunosuppressed) primates have been used as the recipient of pig tissue in experiments designed to test rejection processes. Some work had been done to test them to see if any pathogens had arisen - there were no results at present, but it was thought that this work should continue. (However, it was noted that as the pigs involved in xenotransplantation over the years would not all be from the same genetic lines, it may be necessary to continue to use primates as recipients to test tissue for pathogens. This continued, and possibly large scale, use of primates carried its own ethical difficulties.) (Prof Weber/Dr Schild/Mr Talbot)

❖ A possible approach might be to transplant human cells into immunosuppressed pigs and monitoring for pathogens (Dr Hall).

❖ Co-culture experiments were thought to be important. Of the two C-type retroviruses identified in pigs, one was known to be infectious but the other - sourced from the mini pig kidney cell line - had not been shown to be infectious (but a limited amount of testing had taken place). More co-culture work was needed on these (Prof Weiss).

❖ Co-culture experiments might also be useful for other viruses eg CMV, circovirus (Dr Alexander/Dr Preston).

❖ A generic probe for retroviruses was being developed by Imutran who would report on this work when it was completed (Mr Talbot).

❖ Physiology and immunology: more research involving the transplantation of organs into primates would also be useful to monitor the organ's function, and the safety and efficacy of the immunosuppression, over a longer time than had happened to date (Dr Tyrrell). Mr Talbot reported that this was already part of Imutran's programme.

❖ Many viruses use immunological molecules as receptors and more research to identify the receptors for the viruses of concern would be useful.

❖ Survey the proposed source animals' handlers to see if infections had been transmitted.

❖ The antigenicity of / tolerance to xenotransplants in recipients should be tested over a prolonged period (Dr Desselberger).

❖ The potential for development of immune and auto-immune disease should be monitored.

A number of experiments were identified as providing useful information. However, a useful caveat was provided by Dr Bangham who questioned whether the results of such research would change the decision about whether to proceed to xenotransplantation in humans. It was unlikely that they would provide information such that xenotransplantation would be prohibited or that it would be approved as being definitely safe. A good illustration of this problem was raised by Dr Stoye when he asked what the implications were if it was found that an endogenous C-type retrovirus of pigs was infectious for human cells (as would be demonstrated by co-culture experiments) but it was not known whether it was pathogenic. Would this rule out the use of pigs? As it was not possible to predict whether the viruses would be harmful in humans, this question could not be answered with certainty.

ANNEX C:

APPENDIX 1

ADDITIONAL COMMENTS FROM DELEGATES MADE FOLLOWING THE WORKSHOP

At the end of the workshop delegates were asked to write to the two Secretariats with any additional thoughts or comments they may have, in particular, on research that may be required before xenotransplantation could proceed to trials including humans. A number of comments were received. A summary of the points made is provided here.

RISKS

It was thought that it was important to distinguish clearly between risks to the recipient and risks to the wider population. There was a general agreement that the probability of a known or unknown porcine virus causing disease in the tissue is low and the consequence for the recipient is small in relation to probable life expectancy. On the other hand, while the probability of transmission into the community is very low, it was thought that the consequence may be unacceptably large. Particular comments were as follows

❖ Xenografting will probably be alright, but is 'probably all right' good enough in view of the consequences? There is a risk. (Prof Minson)

❖ In assessing possible precautions that could be taken, we should not overestimate our ability to detect and characterise infectious agents. For example, Hepatitis B and Hepatitis C were discovered as a result of allografting, but it took 5 and 15 years respectively to do so. (Prof Minson)

❖ In recipients of xenotransplants, who may be more heavily immunosuppressed than recipients of human tissue, the risk from recognised human pathogens (bacterial, viral, fungal and protozoal) could be greater. Opportunistic infection could be more severe and there may be increased risk of tumour formation which is clearly linked to the quantity of immunosuppression. (Dr Moore)

MINIMISING ANY RISKS

Delegates suggested various methods by which the risks from some pathogens could be lessened or controlled.

❖ Dr Farrington reinforced the point made during discussion that an important emphasis should be placed on the controlling of risks of bacterial and parasitic infections through the use of 'good medical practice / good laboratory practice' (GMP/GLP).

❖ Prof Biggs, taking pigs as the most likely source animals, confirmed the use of the SPF system described by Dr Alexander as having an important part in the reduction of risks from infectious agents but placed great emphasis on the need for extensive testing of animals at all stages up to as near to the time that an animal is used as a source of tissue as possible.

❖ Dr Farrington agreed with the view expressed that source animals should not be subjected to blanket antibiotic therapy to eliminate bacterial pathogens. However, he thought that there was a case for the judicious use of carefully chosen antibiotics. This would be more likely to be effective, as it would eliminate certain pathogens from an animal reliably, rather than a policy of withholding therapy until infected tissue was transplanted into an immunosuppressed recipient.

❖ If risks from retroviruses, herpesviruses and unknown pathogens exist but remain unquantifiable, Dr Farrington felt that at the very least we must have a clear understanding of which actions should be taken to detect them; which are necessary to restrict the likelihood of any spread (perhaps before any infection is detected); and which are appropriate for the best management of patients in whom infections may be detected.

❖ The importance of systems to monitor tissue recipients, and the difficulties involved in doing so, was also recognised. One point made, additionally to those made during the workshop, was that most infection control procedures for hospitals required some further thought (Dr Farrington).

AREAS OF RESEARCH SUGGESTED

As invited, the delegates who wrote following the workshop suggested some general areas of research and a number of specific proposals for research which should be carried out. These are as follows:

❖ Professor Weiss reported that one of the porcine retroviruses may infect some lines of human cells in culture. He suggested that further work needed to be done to characterise the retrovirus, for example to see whether it was endogenous and to determine its prevalence. Dr Stoye advised testing to determine whether the retrovirus was present in the herds of potential source animals.

❖ Professor Weiss re-emphasised the possibility that an animal microbe could adopt to human infection through xenotransplantation and then cause human to human infection. He emphasised accordingly the importance of monitoring xenotransplant recipients.

❖ Dr Preston made the general comment that research on xenotransplantation should be split equally between studies concerned with the transplant recipient and investigation of potential and known infectious agents, which could have an impact on the wider population. Thus porcine CMV should be characterised better to understand its host range, relationship to other CMVs and rates of transmission. Model conditions should be set up to mimic the clinical situation so that organs may be examined for release of viruses.

❖ If infectious virus is found within source herds and cannot be eliminated, it was thought that it would be advisable to carry out long term trials (in fairly limited numbers of) immunosuppressed primates in an attempt to assess the oncogenic potential of the virus prior to starting clinical trials (this may also allow assessment of transplant efficacy) (Dr Stoye). It would also be worthwhile to work on "knocking out" endogenous retroviruses in the pigs through breeding techniques (Prof Biggs) and to attempt to isolate 'unknown' retroviruses either by PCR or more conventional virological techniques (Dr Stoye).

The following were indicated as research worth undertaking that may identify potential agents of concern (Prof Minson):

❖ trying to establish whether reactivated endogenous porcine retroviruses will infect a variety of human cells

❖ Eliminating CMV from source animals

❖ Immunosuppressing source animals and searching for evidence of unknown viruses by

- histological examination of suspect tissues on the basis of disease symptoms

- culture of PBMC

- co-culture of PBMs with human cells

(In each instance followed by EM and immunohistochemistry with tagged IgG from source animals)

❖ Histological and electron microscopical examination of xenografts from primates

❖ Culture of PBMCs from primate xenograft recipients, followed by electron microscopy and immunohistochemistry with source pig serum.

❖ Investigation of the cidal activity of newly-developed antibiotics such as the quiolones, rifampicin and newer beta-lactins to replace the traditional veterinary streptomycin and tetracycline. (Dr Farrington)

❖ More general comments included that any research should concentrate on the possible generation of new pathogens (Prof Beringer). A salutary comment was that in experiments designed to identify precisely unknown pathogens, negative results were not necessarily reassuring.

ANNEX C:

APPENDIX 2

Infectious Disease and Xenotransplantation Workshop

Thursday 25 April 1996, The Holiday Inn, Kings Cross Road, London WC1

PROGRAMME

9.30am-10.00am	**Registration and coffee**

Session one   **Introduction**
Session Chairman - Dr David Harper, Department of Health

10.00am-10.10am	**Welcome**

Sir Kenneth Calman, Chief Medical Officer, Department of Health

10.10am -10.20am	**Background**

Professor Ian Kennedy, Chairman of the Advisory Group on the Ethics of Xenotransplantation

10.20am-10. 35am	**General Overview**

Dr Michael Crumpton, Chairman of the Advisory Committee on Dangerous Pathogens

Session two   **Overview of the risk of transmission of infectious disease in transplantation**
Session Chairman - Professor Mark Walport, Head of the Rheumatology Unit,
Royal Postgraduate Medical School, Hammersmith Hospital

10.35am-11.20am	**Allotransplantation – infection risks associated with human to human transplantation**

Dr Philip Minor, Head of Virology Department, National Institute of Biological Standards and Control

11.20am -11. 50am	*Coffee Break*

11.50am-12.20pm	**Xenotransplantation – infection risks associated with animal to human transplantation**

Dr Tom Alexander, Veterinary School, Cambridge University

12.20am-12.50pm	**Prions**

Dr David Taylor, Institute for Animal Health, Edinburgh

12.50pm- 1.30pm	*Lunch*

Session three — **Risk of transmission of viruses**
Session Chairman - Dr Geoffrey Schild, Director of the National Institute of
Biological Standards and Control

1.30pm-1.45pm — **Herpesviruses**
Dr Christopher Preston, MRC Virology Unit, Institute of Virology, Glasgow

1.45pm-2.00pm — **Retroviruses**
Professor Robin Weiss, Director of Research, Institute of Cancer Research, London

2.00pm-2.30pm — **Discussion**

Session four — **Risk Assessment**
Session Chairman- Dr John Skehel, Director, Division of Virology,
National Institute for Medical Research

2.30pm-4.00pm — **Risk Assessment – Panel Discussion**

Dr Michael Crumpton, Chairman of the Advisory Committee on Dangerous Pathogens

Professor John Beringer, Chairman of Advisory Committee on Releases to the Environment

Dr Roger Gross, Head of Scientific Programmes, Public Health Laboratory Service

Dr Graham Hall, Head of Biological Resources, Centre for Applied
Microbiology and Research, Porton Down

Dr David Tyrrell, Retired Expert Member of the Advisory Committee on Dangerous Pathogens

Professor Robin Weiss, Director of Research, Institute of Cancer Research, London

4.00pm-4.30pm	*Coffee Break*

4.30pm-4.50pm — **Summary of the day's discussion**

ANNEX C:

APPENDIX 3

LIST OF DELEGATES ATTENDING:

Dr TJL Alexander	Deputy Head Dept Clinical Veterinary Medicine	University of Cambridge
Ms R Arrundale	Secretary, Advisory Group on Ethics of Xeno.	Department of Health
Dr CRM Bangham	Head of Dept of Immunology	Imperial College of Science, Tech & Medicine
Dr R Bartlett	Deputy Executive Secretary	Nuffield Council on Bioethics
Prof J Beringer	Biological Sciences Dept.	Bristol University
Mrs VM Bevan	Head of Technical Services	Public Health Laboratory Service, London
Prof P Biggs	(Retired) Director of Animal Health	Agricultural and Food Research Council
Sir K Calman	Chief Medical Officer	Department of Health
Dr EM Cooke	Project Co-ordinator, NISU	Public Health Laboratory Service
Mr M Cox		Medical Devices Agency, London
Dr MJ Crumpton	Deputy Chief Executive & Managing Director	Imperial Cancer Research Technology. London
Ms N Davies QC	Barrister,	Advisory Group on the Ethics of Xenotransplantation
Ms J Deans		Health & Safety Executive

Dr U Desselberger	Consultant Virologist & Director	Regional Public Health Laboratory, Cambridge
Dr P Doyle	Senior Medical Officer	Department of Health
Mr C Evans	Assistant Secretary to Advisory Group	Department of Health
Prof J Fabre	Head of Dept of Paediatric Cardiology	Institute of Child Health, London.
Dr M Farrington	Consultant Mircobiologist	PHLS Addenbrooke's Hospital, Cambridge
Dr HJ Field	Lecturer	Cambridge University Centre for Veterinary Science
Mr PJR Gayford	Veterinary Advisor	Animal Health and Veterinary Group MAFF
Dr PJ Gosling	ACDP Secretariat	Department of Health
Dr E Gray	Reader in Transplantation/ Consultant Surgeon	John Radcliffe Hospital, Oxford
Prof GE Griffin	Dead of Division of Infectious Diseases	St George's Hospital Medical School, London
Dr R Gross	Head of Scientific Programmes	Public Health laboratory Service, London
Dr G Hall	Head of Biological Resources	CAMR Porton Down
Dr D Harper	Chief Scientific Officer	Department of Health
Dr J Hilton	Senior Medical Officer	Department of Health
Dr P Jones	Head, Division of Env. Microbiology	Institute of Animal Health
Prof I Kennedy	Professor of Medical Law & Ethics Chairman of Advisory Group.	Kings College, London Law School.

Dr J Kinderlerer		University of Sheffield
Mrs E Lawrence	ACDP Secretariat	Department of Health
Dr A Leigh	Scientific Secretary to Advisory Group	Department of Health
Mr PA Lister	ACDP Secretariat	Health and Safety Executive
Mrs J MacArthur Clark	Consultant in Laboratory Animal Science & Ethics	Advisory Group on the Ethics of Xenotransplantation
Ms J McIntyre	Nursing Officer	Department of Health
Dr P Minor	Head of Virology Department	National Institute of Biological Standards and Control
Prof A Minson	Professor of Virology	University of Cambridge
Dr R Moore	Surgeon	Cardiff Royal Infirmary
Ms K Norman	ACDP Secretariat	Department of Health
Dr R Owen	Consultant	OMLB and Trades Union Congress
Dr D Paton	Senior Research Officer	Central Veterinary Laboratory
Dr JF Peutherer	Senior Lecture, Head of Department	Medical Microbiology, Edinburgh University
Dr C Preston	MRC Virology Unit	Institute of Virology, Glasgow
Prof J Salaman	(Retired) Professor of Transplant Surgery	Advisory Group on the Ethics of Xenotransplantation
Dr R Salmon	Consultant Epidemiologist	PHLS Communicable Disease Surveillance Centre
Dr G Schild	Director	National Institute of Biological Standards & Control
Dr TF Schulz	Department of Medical Microbiology & GU Medicine	Liverpool University

Prof H Sewell	Professor of Immunology Queen Elizabeth Hospital Nottingham	Advisory Group on the Ethics of Xenotransplantation
Prof E Simpson	Head, Transplantation Biology Group	MRC Clinical Sciences Centre
Dr J Skehel	Director	National Institute of Medical Research
Dr J Stoye	Group Leader	National Institute of Medical Research
Dr A Suckling	Director of Scientific Affairs, RSPCA	Advisory Group on the Ethics of Xenotransplantation
Prof A Tait	Veterinary Department	University of Glasgow
Mr T Talbot	Director of Product Development	Imutran Ltd
Mr A Taylor	Secretary, Gene Therapy Advisory Committee	Department of Health
Dr D Taylor	Microbiologist	Institute for Animal Health, Edinburgh
Dr H Tranter	Head, Developmental Production	CAMR
Mr A Tucker	Veterinary Surgeon	Imutran Ltd.
Dr D Tyrell	(retired)	Ex MRC
Prof H Waldmann	Professor of Pathology	Oxford University
Prof M Walport	Head, Rheumatology Unit	Royal Postgraduate Medical School
Prof J Weber	Head, Dept. GU Medicine & Communicable Diseases	Imperial College School of Medicine at St Mary's
Prof R Weiss		Institute of Cancer Research, London
Dr T Wyatt	Consultant Clinical Scientist	Mater Hospital Trust
Ms M Young	ACDP Secretariat	Department of Health

ANNEX D

THE PRODUCTION OF TRANSGENIC PIGS FOR XENOTRANSPLANTATION

ANNEX D:

THE PRODUCTION OF TRANSGENIC PIGS FOR XENOTRANSPLANTATION

MICROINJECTION AND INITIAL BREEDING:

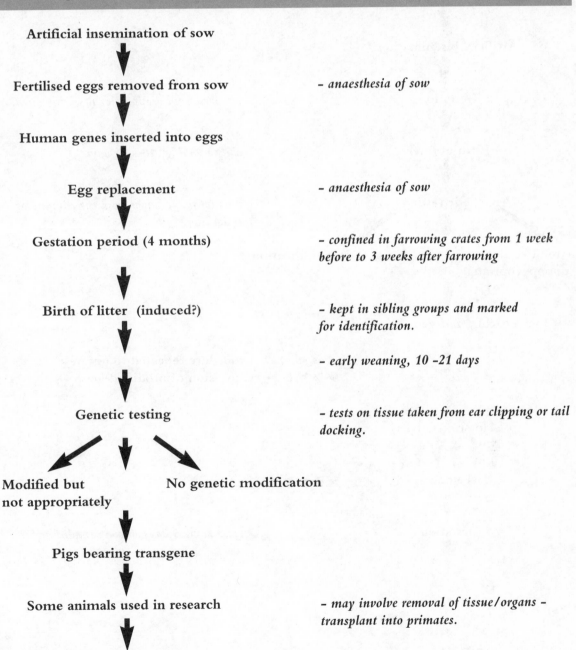

Artificial insemination of sow

Fertilised eggs removed from sow — *anaesthesia of sow*

Human genes inserted into eggs

Egg replacement — *anaesthesia of sow*

Gestation period (4 months) — *confined in farrowing crates from 1 week before to 3 weeks after farrowing*

Birth of litter (induced?) — *kept in sibling groups and marked for identification.*

— *early weaning, 10 –21 days*

Genetic testing — *tests on tissue taken from ear clipping or tail docking.*

Modified but not appropriately   No genetic modification

Pigs bearing transgene

Some animals used in research — *may involve removal of tissue/organs – transplant into primates.*

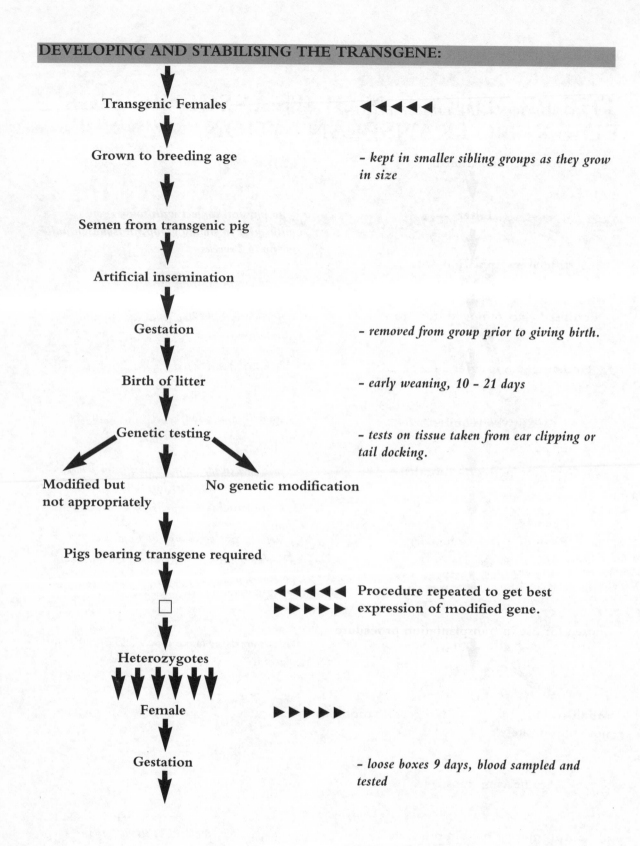

DEVELOPING AND STABILISING THE TRANSGENE:

Transgenic Females ◄◄◄◄◄

Grown to breeding age — *kept in smaller sibling groups as they grow in size*

Semen from transgenic pig

Artificial insemination

Gestation — *removed from group prior to giving birth.*

Birth of litter — *early weaning, 10 – 21 days*

Genetic testing — *tests on tissue taken from ear clipping or tail docking.*

Modified but not appropriately / No genetic modification

Pigs bearing transgene required

◄◄◄◄◄ Procedure repeated to get best ►►►►► expression of modified gene.

Heterozygotes

Female ►►►►►

Gestation — *loose boxes 9 days, blood sampled and tested*

BREEDING THE SOURCE ANIMAL:

SPF CONDITIONS ARE LIKELY TO START NOW

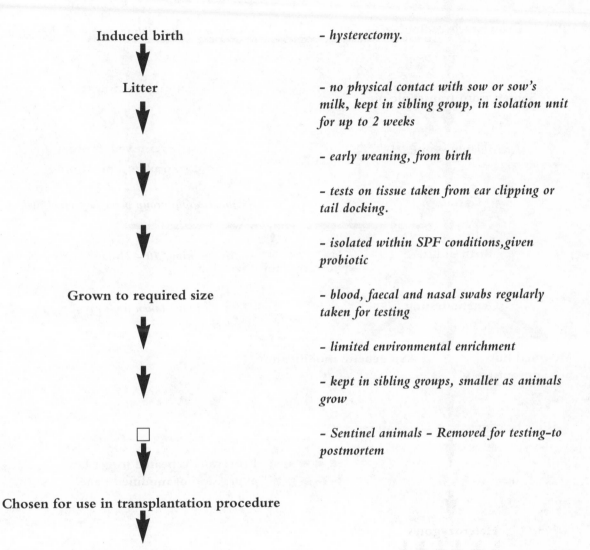

Induced birth   – *hysterectomy.*

Litter   – *no physical contact with sow or sow's milk, kept in sibling group, in isolation unit for up to 2 weeks*

– *early weaning, from birth*

– *tests on tissue taken from ear clipping or tail docking.*

– *isolated within SPF conditions, given probiotic*

Grown to required size   – *blood, faecal and nasal swabs regularly taken for testing*

– *limited environmental enrichment*

– *kept in sibling groups, smaller as animals grow*

– *Sentinel animals – Removed for testing–to postmortem*

Chosen for use in transplantation procedure

ORGAN RETRIEVAL:

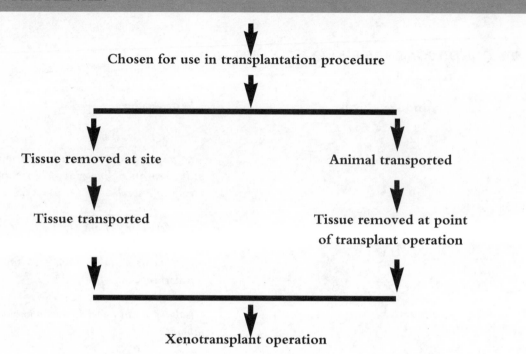